COLLEGE
ALGEBRA

College Algebra

RAYMOND A. BARNETT
Department of Mathematics
Merritt College, California

McGRAW-HILL BOOK COMPANY

New York   St. Louis   San Francisco   Auckland   Düsseldorf   Johannesburg
Kuala Lumpur   London   Mexico   Montreal   New Delhi   Panama   Paris
São Paulo   Singapore   Sydney   Tokyo   Toronto

Library of Congress Cataloging in Publication Data

Barnett, Raymond A
    College algebra.

    Based on the author's College algebra with trigonometry, with sections on trigonometry omitted.
    Includes index.
    1. Algebra. I. Title.
QA154.2.B35   512.9   75-26826
ISBN 0-07-003764-7

College Algebra

1 2 3 4 5 6 7 8 9 0 D O D O 7 9 8 7 6 5

This book was set in Times Roman. The editors were A. Anthony Arthur and Shelly Levine Langman; the cover was designed by Pencils Portfolio, Inc.; the production supervisor was Joe Campanella.
R. R. Donnelley & Sons Company was printer and binder.

Contents

v |

Preface

"Another college algebra?" Considering the large number of college algebras on the market, clearly, any new text must have some special features or innovations to distinguish it from the rest. In this book, these are:

1. First, and foremost, the text is written for students. Each concept is illustrated with an example, and following the example is a parallel problem with an answer so that a student can immediately check his understanding of the concept. These follow-up problems also serve to encourage active rather than passive reading of the text.
2. An informal style is used for exposition, statements of definitions, and proofs of theorems.

3. The text includes approximately 3,300 carefully selected and graded problems. Each set of problems is divided into A, B, and C levels, and ranges from easy and routine (A section) to challenging and nonroutine (C section). By suitably choosing problems from these three categories (see chart, page xiii) courses may be designed to suit various class needs as well as various individual needs within a class. For example, a student reasonably well prepared in intermediate algebra would work a few A problems, a large number of B problems, and a few C problems. A weaker student would be encouraged to work many A problems followed by problems from the B group. A very strong student would place equal emphasis on the B and C groups. The C problems often fill in and extend theoretical developments in the text. In short, the text is designed so that an average or below-average student will be able to experience success, and a very capable student will be challenged.

4. The subject matter is related to the real world through many carefully selected realistic applications from the social, natural, and physical sciences. Thus, the text is equally suited for students interested in the social and natural sciences, as well as students primarily interested in the physical sciences.

5. Following the recommendations of CUPM, other national and international mathematical organizations, and the author's own convictions, the function concept is used as a unifying notion from the fourth chapter onward.

Now for some general comments regarding the text and its organization. Chapter 1, on sets and real and complex numbers, provides foundation material for the rest of the text. The emphasis placed on this material will vary from class to class and instructor to instructor—let your conscience be your guide.

Chapters 2 and 3 primarily review material from intermediate algebra. Absolute value and inequalities usually need some attention, particularly for students intending to take calculus next.

Chapter 4, on relations and functions, provides a unifying theme for the rest of the book. Relations and functions are defined statically in terms of ordered pairs of elements, and dynamically as mappings. The straight line and slope are discussed in detail, and a brief introduction to conics is included. In fact, a fair amount of analytic geometry is dispersed throughout the text.

Chapter 5 generalizes the polynomial in terms of polynomial functions, and provides a systematic treatment for finding or approximating all real zeros of polynomial functions with real coefficients. A section on partial fractions is included at the end.

Chapter 6; in part, reviews material generally covered in intermediate algebra; however, the functional properties of the exponential and logarithmic functions are emphasized. Exponential functions with base e receive some attention.

Chapter 7 includes some review of systems of linear and nonlinear equations. The matrix idea is introduced in a natural way as an outgrowth of solving third-order systems. It is then formalized and developed further in succeeding sections.

Chapter 8 includes a careful but highly motivated treatment of mathematical induction, as well as a review of sequences and series.

I wish to thank those who have read the book in its manuscript form for their many kind comments and helpful suggestions. In addition, special thanks goes to Mrs. Iku Workman and to my daughter Margaret for their final typing of the manuscript.

Raymond A. Barnett

POSSIBLE COURSES

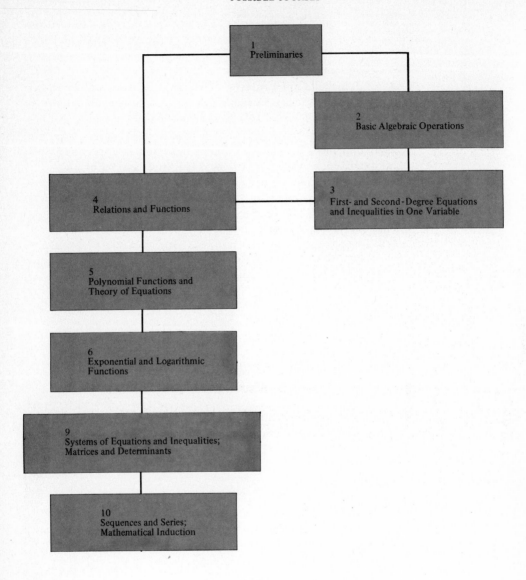

USE OF A, B, and C EXERCISES

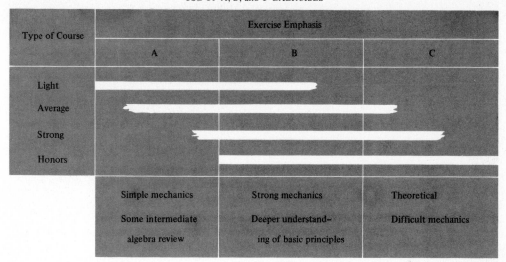

Type of Course	Exercise Emphasis		
	A	B	C
Light			
Average			
Strong			
Honors			
	Simple mechanics	Strong mechanics	Theoretical
	Some intermediate	Deeper understand–	Difficult mechanics
	algebra review	ing of basic principles	

INDIVIDUALIZED ASSIGNMENTS (AVERAGE COURSE)

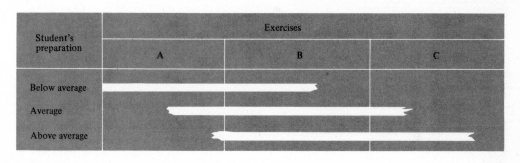

Student's preparation	Exercises		
	A	B	C
Below average			
Average			
Above average			

Chapter

Preliminaries

In this chapter we will review some of the basic ideas about sets and summarize some fundamental properties of the real- and complex-number systems. If most of this material is familiar, as it no doubt is for many, then a brief review is all that is necessary. Of course, if some of the material is new, then something more than a glance is required.

1.1 SETS

George Cantor (1845–1918), when about 30, created a new mathematical concept, the theory of sets. This new theory, an outgrowth of his studies on infinity, has become a milestone in the development of mathematics. Ironically, Cantor's mathematical contemporaries received his theory with scorn and contempt. And it was not until the first part of this century, just before Cantor's death, that his fellow mathematicians began to recognize the importance of his contributions.

We can think of a *set* as any collection of objects with the important property that any given object either is a member of the set or it is not. In this course we will be primarily interested in sets of numbers. Capital letters, A, B, C, ..., are often used to designate sets. Symbolically, a set is usually described either by listing all its elements within braces { }, or by enclosing within braces a rule which determines whether or not a given object is a member of the set. Each object in a set is called a *member* or *element* of the set. If *a is an element of set A*, we write $a \in A$; if *a* is not an element of set A, we write $a \notin A$. Thus, if N is the set of natural numbers, we write $5 \in N$ and $\sqrt{5} \notin N$.

Example 1. Let A be the set of all numbers x such that $x^2 = 4$. The set A may be specified symbolically as follows:

BY LISTING: $A = \{-2, 2\}$
BY RULE: $A = \{x \mid x^2 = 4\}$, which is read, "A is the set of all x such that $x^2 = 4$."

Problem 1. Let B be the set of all numbers x such that $x^2 = 64$. (A) Denote B by the listing method. (B) Denote B by the rule method. (C) Indicate which of the following are true: $4 \in B$, $8 \in B$, $16 \notin B$.

ANSWER

(A) $B = \{-8, 8\}$; (B) $B = \{x \mid x^2 = 64\}$; (C) F, T, T.

The letter x used in Example 1 is a variable, and 4 and 2 are constants. In general, a *constant* is any symbol used to name exactly one thing; a *variable* is any symbol used as a placeholder for constants from a set of two or more constants. Set A in Example 1 is called the solution set for the equation $x^2 = 4$. The *solution set* for any equation is the set of all solutions for that equation. What are the constants and variables in $x^2 = 64$? What is the solution set for this equation? (*Answer:* variable: x; constants: 2 and 64; solution set $= \{-8, 8\}$.)

If each element of set A is also an element of set B, we say that *A is a subset of B* and write $A \subseteq B$ or $B \supseteq A$. (Note that this definition allows a set to be a subset of itself.) If $A \subseteq B$ and $B \subseteq A$, that is, if every element in set A is in B and every element of set B is in A, we say that $A = B$. If A is a subset of B, but A is not all of B, we say that *A is a proper subset of B* and sometimes write $A \subset B$ or $B \supset A$.

A set of special interest is the *empty or null set*; it is the set that contains no elements, and it is denoted by the symbol $\emptyset$. This set is a subset of every set, since it is certainly true that every element of $\emptyset$ is an element of any given set since $\emptyset$ has no elements.

Example 2. Let $A = \{1, 2, 3\}$, $B = \{1, 2, 3, 4, 5\}$, and $C = \{3, 4, 2, 1, 5\}$, then

   (A) $A \subseteq B$ (B) $B \subseteq C$ (C) $C \subseteq B$ (D) $B = C$
   (E) $A \subset B$ (F) $\emptyset \subseteq A$ (G) $\emptyset \subset B$ (H) $B \supseteq A$

Problem 2. For $A = \{3, 4, 5, 6\}$, $B = \{4, 5\}$, and $C = \{4, 6, 5, 3\}$, which of the following are true?

   (A) $B \subseteq C$ (B) $B \supseteq C$ (C) $A \subseteq C$ (D) $C \subseteq A$
   (E) $A = C$ (F) $A \subset C$ (G) $\emptyset \subseteq B$ (H) $\emptyset \subseteq A$

ANSWER

(A) T; (B) F; (C) T; (D) T; (E) T; (F) F; (G) T; (H) T.

The *union* of sets A and B, denoted by $A \cup B$, is the set of elements formed by combining all the elements of A and all the elements of B into one set. The *intersection* of A and B, denoted by $A \cap B$, is the set of elements of A that are also in B. If $A \cap B = \emptyset$, the sets A and B are said to be *disjoint*.

Example 3. If $A = \{1, 2, 3, 4\}$, $B = \{1, 3, 5, 7\}$, and $C = \{2, 4, 6\}$, then

$$A \cup B = \{1, 2, 3, 4, 5, 7\}$$
$$A \cap B = \{1, 3\}$$
$$B \cap C = \emptyset \qquad (B \text{ and } C \text{ are disjoint})$$

Problem 3. If $A = \{3, 6, 9\}$, $B = \{3, 4, 5, 6, 7\}$, and $C = \{4, 5, 7, 8\}$, find

   (A) $A \cup B$ (B) $A \cap B$ (C) $A \cap C$

ANSWER

(A) $\{3, 4, 5, 6, 7, 9\}$; (B) $\{3, 6\}$; (C) $\emptyset$.

We say that a *one-to-one correspondence* exists between two sets A and B if each element in A can be associated with a unique (one and only one) element in B, and each element in B can be associated with a unique element in A. There is, for example, a one-to-one correspondence between the students and the chairs in a classroom if every student has a chair and no chair is left empty. A set A is said to be *infinite* if one can establish a one-to-one correspondence between A and a proper subset of A, otherwise, the set is said to be *finite*.

EXERCISE 1

A *In Probs. 1 to 18 write each set by listing its elements between braces.*

1. The set of digits between 1 and 5, inclusive.
2. The set of digits between 3 and 8, inclusive.
3. The set of natural numbers between 12 and 16, inclusive.
4. The set of natural numbers between 21 and 26, inclusive.
5. The solution set for $x - 3 = 0$
6. The solution set for $x + 5 = 0$
7. The solution set for $x^2 = 49$.
8. The solution set for $x^2 = 36$.
9. $\{x \mid x - 3 = 0\}$
10. $\{x \mid x + 5 = 0\}$
11. $\{x \mid x^2 = 49\}$
12. $\{x \mid x^2 = 36\}$
13. $\{1, 3, 5\} \cup \{2, 3, 4\}$
14. $\{3, 4, 6, 7\} \cup \{3, 4, 5\}$
15. $\{1, 3, 4\} \cap \{2, 3, 4\}$
16. $\{3, 4, 6, 7\} \cap \{3, 4, 5\}$
17. $\{1, 5, 9\} \cap \{3, 4, 6, 8\}$
18. $\{6, 8, 9, 11\} \cap \{3, 4, 5, 7\}$

In Probs. 19 to 31, indicate which of the statements are true.

19. $7 \notin \{3, 5, 7\}$
20. $4 \in \{2, 3, 4\}$
21. $\{7\} \subseteq \{3, 5, 7\}$
22. $\{4\} \subset \{2, 3, 4\}$
23. $\{2, 3, 4\} \subseteq \{1, 2, 3, 4, 5\}$
24. $\{1, 2, 3\} \subseteq \{1, 2, 3\}$
25. $\{1, 2, 3\} \subset \{1, 2, 3\}$
26. $\{2, 5, 7, 9\} = \{7, 5, 3, 9\}$
27. $\{3, 4, 5\} = \{5, 3, 4\}$
28. $33 \in \{x \mid x \text{ is an odd number}\}$
29. $24 \notin \{x \mid x \text{ is an even number}\}$
30. $\{3, 4, 7\} \subseteq \{x \mid x \text{ is an odd number}\}$
31. $\{2, 4, 6\} \subset \{x \mid x \text{ is an even number}\}$

B
32. Let A be the set of all numbers x, such that $x^2 = 9$. Which of the following are true?
    (A) $A = \{3\}$ (B) $A = \{-3, 3\}$ (C) $A = \{x \mid x^2 = 9\}$
    (D) $A = \{x \mid x = 3\}$ (E) $-3 \in A$ (F) $9 \notin A$

33. Let B be the set of all numbers x, such that $x^2 = 25$. Which of the following are true?
    (A) $B = \{-5, 5\}$ (B) $B = \{25\}$ (C) $B = \{x \mid x = 5\}$
    (D) $B = \{x \mid x^2 = 25\}$ (E) $-5 \notin B$ (F) $5 \in B$

34. Let B be the set of all numbers x, such that $x^2 = 81$.
    (A) Denote B by the listing method.
    (B) Denote B by the rule method.
    (C) Indicate which of the following are true: $9 \in B$, $-9 \notin B$, $81 \notin B$.

35. Let A be the set of all numbers x such that $x^2 = 16$.
    (A) Denote A by the listing method.
    (B) Denote A by the rule method.
    (C) Indicate which of the following are true: $-4 \in A$, $16 \notin A$, $8 \in A$.

36. If $A = \{11, 12, 13, 14\}$, then $\{x \mid x \in A$ and x is even$\} = \{$(list elements)$\}$
37. If $B = \{11, 12, 13, 14\}$, then $\{x \mid x \in B$ and x is odd$\} = \{$(list elements)$\}$
38. If $A = \{2, 4, 6\}$, $B = \{1, 2, 3, 4, 5, 6\}$, and $C = \{4, 1, 3, 2, 6, 5\}$, which of the following are true?

    (A) $A \subset B$ (B) $B \supseteq A$ (C) $A = C$ (D) $B = C$
    (E) $B \subseteq C$ (F) $C \subseteq B$ (G) $\emptyset \subseteq A$ (H) $\emptyset \subset B$

39. If $A = \{2, 4, 6, 8\}$, $B = \{6, 8\}$, and $C = \{6, 2, 4, 8\}$, which of the following are true?

    (A) $B \subseteq C$ (B) $A \subseteq C$ (C) $C \subseteq A$ (D) $A = C$
    (E) $B \supset A$ (F) $B \subset A$ (G) $\emptyset \subset B$ (H) $\emptyset \subseteq A$

40. If $A = \{1, 3, 5\}$, $B = \{0, 1, 2\}$, and $C = \{0, 2, 4\}$, find

    (A) $A \cup B$ (B) $A \cup C$ (C) $B \cup C$
    (D) $A \cap B$ (E) $A \cap C$ (F) $B \cap C$

41. If $A = \{5, 7, 9\}$, $B = \{3, 5, 7\}$, and $C = \{4, 6\}$, find

    (A) $A \cup B$ (B) $A \cup C$ (C) $B \cup C$
    (D) $A \cap B$ (E) $A \cap C$ (F) $B \cap C$

42. For $A = \{1, 2, 3, 4\}$, $B = \{2, 4, 6\}$, and $C = \{3, 4, 5, 6\}$, show that
    (A) $A \cup B = B \cup A$
    (B) $A \cup (B \cup C) = (A \cup B) \cup C$

43. For $A = \{1, 2, 3, 4\}$, $B = \{2, 4, 6\}$, and $C = \{3, 4, 5, 6\}$, show that
    (A) $A \cap B = B \cap A$
    (B) $A \cap (B \cap C) = (A \cap B) \cap C$

44. If $A = \{1, 2, 3, 4\}$ and $B = \{2, 4, 6\}$, find
    (A) $\{x \mid x \in A$ or $x \in B\}$ (B) $A \cup B$

45. If $A = \{1, 2, 3, 4\}$ and $B = \{2, 4, 6\}$, find
    (A) $\{x \mid x \in A$ and $x \in B\}$ (B) $A \cap B$

46. The management of a company (president, vice-president, secretary, and treasurer) wish to select a committee of two persons from among themselves. How many ways can this committee be formed; that is, how many two-person subsets can be formed from the set of four officers of the company?

47. The five-member executive committee of the Associated Students wishes to form a subcommittee of three members to study the problem of student-body cards. In how many ways can this subcommittee be formed? (*Hint:* Replace the word committee with set every place that it appears.)

c 48. Which of the following statements are false?
    (A) $\emptyset = \{0\}$ (B) $\{\emptyset\} = \{0\}$ (C) $\emptyset = \{\emptyset\}$

49. How do the sets $\emptyset$, $\{\emptyset\}$, and $\{0\}$ differ from one another?

50. Which of the following defines $A \cup B$, and which defines $A \cap B$?

    $$G = \{x \mid x \in A \text{ or } x \in B\}$$
    $$H = \{x \mid x \in A \text{ and } x \in B\}$$

51. For $A = \{1, 2, 3, 4\}$, $B = \{2, 4, 6\}$, and $C = \{3, 4, 5, 6\}$, show that $A \cup (B \cap C) = (A \cup B) \cap (A \cup C)$.

52. For $A = \{1, 2, 3, 4\}$, $B = \{2, 4, 6\}$, and $C = \{3, 4, 5, 6\}$, show that $A \cap (B \cup C) = (A \cap B) \cup (A \cap C)$.

53. How many subsets does each of the following sets have? (Try to discover a formula in terms of n for a set with n elements.)
    (A) $\{a\}$ (B) $\{a, b\}$ (C) $\{a, b, c\}$

54. Can a one-to-one correspondence be established between $A = \{1, 2, 3, 4, 5, 6\}$ and $B = \{2, 4, 6\}$? Is A finite or infinite?

55. Establish a one-to-one correspondence between the set of natural numbers $\{1, 2, 3, \ldots\}$ and the set of even natural numbers $\{2, 4, 6, \ldots\}$. Is the set of natural numbers finite or infinite?

56. Which of the following statements are true?
    (A) If $A \cap B = B$, then $B \subseteq A$.
    (B) If $A \cup B = B$, then $A \subseteq B$.
    (C) If A and B are any sets, then $A \cap B \subseteq B$.
    (D) If $A \cap B = \varnothing$, then $B = \varnothing$.
    (E) If $A \cup B = \varnothing$, then $B = \varnothing$.

57. Which of the following statements are true?
    (A) If $A \subseteq B$ and $x \in A$, then $x \in B$.
    (B) If $A \subseteq B$ and $x \in B$, then $x \in A$.

58. If U and V are sets, which of the following statements can never be true?
    (A) $U \subset V$ and $V \subset U$ (B) $U \subset V$ or $V \subset U$
    (C) $U \subseteq V$ and $V \subseteq U$ (D) $U \subseteq V$ or $V \subseteq U$

59. An executive committee decides for or against a given measure as follows. The president and vice-president are each allowed two votes, and the other three members are allowed one vote each; four favorable votes are needed for an issue to pass. If $E = \{a, b, c, d, e\}$ represents the executive committee, where a and b are the president and vice-president, respectively, list all minimal winning coalitions (that is, all subsets of E that have enough votes to carry an issue but would not carry it if one member were deleted).

60. The president of the company is allowed two votes, and each of the other members of the management is allowed one vote each. Three votes are required to carry an issue. If $U = \{P, V, S, T\}$ represents the management, list all minimal winning coalitions. (*Hint:* See Prob. 59.)

1.2 THE FIELD OF REAL NUMBERS

Recall that natural numbers, integers, rational numbers, real numbers, and complex numbers are related to each other as in Fig. 1. In this section we will restrict our attention to the set of real numbers, postponing a discussion of complex numbers until later. What are numbers? Obviously, every one knows what numbers are, or do they? When we use the symbols 5, $-\frac{2}{3}$, and $\sqrt{2}$, what objects do they name? (There is a logical difference between a name and the object being named—the same difference that exists between you and your name.) What does 5 name? What does $\sqrt{2}$ name? The answer to these questions is far more difficult than you might expect. In fact, mathematicians struggled with the idea for over 2,000

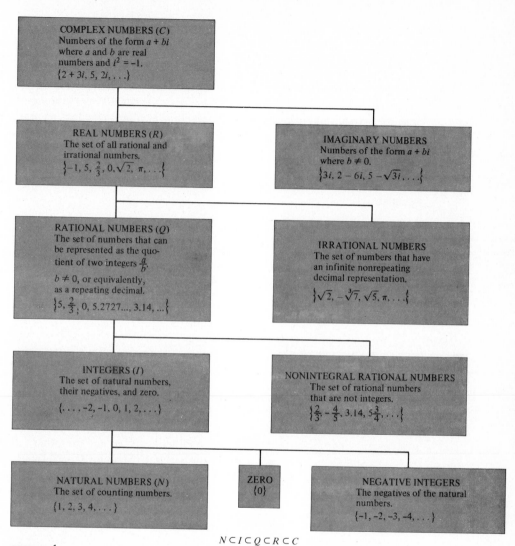

FIGURE 1

years before coming up with a rigorously formulated and workable definition of the concept in the nineteenth century. The German mathematician Gottlob Frege (1848–1925) made one of the earliest attempts to define natural numbers as objects, in a book published in 1893. This work leaned heavily on Cantor's set theory. A more satisfactory definition, still making strong use of sets, was given by John von Neumann (1903–1957) in 1923.

Fortunately, at this stage, we do not need to concern ourselves with this difficult problem, but can accept the results obtained by professional mathematicians. How symbols that name numbers are manipulated is at this point of greater interest to us than a precise knowledge of numbers as objects. Manipulation of number symbols depends on certain basic properties of numbers, properties that have been developed by mathematicians over a considerable period of time and after a great deal of mental and creative effort. We will summarize these properties in this and the next two sections, and will make free use of them throughout the course.

Equality

In mathematics, *equality* is always used in the sense of logical identity; that is, an *equality sign*, $=$, is used to join two expressions if and only if the two expressions are names or descriptions of one and the same thing. In this sense, $=$ means "is identical with."

From the logical meaning of the equality sign, we can easily establish the following basic properties for its consistent use.

Equality Properties

Let x, y, and z be arbitrary elements of a set S.

REFLEXIVE LAW:	$x = x$.
SYMMETRIC LAW:	If $x = y$, then $y = x$.
TRANSITIVE LAW:	If $x = y$ and $y = z$, then $x = z$.
SUBSTITUTION PRINCIPLE:	If $x = y$, then either may replace the other in any expression without changing the truth or falsity of the statement.

These properties, directly or indirectly, control much activity related to the manipulation of algebraic expressions and the solving of algebraic equations. It is interesting to note that the equality sign did not appear until rather late in history—the sixteenth century. It was introduced by the English mathematician Robert Recorde (1510–1558).

Example 4.
(A) If $5 = \sqrt{x - 3}$, then, by the symmetric law of equality, $\sqrt{x - 3} = 5$.

(B) If $2 + 3(x + 5) = 2 + 3x + 15$ and $2 + 3x + 15 = 3x + 17$, then, by the transitive law of equality, $2 + 3(x + 5) = 3x + 17$.

(C) If $a + c = a + c$ and $a = b$, then, by the substitution principle, $a + c = b + c$.

Problem 4. State the property of equality that justifies each statement.

    (A) If $ac = ac$ and $a = b$, then $ac = bc$.
    (B) If $a(b + c) = ab + ac$, then $ab + ac = a(b + c)$.
    (C) If $3x^3 - 3x^2 - 18x = 3x(x^2 - x - 6)$ and $3x(x^2 - x - 6)$
          $= 3x(x - 3)(x + 2)$, then $3x^3 - 3x^2 - 18x = 3x(x - 3)(x + 2)$.

ANSWER

(A) Substitution principle, (B) symmetric law of equality, (C) transitive law of equality.

Field Properties

The set of real numbers has the mathematical structure of a *field*; that is, under the operations of addition and multiplication, real numbers have the following basic properties:

The Field of Real Numbers

Let R be the set of real numbers and x, y, z arbitrary elements of R.

Addition Properties

CLOSURE:	$x + y$ is a unique element in R.
ASSOCIATIVE:	$(x + y) + z = x + (y + z)$.
COMMUTATIVE:	$x + y = y + x$.
IDENTITY:	0 is the additive identity; that is, $0 + x = x + 0 = x$ for all $x \in R$, and 0 is the only element of R with this property.
INVERSE:	For each $x \in R$, $-x$ is its unique additive inverse; that is, $x + (-x) = (-x) + x = 0$, and $-x$ is the only element of R with this property.

Multiplication Properties

CLOSURE:	xy is a unique element in R.
ASSOCIATIVE:	$(xy)z = x(yz)$.
COMMUTATIVE:	$xy = yx$.
IDENTITY:	1 is the multiplicative identity; that is, $1x = x1 = x$ for $x \in R$, and 1 is the only element of R with this property.
INVERSE:	For each $x \in R$, $x \neq 0$, x^{-1} is its unique multiplicative inverse; that is, $xx^{-1} = x^{-1}x = 1$, and x^{-1} is the only element of R with this property.

Combined Property

DISTRIBUTIVE:	$x(y + z) = xy + xz$.

Example 5.   The replacement set for all variables is the set of real numbers.

	Statement	*Property Illustrated*
(A)	$(7x)y = 7(xy)$	Associative property of multiplication
(B)	$a(b + c) = (b + c)a$	Closure property of addition and commutative property of multiplication
(C)	$(a + b) + xy = a + (b + xy)$	Closure property of multiplication and associative property of addition
(D)	If $a + b = 0$, then $b = -a$	Uniqueness of additive inverse
(E)	$7x + 9x = x7 + x9$	Commutative property of multiplication
	$= x(7 + 9)$	Distributive property
	$= x16$	Substitution principle
	$= 16x$	Commutative property of multiplication

Problem 5.   If the replacement set for all variables is the set of real numbers, indicate the property or properties of real numbers that justify each statement.

(A) $4 + (2 + x) = (4 + 2) + x$
(B) $(a + b) + c = c + (a + b)$
(C) $(7x)2 = 2(7x)$
(D)   If $ab = 1$, then $b = a^{-1}$
(E) $(y + z)x = x(y + z)$
$\qquad\qquad\quad = xy + xz$
$\qquad\qquad\quad = yx + zx$

ANSWER

(A) Associative property of addition; (B) closure and commutative property of addition; (C) closure and commutative property of multiplication; (D) uniqueness of the multiplicative inverse; (E) closure for addition and commutative property of multiplication, distributive property, commutative property of multiplication.

   From the few basic properties of real numbers listed above, we can derive many other useful properties, some of which will be discussed in the next section, and together these properties form the operating rules for the algebra of real numbers.

EXERCISE 2

A   1. (A)   Give an example of a real number that is not a rational number.
      (B)   Give an example of an integer that is not a natural number.
      (C)   Give an example of a rational number that is not an integer.
   2. Indicate which of the following statements are true:
      (A)   The set of integers is a subset of the set of natural numbers.
      (B)   The set of rational numbers is a subset of the set of real numbers.
      (C)   The set of integers is a subset of the set of real numbers.
      (D)   The set of natural numbers is a subset of the set of rational numbers.
   3. Given the sets $R =$ the set of real numbers
$$Q = \text{the set of rational numbers}$$
$$I = \text{the set of integers}$$
$$N = \text{the set of natural numbers}$$
   Each of the following numbers belongs to which of the above sets?
      (A) -3 (B)   3.14   (C) $\frac{22}{7}$ (D) $\sqrt[3]{5}$
   4. Using the four sets described in Prob. 3, indicate to which each of the following belongs:
      (A) $3\frac{1}{2}$ (B)   1.73   (C) $\sqrt{3}$ (D) -8
   5. Replace "is" with $=$ or $\neq$ as is appropriate.
      (A) $(5)(7)$ is $5 \cdot 7$ (B)   4 is V   (C)   2 is even
   6. Replace "is" with $=$ or $\neq$ as is appropriate.
      (A) $7 + 4$ is $6 + 5$ (B)   IX is 11   (C)   5 is odd

State the law of equality that justifies each statement.

   7. If $A = p(1 + rt)$, then $p(1 + rt) = A$.
   8. If $3 + x = \sqrt{x - 2}$, then $\sqrt{x - 2} = 3 + x$.
   9. If $2(x - 3) + 4x = 2x - 6 + 4x$ and $2x - 6 + 4x = 6x - 6$, then $2(x - 3) + 4x = 6x - 6$.
   10. If $C = \pi D$ and $\pi D = 2\pi r$, then $C = 2\pi r$.
   11. If $a - c = a - c$ and $a = b$, then $a - c = b - c$.
   12. If $a/c = a/c$ and $a = b$, then $a/c = b/c$.

In Probs. 13 and 14, if the replacement set for all variables is the set of real numbers, indicate the property or properties of the real numbers that justify each statement.

   13. (A) $az = za$ (B) $(12a)b = 12(ab)$
        (C) $(12 + a) + b = b + (12 + a)$ (D) $r(s + t) = rs + rt$
        (E) $c + x$ is a real number   (F) $12 + (a + b) = (12 + a) + b$
        (G) $x^2y + xy^2 = xy(x + y)$ (H) cx is a real number
   14. (A) $y + z$ is a real number   (B) $u + v = v + u$
        (C) $3 \cdot 15 = 15 \cdot 3$ (D) $7(x + y) = 7x + 7y$
        (E) $(3y)z = 3(yz)$ (F) $(3y)z = z(3y)$
        (G) $x^2 + 7x = x(x + 7)$ (H) $5 + (a + b) = (5 + a) + b$

B 15. Every rational number has an infinite repeating-decimal representation. For example,

$$\tfrac{1}{4} = 0.25\overline{00}$$

$$\tfrac{1}{3} = 0.3\overline{33}$$

$$\tfrac{15}{7} = 2.142857\overline{142857}$$

(The bar indicates the block of numbers that continues to repeat indefinitely.) Express each of the following rational numbers in repeating-decimal form:

(A) $\tfrac{3}{8}$ (B) $\tfrac{23}{9}$ (C) $\tfrac{7}{13}$

16. Repeat Prob. 15 for

(A) $\tfrac{37}{6}$ (B) $\tfrac{15}{21}$

17. Every infinitely repeating decimal is a rational number. To find two integers whose quotient is a repeating decimal, say $2.13\overline{535}$, proceed as follows:

$$n = 2.13\overline{535}$$

$$10n = 21.3\overline{535}$$

$$1{,}000n = 2135.3\overline{535}$$

$$1{,}000n - 10n = 2135.3\overline{535} - 21.3\overline{535}$$

$$990n = 2{,}114$$

$$n = \frac{2{,}114}{990} = \frac{1{,}057}{495}$$

Convert each of the following repeating decimals to a quotient of two integer forms:

(A) $0.27\overline{27}$ (B) $3.21\overline{21}$

18. Proceed as in Prob. 17 to convert each of the following repeating decimals to a quotient of two integer forms:

(A) $2.17\overline{17}$ (B) $0.472\overline{72}$

(COMMENT: In general it can be shown that irrational numbers are characterized by infinite nonrepeating-decimal representations, and that rational numbers are characterized by repeating-decimal representations.)

19. What is wrong with the following argument? Four is an even number and 8 is an even number, hence we can write, "4 = even number" and "8 = even number." By the symmetric law for equality, we can write, "even number = 8," and conclude, using the transitive law for equality (since 4 = even number and even number = 8), that 4 = 8.

20. What is wrong with the following argument? Rod is a human and Jan is a human, hence we can write, "Rod = human" and "Jan = human." By the symmetric law for equality, we can write, "human = Jan," and conclude, using the transitive law for equality (since Rod = human and human = Jan), that Rod = Jan.

In Probs. 21 and 22, if the replacement set for all variables is the set of real numbers, indicate the property or properties of the real numbers that justify each statement.

21. (A) $(ab)(cd) = (cd)(ab)$
    (B) $(2+3) + (5+7) = (5+7) + (2+3)$
    (C) $(2+3) + (5+7) = 2 + [3 + (5+7)]$
    (D) $(x+y)(a+b) = (x+y)a + (x+y)b$
    (E) $(xy)(a+b) = x[y(a+b)]$

22. (A) $(z+x) + (c+a) = z + [x + (c+a)]$
    (B) $(zx)(ca) = z[x(ca)]$
    (C) $(x+y) + z = z + (x+y)$
    (D) $(x+3)(x+5) = (x+3)x + (x+3)5$
    (E) $(xy)z = z(xy)$

23. If in the set of real numbers each of the four arithmetic operations were associative, we would be able to write:
    For each real number a, b, and c

    $$(a+b) + c = a + (b+c) \qquad (ab)c = a(bc)$$
    $$(a-b) - c = a - (b-c) \qquad (a \div b) \div c = a \div (b \div c)$$

    Find a counterexample for each false statement; that is, find real-number replacements for a and b that will make the statement false. Conclusion?

24. If in the set of real numbers each of the four arithmetic operations were commutative, we would be able to write:
    For each real number a and b

    $$a + b = b + a \qquad a - b = b - a$$
    $$ab = ba \qquad a \div b = b \div a$$

    Find a counterexample for each false statement; that is, find real-number replacements for a and b that will make the statement false. Conclusion?

25. If in the set of real numbers addition distributed over multiplication, we would be able to write:
    For each real number a, b, and c

    $$a + (bc) = (a+b)(a+c)$$

    How can you show that this statement is false?

26. If the set of natural numbers were closed with respect to the four arithmetic operations, we would be able to write:
    For each pair of natural numbers a and b

    $a + b$ is a natural number
    ab is a natural number
    $a - b$ is a natural number
    $a \div b$ is a natural number

    Find a counterexample for each false statement. Conclusion?

27. How is the distributive law used in the standard multiplication process illustrated in the problem at the right?

$$\begin{array}{r} 37 \\ 62 \\ \hline 74 \\ 222 \\ \hline 2{,}294 \end{array}$$

28. If the replacement set for the variable x is the set of real numbers, then $-x$ (*sometimes*, *always*, *never*) represents a negative real number.

C 29. Which of the field properties are not satisfied by (A) natural numbers, (B) integers?

30. Do rational numbers form a field; that is, do they have the same field properties that real numbers have?

31. Give an example of two rational numbers that are not integers whose sum is an integer.

32. Can the sum of an integer and a rational number that is not an integer ever be an integer?

33. Give an example of two irrational numbers whose sum is a rational number.

34. Can the sum of a rational number and an irrational number ever be rational? Explain.

35. Give an example of a subset of real numbers that is closed with respect to
    (A) $+$ and $\cdot$, but not with respect to $-$ and $\div$.
    (B) $+$, $\cdot$, and $-$, but not with respect to $\div$.

36. Give a reason for each step.

$$\begin{aligned} [a + b] + (-a) &= (-a) + [a + b] \\ &= [(-a) + a] + b \\ &= 0 + b \\ &= b \end{aligned}$$

37. Supply the reasons for each of the following steps (more than one reason may be required for each step).

$$\begin{aligned} (a + b) + [(-a) + (-b)] &= [a + (-a)] + [b + (-b)] \\ &= 0 + 0 \\ &= 0 \end{aligned}$$

Therefore,

$$-(a + b) = (-a) + (-b)$$

38. Show that if a and b are integers, then $x = [(-a) + b]$ is a solution of the equation $x + a = b$, justifying each step with a real-number property.

1.3 MORE PROPERTIES OF REAL NUMBERS

In this section we will review several additional properties of real numbers that can be derived from the basic properties listed in the last section. More properties will be added from time to time as needed. Informal proofs will be given for some of the properties, and proofs for others will be left as exercises. To start, we define *subtraction* and *division*. For $x, y \in R$

$$x - y = x + (-y)$$

$$y\overline{)x} = x \div y = \frac{x}{y} = xy^{-1} \qquad y \neq 0$$

Thus, to subtract y from x, add the negative (the additive inverse) of y to x; to divide x by y, multiply x by the reciprocal (the multiplicative inverse) of y. *Division by zero is not defined.*

Theorem 1. If $a, b, c \in R$ and $a = b$, then

(A) $a + c = b + c$

(B) $a - c = b - c$

(C) $ac = bc$

(D) $\dfrac{a}{c} = \dfrac{b}{c} \qquad c \neq 0$

These are all easy to prove, making direct use of the properties of equality discussed in the last section. We will prove the addition property. From closure for addition, $a + c$ is a real number, hence, from the reflexive law of equality, $a + c = a + c$. Since it is given that $a = b$, we substitute b for a in the right side of the equation, using the substitution principle, to obtain $a + c = b + c$.

Theorem 2. If $a, b \in R$, then*

(A) $a + b = 0 \Rightarrow a = -b$ and $b = -a$

(B) $ab = 1 \Rightarrow a = b^{-1}$ and $b = a^{-1}$

(C) $a + b = a \Rightarrow b = 0$

(D) $ab = a \Rightarrow b = 1$

The proof of this theorem involves the uniqueness of the additive and multiplicative inverses and identities, and is an immediate consequence of these properties of the real numbers. That is, in the case for part (A),

---

* $\Rightarrow$ means "implies," and the statement "$p \Rightarrow q$" is called a *conditional sentence* or an *implication*. The following statements are equivalent in the sense that either all are true or all are false:

| If p, then q | p is sufficient for q | $p \Rightarrow q$ |
| p implies q | q is necessary for p | not $q \Rightarrow$ not p |

for each $a \in R$, there exists a unique (one and only one) element of R, $-a$, such that $a + (-a) = 0$. It follows that if $a + b = 0$, then b must be $-a$.

Theorem 3. If $a, b \in R$, then

(A) $-(-a) = a$
(B) $-(a + b) = -a - b$
(C) $(a^{-1})^{-1} = a$
(D) $(ab)^{-1} = a^{-1}b^{-1}$

To prove part (A), start with $a + (-a) = 0$. By Theorem 2, $a = -(-a)$, and by the symmetric law of equality, $-(-a) = a$. To prove part (B), show that $(a + b) + (-a - b) = 0$ and conclude, because of Theorem 2A, that $-(a + b) = -a - b$.

Theorem 4. If $a, b \in R$, then

(A) $a \cdot 0 = 0$
(B) $ab = 0 \Rightarrow a = 0$ or $b = 0$ (or both)

We start the proof of part (A) by first writing $0 + 0 = 0$. Then, using the multiplication property of equality, we multiply both members of the equation by a to obtain $a(0 + 0) = a \cdot 0$. And, with the distributive property, this becomes $a \cdot 0 + a \cdot 0 = a \cdot 0$. Now, using Theorem 2C, we conclude that $a \cdot 0 = 0$. To prove part (B), start by assuming $a \neq 0$ and multiply both members of $ab = 0$ by a^{-1}.

Theorem 5. If $a, b \in R$, then

(A) $(-a)b = -(ab)$
(B) $(-a)(-b) = ab$
(C) $(-1)a = -a$

This theorem does not tell us that the product of a negative number and a positive number is a negative number. It simply tells us that if a and b are any two real numbers and we multiply the negative of a by b, the product will be the negative of the product of a and b, which may or may not be negative. To prove part (A), we first write $a + (-a) = 0$. Using the multiplication property of equality, multiply both members by b to obtain $b[a + (-a)] = b \cdot 0$. Applying the distributive property to the left member and Theorem 4A to the right, the equation now becomes $ba + b(-a) = 0$, which in turn becomes $ab + (-a)b = 0$ with an application of the commutative property of multiplication. From the last equation we can conclude, because of Theorem 2A, that $(-a)b = -(ab)$.

There are several variations on the distributive property. The following theorem lists a few useful ones.

Theorem 6. For a, b, $c \in R$

(A) $(b + c)a = ba + ca$
(B) $a(b - c) = ab - ac$
(C) $(b - c)a = ba - ca$

The last three theorems in this section deal with fractions.

Theorem 7. If a, b, c, $d \in R$, then*

(A) $\dfrac{a}{a} = 1 \qquad a \neq 0$

(B) $\dfrac{a}{1} = a$

(C) $\dfrac{a}{b} = \dfrac{c}{d} \Leftrightarrow ad = bc \qquad b, d \neq 0 \qquad$ (equality of fractions)

(D) $\dfrac{ka}{kb} = \dfrac{a}{b}, \quad b \neq 0 \qquad$ (fundamental property of fractions)

Part (A) follows from the definition of division and the multiplicative inverse property: $a/a = a \cdot a^{-1} = 1$. The proof of (B) is similar to that of (A), and (D) follows from (C). See if you can supply the reasons in the following proof of (C):

$$\frac{a}{b} = \frac{c}{d} \Leftrightarrow ab^{-1} = cd^{-1} \Leftrightarrow (bd)(ab^{-1}) = (bd)(cd^{-1})$$

$$\Leftrightarrow (ad)(bb^{-1}) = (bc)(dd^{-1}) \Leftrightarrow (ad) \cdot 1 = (bc) \cdot 1 \Leftrightarrow ad = bc$$

Answer

Definition of division; multiplication property of equality; repeated use of associative and commutative properties of multiplication; multiplication inverse property; multiplication identity property.

* $\Leftrightarrow$ means "if and only if," and the statement $p \Leftrightarrow q$ is called a *biconditional*. The following statements are equivalent in the sense that either all are true or all are false:

p if and only if q p is necessary and sufficient for q
$p \Leftrightarrow q$ q is necessary and sufficient for p
$p \Rightarrow q$ and $q \Rightarrow p$

Property (D) in Theorem 7, the fundamental property of fractions, is of great use; it allows us to raise fractions to "higher terms" and to reduce fractions to "lower terms." The former is particularly useful in the process of adding or subtracting fractions with different denominators.

Theorem 8. If $a, b, c, d \in R$, then

(A) $\dfrac{a}{c} + \dfrac{b}{c} = \dfrac{a+b}{c}$ $\qquad c \neq 0$ (B) $\dfrac{a}{c} - \dfrac{b}{c} = \dfrac{a-b}{c}$ $\qquad c \neq 0$

(C) $\dfrac{a}{b} \cdot \dfrac{c}{d} = \dfrac{ac}{bd}$ $\qquad b, d \neq 0$ (D) $\dfrac{a}{b} \div \dfrac{c}{d} = \dfrac{a}{b} \cdot \dfrac{d}{c}$ $\qquad b, c, d \neq 0$

To add or subtract fractions without common denominators, use the fundamental property of fractions (Theorem 7D) to obtain common denominators; then use either (A) or (B). It is interesting to note that all these operations can be established on the basis of the field properties of real numbers, a few derived properties, and the definition of division. Try to supply the reasons for each step in the following proofs of (A) and (B).

(A) $a/c + b/c = ac^{-1} + bc^{-1} = (a+b)c^{-1} = (a+b)/c$
(B) $a/b \cdot c/d = (ab^{-1})(cd^{-1}) = (ac)(b^{-1}d^{-1}) = (ac)(bd)^{-1} = ac/bd$

ANSWER

(A) Definition of division, Theorem 6A, definition of division; (B) definition of division, repeated use of associative and commutative properties of multiplication, Theorem 3D, definition of division.

Theorem 9. If $a, b \in R$, then

(A) $\dfrac{-a}{b} = \dfrac{a}{-b} = -\dfrac{a}{b}$ $\qquad b \neq 0$

(B) $\dfrac{-a}{-b} = \dfrac{a}{b}$ $\qquad b \neq 0$

This last theorem, when completely understood, results in a substantial reduction of sign errors in algebraic work with fractions. All parts follow almost directly from Theorems 7C and 5.

EXERCISE 3

A *Justify each statement on the basis of a theorem or definition given in this section. The replacement set for all variables is the set of real numbers.*

1. If $x + 3 = x + 7$, then $(x + 3) - 3 = (x + 7) - 3$.
2. If $x^2 - 4 = x$, then $(x^2 - 4) + 4 = x + 4$.
3. If $x/3 = 7$, then $3(x/3) = 3 \cdot 7$.
4. If $2x = 4$, then $2x/2 = \frac{4}{2}$.
5. $(-3) - (-2) = (-3) + [-(-2)]$
6. $\frac{7}{6} = 7 \cdot 6^{-1}$
7. If $m + n = 0$, then $m = -n$.
8. If $ab + (-a)b = 0$, then $(-a)b = -(ab)$.
9. If $10x = 1$, then $x = 10^{-1}$.   10. If $ax = 1$, then $x = a^{-1}$.
11. If $5 + x = 5$, then $x = 0$.   12. If $ab + c = ab$, then $c = 0$.
13. $-(-5) = 5$ 14. $-(7x + 2y) = -7x - 2y$
15. $(5^{-1})^{-1} = 5$ 16. $u^{-1}v^{-1} = (uv)^{-1}$
17. If $(x - 3)(x + 2) = 0$, then $x - 3 = 0$ or $x + 2 = 0$.
18. If $x(x + 5) = 0$, then $x = 0$ or $x + 5 = 0$.
19. $(-1)(ab) = -(ab)$ 20. $(-x)(-y) = xy$
21. $3(x - y) = 3x - 3y$ 22. $(a + b)x = ax + bx$
23. $7x + 2x = (7 + 2)x$ 24. $6xy = 3xy = (6 - 3)xy$

25. $\dfrac{6(x - y)}{6(x - y)} = 1$ 26. $6 \cdot \dfrac{\sqrt{3}}{x} = \dfrac{6}{1} \cdot \dfrac{\sqrt{3}}{x}$

27. $\dfrac{6x^3y}{8xy^2} = \dfrac{3x^2}{4y}$ 28. $\dfrac{3}{7} = \dfrac{6(x - 4)}{14(x - 4)}$

29. $\dfrac{3}{2} \cdot \dfrac{x + 1}{x^2} = \dfrac{3(x + 1)}{2x^2}$

30. $\dfrac{x^2}{x + 1} \div \dfrac{(x + 1)^2}{3x^4} = \dfrac{x^2}{x + 1} \cdot \dfrac{3x^4}{(x + 1)^2}$

31. $\dfrac{4y}{3x} + \dfrac{5z}{3x} = \dfrac{4y + 5z}{3x}$

32. $\dfrac{6(x - 3)}{4(x - 3)} - \dfrac{x - 2}{4(x - 3)} = \dfrac{6(x - 3) - (x - 2)}{4(x - 3)}$

33. $\dfrac{5}{-(x - 3)} = -\dfrac{5}{x - 3}$

34. $\dfrac{-7}{-(x^2 + 6)} = \dfrac{7}{x^2 + 6}$

B 35. (A) Zero divided by any real number is (*always, sometimes, never*) zero.
   (B) Any real number divided by zero is (*always, sometimes, never*) zero.
36. If $ab = 1$ does either a or b have to be 1? Explain.
37. If $a, b \in R$, how do we know that $a - b \in R$; that is, R is closed under subtraction? (*Hint:* See definition of subtraction.)
38. If $a, b \in R$, $b \neq 0$, how do we know that $a/b \in R$; that is, R is closed under division? (*Hint:* See definition of division.)

In Probs. 39 to 42 give the reason(s) for each step in each proof. The replacement set for all variables is the set of real numbers. Assume the transitive property of equality without statement.

39. Theorem 1D: $a = b \Rightarrow a/c = b/c$ $c \neq 0$
   PROOF:

Statement	*Reason*
1. $a/c \in R$	1.
2. $a/c = a/c$	2.
3. $a = b$	3.
4. $a/c = b/c$	4.

40. Theorem 4B: $ab = 0 \Rightarrow a = 0$ or $b = 0$
   PROOF: There are two possibilities. If $a = 0$, then the stated conclusion is correct, and the proof is complete. If $a \neq 0$, we must show that $b = 0$.

Statement	*Reason*
1. $ab = 0$	1.
2. a^{-1} exists	2.
3. $a^{-1}(ab) = a^{-1} \cdot 0$	3.
4. $(a^{-1}a)b = 0$	4.
5. $1 \cdot b = 0$	5.
6. $b = 0$	6.

41. Theorem 8B: $(a/c) - (b/c) = (a - b)/c$ $c \neq 0$
   PROOF:

Statement	*Reason*
1. $a/c - b/c = ac^{-1} - bc^{-1}$	1.
2. $= (a - b)c^{-1}$	2.
3. $= (a - b)/c$	3.

42. Theorem 6B: $a(b - c) = ab - ac$
   PROOF:

Statement	*Reason*
1. $a(b - c) = a[b + (-c)]$	1.
2. $= ab + a(-c)$	2.
3. $= ab + [-(ac)]$	3.
4. $= ab - ac$	4.

C *Prove the following theorems, assuming the replacement set of all variables is the set of real numbers, division by zero excluded.*

43. $(b + c)a = ba + ca$

44. $a = b \Rightarrow ac = bc$

45. $-(a + b) = -a - b$

46. $(-a)(-b) = ab$

47. $\dfrac{a}{b} + \dfrac{c}{d} = \dfrac{ad + bc}{bd}$

48. $\dfrac{a}{b} \div \dfrac{c}{d} = \dfrac{a}{b} \cdot \dfrac{d}{c}$

49. $(a^{-1})^{-1} = a$

50. $(ab)^{-1} = a^{-1}b^{-1}$

1.4 ORDER, THE REAL LINE, AND COMPLETENESS

Order Relation

In the last two sections we observed that the set of real numbers satisfied field properties, and we investigated some of the consequences of this fact. Another important property of real numbers is that they form an ordered set—intuitively, they can be arranged in an order from smaller to larger— hence they are often referred to as an *ordered field*. Later we will see that the set of complex numbers is a field, but that it cannot be ordered.

Basic to the ordering process are the two following additional properties of real numbers. These properties characterize the *positive real numbers* R^+.

TRICHOTOMY: For each $x \in R$, one and only one of the following is true: x is positive, $x = 0$, or $-x$ is positive.

CLOSURE FOR R^+: If x and y are positive real numbers, then $x + y$ and xy are positive real numbers.

If x is a positive real number, $-x$ is a negative real number, and the *set of negative real numbers* is denoted by R^-.

With these basic notions, we now order the real numbers as follows. We say that x *is greater than* y (*or y is less than x*), written $x > y$ (or $y < x$), if $x - y$ is a positive real number. The symbols $>$ and $<$ are called *inequality signs*, and expressions such as $x - 3 > 2$ or $3 < x + 5$ are called *inequalities* or *inequality statements*.

Example 6.
(A) If $b - a$ is positive, then $b > a$ and $a < b$.
(B) $5 - (-3) = 8$ is positive, hence $5 > -3$ and $-3 < 5$.
(C) $0 - (-10) = 10$ is positive, hence $0 > -10$ and $-10 < 0$.
(D) $(-1) - (-8) = 7$ is positive, hence $-1 > -8$ and $-8 < -1$.
(E) If $ab - ac$ is positive, then $ab > ac$ and $ac < ab$.
(F) If $b > a$ or $a < b$, then $b - a$ is positive.

Problem 6. Replace each question mark with $>$, $<$, an appropriate numeral, or an algebraic expression.

(A) If ? is positive, then $u > v$ and $v < u$.
(B) $? - ? = 3$ is positive, hence $0 > -3$ and $-3 < 0$.
(C) $(-5) - (-25) = 20$ is positive, hence $? > ?$ and $? < ?$.

(D) $? - ? = 9$ is positive, hence $6 ? -3$ and $-3 ? 6$.
(E)   If $(a + c) - (b + c)$ is positive, then $a + c ? b + c$.
(F)   If $(a - c) > (b - c)$, then $? - ?$ is positive.

ANSWER

(A) $u - v$; (B) $0, -3$; (C) $-5, -25, -25, -5$; (D) $6, -3, >, < $;
(E) $>$; (F) $a - c, b - c$.

The following properties of the order relations $>$ and $<$ follow directly from the properties and definitions above.

Theorem 10.   (A)   For $x, y \in R$, then one, and only one, of the following holds: $x > y$, $x = y$, or $x < y$.
(B)   If $x > y$ and $y > z$, then $x > z$.
(C)   If $x > y$ and z is any real number, then $x + z > y + z$.
(D)   If $x > y$ and z is positive, then $xz > yz$.
(E)   If $x > y$ and z is negative, then $xz < yz$.

Part (A) follows from the trichotomy property of real numbers; that is, $x - y$ is either positive, or 0, or $-(x - y) = y - x$ is positive. Hence, $x > y$, $x = y$, or $y > x$ (that is, $x < y$). To prove part (E), we start with $x > y$, which implies $x - y$ is positive. Since z is given negative, $z(x - y) = zx - zy$ is negative and $zy - zx$ is positive. Thus, $zx < zy$. The proofs of the other parts are left as exercises.

One often encounters statements of the form $x \geq y$, which is read, "x is greater than or equal to y," and $x \leq y$, which is read, "x is less than or equal to y." Theorem 10 is modified in obvious ways to apply to these forms and to the $x < y$ form. In addition, the *double inequalities $a \leq x \leq b$* $(a \leq x$ and $x \leq b)$, $a \leq x < b$ $(a \leq x$ and $x < b)$, $a < x \leq b$ $(a < x$ and $x \leq b)$, and $a < x < b$ $(a < x$ and $x < b)$ are frequently seen and are very useful.

Example 7.   Let $N =$ the set of natural numbers and $I =$ the set of integers.

(A) $\{x \in N \mid x \leq 5\} = \{1, 2, 3, 4, 5\}$
(B) $\{x \in N \mid x < 5\} = \{1, 2, 3, 4\}$
(C) $\{x \in I \mid -3 < x \leq 2\} = \{-2, -1, 0, 1, 2\}$

Problem 7.   List the elements in each of the following sets within braces.

(A) $\{x \in N \mid x < 4\}$
(B) $\{x \in N \mid x \leq 4\}$
(C) $\{x \in I \mid -2 \leq x < 3\}$

ANSWER

(A) $\{1, 2, 3\}$; (B) $\{1, 2, 3, 4\}$; (C) $\{-2, -1, 0, 1, 2\}$.

We will have more to say about inequality statements and their solutions in later sections. Now we turn to the association of real numbers with points on a line.

The Real-Number Line and Completeness

It is extremely useful to be able to associate numbers with points on a line. To start, pick an arbitrary point on a line and label it zero, and another point, usually to the right, and label it one, then divide the whole line into equal line segments having the same length as the segment from 0 to 1. Having done this, we can associate each integer with an end point of a line segment, and each end point of a line segment with an integer—the positive integers to the right of zero and the negative integers to the left. A number associated with a point is called the *coordinate of the point*, and the *graph of a number* is the point associated with the number. Thus,

We note that between two consecutive integers there are no other integers; hence, there are many points left without names (or coordinates).

We now use rational numbers to continue the labeling process. Every rational number a/b can be associated with a point on a line. For example, the point with coordinate $\frac{7}{4}$ is located by dividing the segment between 1 and 2 into four segments and taking the end point of the third segment. Something interesting happens in the case of rational numbers that did not happen with integers. It is easy to show, because of closure and ordering properties of rational numbers, that between any two distinct rational numbers (no matter how close) there always exists another rational number—just take the average of the two. One then naturally speculates that there is a one-to-one correspondence between the set of rational numbers and the points on a line. Not so! It was shown by the Pythagoreans, about 2,500 years ago, that certain line segments cannot be measured by rational numbers—a remarkable discovery for modern mathematics. By use of the Pythagorean theorem, it was found that if c is the hypotenuse of a right triangle having both legs of length 1, then $c^2 = 2$ (see Fig. 2). The question is, "Is there a rational number whose square is 2?" We now prove that there is no rational number whose square is 2.

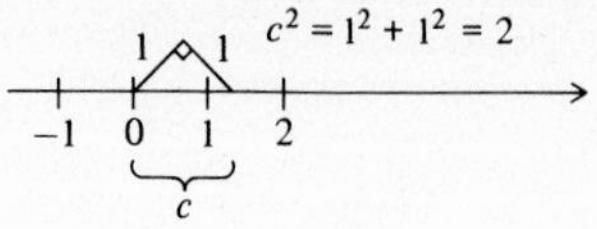

FIGURE 2

We will utilize an indirect proof, that is, a proof by contradiction. In this method of proof, we assume the contrary and show with deductive reasoning that this assumption leads to a contradiction; hence, the assumption must be false. Let us assume there is a rational number a/b, a and b integers, such that

$$\left(\frac{a}{b}\right)^2 = 2$$

then

$$a^2 = 2b^2$$

We now use the fundamental theorem of arithmetic, which states that each integer can be expressed as a product of prime numbers in only one way, except for order and sign. Thus if

$$a = n_1 n_2 \cdots n_p \qquad n_1, n_2, \ldots, n_p \text{ all prime}$$

then

$$a^2 = n_1{}^2 n_2{}^2 \cdots n_p{}^2$$

and we see that each prime factor in a^2 appears an even number of times. Similarly, each prime factor appears in b^2 an even number of times. But, since $a^2 = 2b^2$, the prime number 2 must appear on the right an odd number of times and on the left an even number of times, if at all. This contradicts the fundamental theorem of arithmetic; hence, our assumption must be false—there is no rational number whose square is 2.

There are infinitely many other points on the number line that do not have rational-number coordinates. Let us look at another type of "gap" on the rational-number line—one not associated with the solution of a polynomial equation. Suppose that we "unroll" the circumference of a circle with diameter 1 on a number line starting at zero (see Fig. 3). The

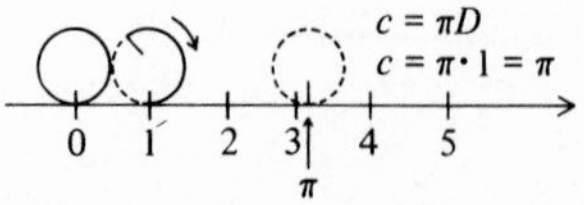

FIGURE 3

terminal point will be labeled π (recall that $C = \pi D$). We can show, though the proof is difficult, that there is no rational number equal to π— not even $\frac{22}{7}$, 3.14, or 3.14159 (these are all rational-number approximations of π).

The points on the number line not named by rational numbers will be named by irrational numbers, and it is a remarkable fact that we have the following theorem, the *fundamental theorem of analytic geometry*, which we state without proof.

Theorem 11. There exists a one-to-one correspondence between the set of real numbers and the points on a line.

It is for this reason that we call the real numbers *complete*, and refer to them as a *complete ordered field*. A line having real-number coordinates is called a *real-number line*, or simply a *real line*. As a consequence of Theorem 11, some of the graphs in the next example are solid lines. Note also, that any number to the right of another is larger than that number.

Example 8. $R =$ the set of real numbers, and $I =$ the set of integers.

(A) The graph of the set $\{x \in R \mid -2 < x \le 5\}$ is

(a)
```
 ├──┼──┼──┼──○━━━━━━━━━━━━━━●──┼──→
-6  -5 -4 -3 -2 -1  0  1  2  3  4  5  6
```

(B) The graph of the set $\{x \in I \mid -2 < x \le 5\}$ is

(b)
```
 ├──┼──┼──┼──┼──┼──●──●──●──●──●──●──●──┼──→
-6  -5 -4 -3 -2 -1  0  1  2  3  4  5  6
```

(C) The graph of the set $\{x \in R \mid x > -\frac{3}{2}\}$ is

(c)
```
 ├──┼──┼──┼──┼──○━━━━━━━━━━━━━━━━━━━→
-6  -5 -4 -3 -2 -1  0  1  2  3  4  5  6
```

Problem 8. Graph each of the following sets on a real-number line.

(A) $\{x \in R \mid -3 \le x < 4\}$
(B) $\{x \in I \mid -3 \le x < 4\}$
(C) $\{x \in R \mid x \le \frac{5}{2}\}$

ANSWER

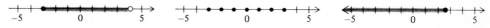

We conclude this section by stating without proof the following theorem.

Theorem 12. Between any two $\begin{pmatrix} \text{real} \\ \text{rational} \\ \text{rational} \\ \text{irrational} \\ \text{irrational} \end{pmatrix}$ numbers there is always a (an) $\begin{pmatrix} \text{real} \\ \text{rational} \\ \text{irrational} \\ \text{rational} \\ \text{irrational} \end{pmatrix}$ number.

This theorem tells us, among other things, that we can approximate any irrational number as closely as we like with rational numbers.

EXERCISE 4

In the following problems
N = the set of natural numbers
I = the set of integers
Q = the set of rational numbers
R = the set of real numbers

A *Replace each question mark with an appropriate symbol.*

1. $(-3) - (-9) = 6$ is positive, hence $-3 > -9$ and $? < ?$
2. $(-5) - (-8) = 3$ is positive, hence $? > ?$ and $-8 < -5$.
3. $? - ? = 9$ is positive, hence $0 > -9$ and $? < ?$
4. $? - ? = 5$ is positive, hence $-1 > -6$ and $? < ?$
5. If $a - b$ is positive, then $a > b$ and $? < ?$
6. If $? - ?$ is positive, then $u > v$ and $? < ?$
7. If $uv - wx$ is positive, then $? > ?$ and $wx < uv$.
8. If $? - ?$ is positive, then $a + c > b + c$.

List the elements of each set within the braces.

9. $\{x \in N \mid x \le 5\}$
10. $\{x \in N \mid x < 3\}$
11. $\{x \in I \mid -2 \le x < 2\}$
12. $\{x \in I \mid -1 < x \le 3\}$
13. $\{x \in I \mid -3 \le x \le 1\}$
14. $\{x \in I \mid -3 < x < 1\}$

Graph each set on a real number line.

15. $\{x \in N \mid x \le 6\}$
16. $\{x \in N \mid x < 4\}$
17. $\{x \in I \mid -1 \le x < 2\}$
18. $\{x \in I \mid -2 < x \le 2\}$
19. $\{x \in R \mid -1 \le x < 2\}$
20. $\{x \in R \mid -2 < x \le 2\}$
21. $\{x \in R \mid -3 < x < 3\}$
22. $\{x \in R \mid -2 \le x \le 2\}$
23. $\{x \in R \mid x \ge -2\}$
24. $\{x \in R \mid x < 4\}$

B 25. Replace the question marks with appropriate symbols:
   (A) $\{x \mid x < 8, x \in N\} = \{1, ?, ?, ?, ?, ?, 7\}$
   (B) $\{u \mid 99 < u \le 102, u \in N\} = \{(\text{list elements})\}$
   (C) $\{? \mid ? > ?, y \in N\} = \{10, 11, 12, \ldots\}$

26. Replace the question marks with appropriate symbols:
   (A) $\{x \mid x \le 5, x \in N\} = \{1, ?, ?, ?, 5\}$
   (B) $\{t \mid 2 \le t < 6, t \in N\} = \{(\text{list elements})\}$
   (C) $\{y \mid ? < ? \le ?, ? \in N\} = \{3, 4, 5, 6, 7\}$

27. If the graph of set S is

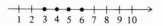

then
(A) $S =$ (list the elements)
(B) $S = \{t \mid ? < t \le ?, t \in N\}$

28. If the graph of the set M is

then
(A) $M =$ (list the elements)
(B) $M = \{x \mid ? \le ? < ?, x \in N\}$

29. Describe each of the following sets as empty, nonempty but finite, or infinite:
(A) $\{x \mid 5 < x < 6, x \text{ a natural number}\}$
(B) $\{x \mid -3 < x < -2, x \text{ an integer}\}$
(C) $\{x \mid 5 < x < \frac{11}{2}, x \text{ a rational number}\}$
(D) $\{x \mid 3 < x < \pi, x \text{ a real number}\}$

30. Indicate whether each set is empty, finite (but nonempty), or infinite.
(A) $\{x \mid -1 < x < 0, x \in I\}$
(B) $\{x \mid -1 \le x \le 0, x \in I\}$
(C) $\{x \mid -1 < x < 0, x \in Q\}$
(D) $\{x \mid -1 < x < 0, x \in R\}$

31. Graph $\{x \in I \mid -\pi \le x \le \frac{9}{4}\}$
32. Graph $\{x \in I \mid -\sqrt{5} \le x < \pi\}$
33. Graph $\{x \in R \mid -\pi \le x \le \frac{9}{4}\}$
34. Graph $\{x \in R \mid -\sqrt{5} \le x < \pi\}$

Give the reasons for the statements in the proofs for the following theorems.

35. If $x > y$ and z is any real number, then $x + z > y + z$.
PROOF:

Statement		Reason
1. $x > y \Rightarrow x - y$ is positive.	1.	
2. $x + z - y - z$ is positive.	2.	
3. $(x + z) - (y + z)$ is positive.	3.	Definition of subtraction, and $-(y + z) = -y - z$
4. $x + z > y + z$	4.	

36. If $x > y$ and z is negative, then $\dfrac{x}{z} < \dfrac{y}{z}$.

PROOF:

Statement		Reason
1. $x > y \Rightarrow x - y$ is positive.	1.	

2. $\dfrac{1}{z}$ is negative.   2. Sign property of R

3. $\dfrac{1}{z}(x - y) = \dfrac{x}{z} - \dfrac{y}{z}$ is negative.   3.

4. $\dfrac{y}{z} - \dfrac{x}{z}$ is positive.   4. $a - b$ positive $\Rightarrow b - a$ negative

5. $\dfrac{x}{z} < \dfrac{y}{z}$ 5.

C 37. In the set of all rational numbers less than a given rational number, is there a largest rational number?

38. In the set of all rational numbers less than a given irrational number, is there a largest rational number?

39. (A) Find the two integers nearest $\frac{17}{4}$.
(B) Can you find two rational numbers, one above $\frac{17}{4}$ and the other below $\frac{17}{4}$, that are nearer $\frac{17}{4}$ than any other rational numbers? Explain.

40. (A) Find the two integers nearest $\sqrt{2}$.
(B) Can you find two rational numbers, one above $\sqrt{2}$ and the other below $\sqrt{2}$, that are nearer $\sqrt{2}$ than any other rational numbers? Explain.

41. Prove that if $x > y$ and z is positive, then $xz > yz$.

42. Prove that if $x > y$ and $y > z$, then $x > z$.

43. Prove that there is no rational number whose square is 3.

44. Prove that there is no rational number whose square is 5.

45. Prove that if a/b is a positive, nonintegral rational number, a and b natural numbers, then there exists a natural number n such that $n < a/b < n + 1$. (*Hint:* Assume that for each positive rational number a/b there exist unique natural numbers q and r such that $a = bq + r$, $0 < r < b$.)

1.5 THE FIELD OF COMPLEX NUMBERS

The real-number system is closed with respect to the four basic operations of arithmetic, except for division by zero. In addition, any root of a positive real number is a real number, and some roots of negative real numbers are real numbers. It is still easy, however, to make up simple equations, using only integers and a variable, that do not have solutions in real numbers. For example

$$x^2 = -1$$

has no solution in real numbers (since no real number squared can be negative). We are thus motivated to extend the real-number system to include numbers whose squares are negative. To this end, we define a new kind of number, called a *complex number*, as a number of the form

---

$$a + bi$$

---

where a and b are real numbers, and i is called the imaginary unit. Thus,

$$3 - 2i \qquad \tfrac{1}{2} + 5i \qquad \sqrt{2} - \tfrac{1}{3}i$$
$$0 + 3i \qquad 5 + 0i \qquad 0 + 0i$$

are all complex numbers. We define particular types of complex numbers as follows:

$$a + 0i = a \qquad \text{(real number)}$$
$$0 + bi = bi \qquad \text{(pure imaginary number)}$$
$$1i = i \qquad \text{(imaginary unit)}$$

Hence, every real number is a complex number (just as every integer is a rational number). Shortly we will show that there are some complex numbers that are not real numbers, and thus establish the fact that the set of real numbers is a proper subset of the set of complex numbers.

We define *equality*, *addition*, and *multiplication* as follows:

$$a + bi = c + di \qquad \text{if and only if } a = c \text{ and } b = d$$
$$(a + bi) + (c + di) = (a + c) + (b + d)i$$
$$(a + bi)(c + di) = (ac - bd) + (ad + bc)i$$

Fortunately, we will not have to memorize the definitions for addition and multiplication. First, let us see what happens when we square i:

$$i^2 = i \cdot i = (0 + 1i)(0 + 1i) = [0 \cdot 0 - 1 \cdot 1] + [0 \cdot 1 + 1 \cdot 0]i$$
$$= -1 + 0 = -1$$

Thus,

$$i^2 = -1$$

---

and we have a number whose square is negative (and a solution to $x^2 = -1$). We choose to let

$$i = \sqrt{-1}$$
$$-i = -\sqrt{-1}$$

Under the definitions of addition and multiplication above, one can show that the set of complex numbers C satisfies the same field properties that real numbers R do (the details will be left as exercises). Also, a, b, and i in the $a + bi$ form can be treated as individual complex numbers, since $a + bi = (a + 0i) + (b + 0i)(0 + 1i)$. All this is very useful to know, because it means that we can manipulate the $a + bi$ form in the same way we manipulate binomial forms in the algebra of real numbers. The only difference is that we replace i^2 with -1 whenever it appears.

Example 9.   (A) $(2 - 3i) + (6 + 2i) = 2 - 3i + 6 + 2i = 2 + 6 - 3i + 2i = 8 - i$
                (B) $(7 - 3i) - (6 + 2i) = 7 - 3i - 6 - 2i = 1 - 5i$
                (C) $(2 - 3i)(6 + 2i) = 12 - 14i - 6i^2 = 12 - 14i + 6 = 18 - 14i$

(D) $\dfrac{3 + 2i}{5 + 3i} = \dfrac{(3 + 2i)(5 - 3i)}{(5 + 3i)(5 - 3i)} = \dfrac{15 + i - 6i^2}{25 - 9i^2} = \dfrac{21 + i}{25 + 9} = \dfrac{21}{34} + \dfrac{1}{34}i$

In part (D), notice that to carry out the division we multiplied the numerator and denominator by $5 - 3i$. This effectively eliminates i from the denominator. We have actually multiplied the numerator and denominator by the conjugate of the denominator. The *conjugate* of $a + bi$ is defined to be $a - bi$.

Problem 9.   Carry out the following operations and write each answer in the $a + bi$ form.

          (A) $(3 + 2i) + (6 - 4i)$
          (B) $(3 - 5i) - (1 - 3i)$
          (C) $(2 - 4i)(3 + 2i)$

          (D) $\dfrac{2 + 4i}{3 + 2i}$

ANSWER

(A) $9 - 2i$; (B) $2 - 2i$; (C) $14 - 8i$; (D) $\frac{14}{13} + \frac{8}{13}i$.

We say that y *is a square root of* x if $y^2 = x$. It can be shown that if x is a positive or negative real number, then x has two square roots. We denote one by $\sqrt{x}$, and the other by $-\sqrt{x}$. If x is negative, the square roots of x are complex numbers. If we let $x = -a$, $a > 0$, then

$$\sqrt{-a} = i\sqrt{a} \qquad a > 0$$

This is readily verified by noting that $(i\sqrt{a})^2 = i^2 a = -a$. Hence a square root of any negative real number can be written as the product of i and a square root of a positive real number. Thus

$$\sqrt{-3} = i\sqrt{3} \qquad \sqrt{-4} = i\sqrt{4} = 2i$$

What are $\sqrt{-7}$ and $\sqrt{-9}$? (*Answer:* $i\sqrt{7}$ and $3i$.) To solve the equation

$$(2x - 3)^2 = -16$$

we use the definition of square root of a number and write

$$2x - 3 = \pm\sqrt{-16}$$
$$2x = 3 \pm i\sqrt{16}$$
$$x = \frac{3 \pm 4i}{2} = \frac{3}{2} \pm 2i$$

Thus $\frac{3}{2} + 2i$ and $\frac{3}{2} - 2i$ are solutions to the equation, as can easily be checked.

We have noted that complex numbers form a field, but contrary to real numbers, complex numbers cannot be ordered. That is to say, it is impossible to say that one complex number is smaller than or larger than another. Complex numbers have widespread use in advanced applied mathematics, as well as in pure mathematics. Our first use of them will be in connection with solutions of equations.

EXERCISE 5

A *Perform the indicated operations and write the answer in the form* $a + bi$.

1. $(2 - 3i) + (5 - 2i)$
2. $(-8 + 5i) + (3 - 2i)$
3. $(9 - 3i) - (12 - 5i)$
4. $(4 + 7i) - (-2 - 6i)$
5. $12 + (5 - 2i)$
6. $(3 - 7i) + 5i$
7. $(\frac{1}{2} - 5i) + (\frac{2}{3} + \frac{1}{2}i)$
8. $(\frac{7}{8} - \frac{1}{3}i) - (\frac{3}{4} + \frac{1}{4}i)$
9. $(2i)(4i)$
10. $(5i)(3i)$
11. $3i(2 - 4i)$
12. $-2i(5 - 3i)$

13. $(2-3i)(3+3i)$
14. $(3-5i)(-2-3i)$
15. $(2-i)(3+2i)$
16. $(7-6i)(2-3i)$
17. $(5-3i)(5+3i)$
18. $(7+4i)(7-4i)$
19. $(u-vi)(u+vi)$
20. $(a+bi)(a-bi)$

21. $\dfrac{15-3i}{2-3i}$
22. $\dfrac{13+i}{2-i}$

23. $\dfrac{8+25i}{3-2i}$
24. $\dfrac{-1+8i}{3+2i}$

Write each of the following in the form $a+bi$ or $a+ib$.

25. $3+\sqrt{-4}$
26. $2-\sqrt{-9}$
27. $2+\sqrt{-3}$
28. $7-\sqrt{-5}$

29. $\dfrac{4-\sqrt{-16}}{2}$
30. $\dfrac{6-\sqrt{-9}}{3}$

B *In Probs. 31 to 46 convert square roots of negative numbers to complex form, perform the indicated operations, and write the answers in the form $a+bi$ or $a+ib$.*

31. $(-8+\sqrt{-25})+(3-\sqrt{-4})$
32. $(5-\sqrt{-9})+(2-\sqrt{-4})$
33. $(4+\sqrt{-49})-(-2-\sqrt{-36})$
34. $(9-\sqrt{-9})-(12-\sqrt{-25})$
35. $(5+\sqrt{-9})(2-\sqrt{-1})$
36. $(-2+\sqrt{-49})(3-\sqrt{-4})$

37. $\dfrac{6-\sqrt{-64}}{2}$
38. $\dfrac{5-\sqrt{-4}}{3}$

39. $\dfrac{1}{3-\sqrt{-16}}$
40. $\dfrac{1}{2-\sqrt{-9}}$

41. $\dfrac{1}{3i}$
42. $\dfrac{2}{5i}$

43. $\dfrac{2-i}{3i}$
44. $\dfrac{1+3i}{2i}$

45. $(2-3i)^2-2(2-3i)+9$
46. $(2-i)^2+3(2-i)-5$
47. Evaluate x^2-2x+2 for $x=(1+i)$.
48. Evaluate x^2-2x+2 for $x=(1-i)$.

Solve each of the equations in Probs. 49 to 52.

49. $x^2=-25$
50. $y^2=-36$
51. $(x-3)^2=-4$
52. $(x-9)^2=-9$
53. Simplify: i^2, i^3, i^4, i^5, i^6, i^7, and i^8.
54. Simplify: i^{12}, i^{13}, i^{14}, i^{15}, and i^{16}.
55. For what real values of x and y will $(2x-1)+(3y+2)i=5-4i$?
56. For what real values of x and y will $(3x)+(y-2)i=(5-2x)+(3y-8)i$?

Supply the reasons in the proofs for the following two theorems.

57. Complex numbers are commutative under addition.

    PROOF: Let $a + bi$ and $c + di$ be two arbitrary complex numbers. Then

Statement		Reason
1. $(a + bi) + (c + di) = (a + c) + (b + d)i$		1.
2. $\qquad = (c + a) + (d + b)i$		2.
3. $\qquad = (c + di) + (a + bi)$		3.

58. Complex numbers are commutative under multiplication.

    PROOF: Let $a + bi$ and $c + di$ be two arbitrary complex numbers. Then

Statement		Reason
1. $(a + bi)(c + di) = (ac - bd) + (ad + bc)i$		1.
2. $\qquad = (ca - db) + (da + cb)i$		2.
3. $\qquad = (c + di)(a + bi)$		3.

C 59. For what values of x will $\sqrt{x - 10}$ be real?

60. When will $(-b \pm \sqrt{b^2 - 4ac})/2a$ represent a complex number, assuming a, b, and c are all real numbers $(a \neq 0)$?

61. Show that $i^{4k} = 1$, $k \in N$.

62. Show that $i^{4k+1} = i$, $k \in N$.

63. $i^{4k+2} = ?$, $k \in N$. Prove your answer.

64. $i^{4k+3} = ?$, $k \in N$. Prove your answer.

In the following proofs use only the definitions of equality, addition, and multiplication of complex numbers and properties of real numbers.

65. Prove that $0 = 0 + 0i$ is the additive identity for the set of complex numbers C.

66. Prove that $1 = 1 + 0i$ is the multiplicative identity for the set of complex numbers C.

67. Prove that for each complex number $a + bi$, its additive inverse is $-a - bi$.

68. Prove that for each complex number $a + bi$, except 0, its multiplicative inverse is

$$\frac{a}{a^2 + b^2} - \frac{b}{a^2 + b^2} i$$

69. Prove the distributive property for complex numbers.

70. Let $u, v \in C$ and $\bar{u}, \bar{v}$ their conjugates. Show that

    (A) $\overline{uv} = \bar{u}\bar{v}$

    (B) $\overline{u + v} = \bar{u} + \bar{v}$

    (C) $\bar{u} = u$ if u is real.

EXERCISE 6   CHAPTER-REVIEW EXERCISES

A 1. $\{x \mid x^2 = 36\} = \{(\text{list elements})\}$

Problems 2 and 3 refer to the following sets:
$A = \{1, 2, 3, 4, 5, 6\}$
$B = \{1, 3, 5\}$
$C = \{3, 4, 5\}$
$D = \{2, 4, 6\}$

2. Find each of the following:
   (A) $B \cup C$,   (B) $B \cap C$,   (C) $B \cap D$,   (D) $A \cap C$
3. Which of the following are true?
   (A) $B \subset C$,   (B) $D \subset A$,   (C) $3 \in A$,
   (D) $3 \notin D$,   (E) $B \subseteq A$
4. Indicate which of the following statements are true:
   (A) π is an irrational number and a real number.
   (B) $-\frac{2}{3}$ is a rational number and a real number.
   (C) A natural number is a rational number and a real number.
5. Given the amount formula for simple interest $S = p + I$ and the simple interest formula $I = prt$, what law of equality permits us to write $S = p + prt$?
6. What field properties of the real numbers R justify each statement $(a, b, c \in R)$?
   (A) $7 + a = a + 7$ (B) $(3a)b = 3(ab)$
   (C) $3(a + b) = 3a + 3b$ (D) $5c \in R$
7. Replace each question mark with an appropriate symbol: $-8 - (-10) = 2$ is positive, hence $? > ?$ and $? < ?$
8. Graph each set on a real-number line:
   (A) $\{x \in I \mid -3 < x \leq 1\}$
   (B) $\{x \in R \mid -3 < x \leq 1\}$

Perform the indicated operations and write the answer in the form $a + bi$.

9. $(-3 + 2i) + (6 - 8i)$
10. $(3 - 3i)(2 + 3i)$

11. $\dfrac{13 - i}{5 - 3i}$

B 12. Let A be the set of all numbers x, such that $x^2 = 25$. (A) Denote A by the listing method. (B) Denote A by the rule method.
13. Let $A = \{x \in I \mid -1 \leq x < 2\}$ and $B = \{x \in N \mid x < 4\}$.
   (A) Find $A \cup B$ (B) Find $A \cap B$ (C) Is $-3 \in B$?
   (D) Is $\varnothing \subset A$?   (E) Is $B \subset A$?
14. If the replacement set for all variables is the set of real numbers, which field property in addition to closure justifies each statement?
   (A) $7 + (x + y) = (x + y) + 7$
   (B) $(a + b) + (x + y) = a + [b + (x + y)]$
   (C) $(a + b)(x + y) = (a + b)x + (a + b)y$
15. (A) Represent $\frac{1}{7}$ as a repeating decimal.
    (B) Represent $0.12\overline{12}$ as the quotient of two integers.
16. Are any of the number systems we studied in this chapter associative or commutative relative to subtraction?
17. Is R closed under subtraction? Explain.
18. Replace each question mark with an appropriate symbol: If $ab - ac$ is positive, then $? > ?$ and $? < ?$.
19. If the graph of set A is then $A = \{x \in ? \mid ?\}$.

Perform the indicated operations and write the answer in the form $a + bi$.

20. $(2 - 2\sqrt{-4}) - (3 - \sqrt{-9})$

21. $\dfrac{2 - \sqrt{-1}}{3 + \sqrt{-4}}$

22. $(3 + i)^2 - 2(3 + i) + 3$

23. i^{27}

C 24. Which of the following sets is the empty set: $\emptyset$, $\{0\}$, $\{\emptyset\}$?

25. $\{x \mid x \in A$ and $x \in B\}$ defines $A \cup B$ or $A \cap B$?

26. Which of the following statements are true?
    (A) $A \cap B = A \Rightarrow A \subseteq B$ (B) $A \cup B = A \Rightarrow A \subseteq B$
    (C) $A \subseteq B \Rightarrow A \cup B = B$

27. (A) Which of the following sets of numbers have the multiplicative identity property: N, I, Q, R?
    (B) Which have the multiplicative inverse property?

28. Give an example of a proper subset of the set of real numbers that is closed with respect to addition, subtraction, and multiplication, but not with respect to division.

29. Prove that if a, b, $c \in R$ and $a = b$, then $a + c = b + c$.

30. Prove that if $a > b$ and c is any real number, then $a + c > b + c$.

31. In the set of all rational numbers larger than $\sqrt{2}$ is there a smallest one?

32. Prove that there is no rational number whose square is 5.

33. What is the additive identity for the set of complex numbers? Prove your answer.

34. Evaluate

$$(a + bi)\left(\frac{a}{a^2 + b^2} - \frac{b}{a^2 + b^2} i\right) \qquad a \neq 0 \quad \text{and} \quad b \neq 0$$

thus showing that the set of complex numbers satisfies which field property?

Chapter

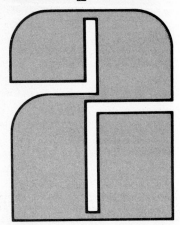

Basic Algebraic Operations

2.1 ARITHMETIC OPERATIONS ON POLYNOMIALS

Polynomials

Recall that if n is a natural number and a is any real number, then

$$a^n = aa \cdots a \qquad (n \text{ factors of } a)$$

For our work on polynomials we also need to recall the following exponent laws (more will be said about exponents and their laws later in the chapter).

Laws of Exponents

If $m, n \in N$ and $a, b \in R$

(A) $a^m a^n = a^{m+n}$

(B) $(ab)^n = a^n b^n$

(C) $(a^n)^m = a^{mn}$

(D) $\left(\dfrac{a}{b}\right)^n = \dfrac{a^n}{b^n}$

(E) $\dfrac{a^n}{a^m} = \begin{cases} a^{n-m} & \text{if } n > m \\ 1 & \text{if } n = m \\ \dfrac{1}{a^{m-n}} & \text{if } m > n \end{cases}$

A *polynomial in one variable* is an algebraic expression of the form

$$P(x) = a_n x^n + a_{n-1} x^{n-1} + \cdots + a_1 x + a_0$$

where n is a natural number, x a variable, and the coefficients $a_0, a_1, \ldots, a_n$ are constants. There are also *polynomials with more than one variable*. These are algebraic expressions of the same type having one or more terms of the form $a_i x^m y^n \cdots z^p$, where the exponents are natural numbers, and the coefficients are constants. If the coefficients of $P(x)$ are real numbers and the replacement set for the variable is the set of real numbers, then $P(x)$ is called a *real polynomial*.

The *degree of a term* in a polynomial is the power of the variable present in the term; if more than one variable is present as a factor, then the sum of the powers of the variables in the term is the degree of the term. The *degree of a polynomial* is the degree of the term with the highest degree in the polynomial. A nonzero constant is defined to be a *polynomial of degree zero*. The number 0 is called the zero polynomial and is not assigned a degree.

Example 1.

(A) Polynomials in one variable:

$$x^2 - 3x + 2 \qquad 6x^3 - \sqrt{2}\,x - \tfrac{1}{3}$$

(B) Polynomials in several variables:

$$3x^2 - 2xy + y^2 \qquad 4x^3 y^2 - \sqrt{3}\,xy^2 z^5$$

(C) Nonpolynomials:

$$\sqrt{2x} - \frac{3}{x} + 5 \qquad \frac{x^2 - 3x + 2}{x - 3} \qquad \sqrt{x^2 - 3x + 1}$$

(D) The degree of the first term in $6x^3 - \sqrt{2}\,x - \tfrac{1}{3}$ is 3, the second term 1, the third term 0, and the whole polynomial 3.

(E) The degree of the first term in $4x^3 y^2 - \sqrt{3}\,xy^2$ is 5, the second 3, and the whole polynomial 5.

Problem 1.   (A)   Which of the following are polynomials?

$$3x^2 - 2x + 1 \qquad \sqrt{x-3} \qquad x^2 - 2xy + y^2 \qquad \frac{x-1}{x^2+2}$$

(B)   Given the polynomial $3x^5 - 6x^3 + 5$, what is the degree of the first term? The second term? The whole polynomial?

(C)   Given the polynomial $6x^4y^2 - 3xy^3$, what is the degree of the first term? The second term? The whole polynomial?

ANSWER

(A) $3x^2 - 2x + 1$, $x^2 - 2xy + y^2$; (B) 5, 3, 5; (C) 6, 4, 6.

For any replacement of a variable(s) in a real polynomial by real numbers, the resulting expression names a real number; hence all the real-number properties discussed in Chap. 1 apply to real polynomials. We now review the four arithmetic operations on polynomials in light of these remarks.

Addition and Subtraction of Polynomials

From elementary algebra you learned that two terms are called *like terms* if they are exactly the same except for numerical coefficients. You also learned that two or more like terms can always be combined into a single term of the same type where the numerical coefficient of the single term is the sum of the numerical coefficients of the several terms. This mechanical rule is a consequence of the distributive, associative, and commutative properties of real numbers, and the fact that $a - b = a + (-b)$. Thus

$$3x - 5y + 6x + 2y \begin{array}{l} = 3x + 6x + 2y - 5y \quad * \\ = (3+6)x + (2-5)y \\ = 9x + (-3)y \end{array}$$
$$= 9x - 3y$$

Addition and subtraction of polynomials can often be thought of in terms of removing parentheses, or other symbols of grouping, and then proceeding as illustrated above. The process of removing parentheses is based primarily on three principles: (1) Any expression involving subtraction can be converted to addition, (2) multiplication distributes over

---

* Dashed-line boxes enclose steps done mentally, or illustrate principles behind mechanical processes.

addition, and, (3) parentheses may be inserted and removed at will relative to the operation of addition (associative property).

Mechanically, each term within parentheses (including the sign that precedes it) is multiplied by the coefficient of the parentheses.

Example 2. (A) $2(x^2 - 3) - (x^2 + 2x - 3) = 2x^2 - 6 - x^2 - 2x + 3 = x^2 - 2x - 3$
(B) $(2x - 3y) - [x - 2(3x - y)] = (2x - 3y) - [x - 6x + 2y]$
$$= 2x - 3y - x + 6x - 2y = 7x - 5y$$
(C) $3x - \{5 - 3[x - x(3 - x)]\} = 3x - \{5 - 3[x - 3x + x^2]\}$
$$= 3x - \{5 - 3x + 9x - 3x^2\}$$
$$= 3x - 5 + 3x - 9x + 3x^2$$
$$= 3x^2 - 3x - 5$$

Problem 2. Remove all symbols of grouping and simplify.

(A) $3(y^2 + 2y) - (y^2 - 2y + 1)$
(B) $(4x + 2y) - [3x - 5(x - 3y)]$
(C) $2t - \{7 - 2[t - t(4 + t)]\}$

ANSWER

(A) $2y^2 + 8y - 1$; (B) $6x - 13y$; (C) $-2t^2 - 4t - 7$.

Multiplication of Polynomials

The distributive property is the important principle behind multiplying polynomials. It leads directly to the following mechanical procedure: To multiply two polynomials, multiply each term of one by each term of the other and combine like terms. The commutative and associative properties are, of course, also used in simplifying the result.

Example 3. Multiply $(2x - 3)(3x^2 - 2x + 3)$.

SOLUTION

$(2x - 3)(3x^2 - 2x + 3)$
$= 2x(3x^2 - 2x + 3) - 3(3x^2 - 2x + 3)$
$= 6x^3 - 4x^2 + 6x - 9x^2 + 6x - 9$
$= 6x^3 - 13x^2 + 12x - 9$

or

$$\begin{array}{r} 3x^2 - 2x + 3 \\ 2x - 3 \\ \hline 6x^3 - 4x^2 + 6x \\ -9x^2 + 6x - 9 \\ \hline 6x^3 - 13x^2 + 12x - 9 \end{array}$$

Problem 3. Multiply $(2x - 3)(2x^2 + 3x - 2)$.

ANSWER

$4x^3 - 13x + 6.$

Division of Polynomials

It is often useful to find quotients of polynomials by a long-division algorithm similar to that used in arithmetic. An example will illustrate the process.

Example 4. Divide $5 + 4x^3 - 3x$ by $2x - 3$.

SOLUTION

$$
\begin{array}{r}
2x^2 + 3x + 3 \\
2x - 3)\overline{4x^3 + 0x^2 - 3x + 5} \\
\underline{4x^3 - 6x^2} \\
6x^2 - 3x \\
\underline{6x^2 - 9x} \\
6x + 5 \\
\underline{6x - 9} \\
\text{(remainder)} \quad 14
\end{array}
$$

Arrange the dividend and the divisor in descending powers of the variable. Insert, with zero coefficients, any missing terms of degree less than 3. Divide the first term of the divisor into the first term of the dividend. Multiply the divisor by $2x^2$, line up like terms, subtract as in arithmetic, and bring down $-3x$. Repeat the process until the degree of the remainder is less than that of the divisor.

CHECK:
$(2x - 3)(2x^2 + 3x + 3) + 14$
$= 4x^3 - 3x + 5$

Problem 4. Divide $6x^2 - 30 + 9x^3$ by $3x - 4$.

ANSWER

$3x^2 + 6x + 8, \ R = 2.$

We note in Example 4 that if we let $P(x) = 4x^3 - 3x + 5$, $D(x) = 2x - 3$, $Q(x) = 2x^2 + 3x + 3$, and $R(x) = 14$, then $P(x) = D(x) \cdot Q(x) + R(x)$, where $P(x)$ is the dividend, $D(x)$ the divisor, $Q(x)$ the quotient, and $R(x)$ the remainder. This is an illustration of the following important theorem, which we state without proof.

Theorem 1. Let $P(x)$ and $D(x)$ be real polynomials with the degree of $D(x) \leq$ the degree of $P(x)$, then there exist unique polynomials $Q(x)$ and $R(x)$, such that

$$P(x) = D(x)Q(x) + R(x)$$

where the degree of $R(x)$ is less than the degree of $D(x)$ or $R(x) = 0$.

This theorem will be particularly useful to us in Chap. 5 when we study the theory of equations.

EXERCISE 7

A *Perform the indicated operations and simplify.*

1. $5x + (3x - 7)$
2. $2t - (3t - 5)$
3. $(3x - 1)(2x + 3)$
4. $(4x + 3)(2x - 5)$
5. $(2x^2 + x - 6)/(x + 2)$
6. $(6x^2 + 5x - 6)/(3x - 2)$
7. $2(x - 1) + 3(2x - 3) - (4x - 5)$
8. $-3(-t + 7) - (t - 1)$
9. $(3y + 2)(2y^2 + 5y - 3)$
10. $(2x - 1)(x^2 - 3x + 5)$
11. $(6x^2 + 5x - 6)/(3x - 2)$
12. $(8x^2 - 14x + 3)/(2x - 3)$
13. $3x - 2[x - (x - 7)]$
14. $2t - 3t[4 - 2(t - 1)]$
15. $(a + b)(a^2 - ab + b^2)$
16. $(a - b)(a^2 + ab + b^2)$
17. $(y^2 - 9)/(y + 3)$
18. $(4m^2 - 1)/(2m - 1)$
19. $(x^3 - 1)/(x - 1)$
20. $(a^3 + 27)/(a + 3)$
21. $(8x^2 - 6x + 6)/(2x - 1)$
22. $(12x^2 + 11x - 2)(3x + 2)$
23. $(-7x + 2x^2 - 1)/(2x + 1)$
24. $(13x - 12 + 3x^2)/(3x - 2)$

B *In Probs. 25 to 44 perform the indicated operations and simplify.*

25. $x - \{x - [x - (x - 1)]\}$
26. $2t - 3\{t + 2[t - (t + 5)] + 1\}$
27. $(x^2 - 3x + 5)(2x^2 + x - 2)$
28. $(a^2 - 2ab + b^2)(a^2 + 2ab + b^2)$
29. $(2y^3 + 5y^2 - y - 6)/(y + 2)$
30. $(x^3 - 5x^2 + x + 10)/(x - 2)$
31. $(x^4 - 16)/(x + 2)$
32. $(x^4 - 81)/(x - 3)$
33. $3x^2 - 2\{x - x[x + 4(x - 3)] - 5\}$
34. $-2t(-t - 3) - [t^2 - t(2t + 3)]$
35. $(x + 2y)^3$
36. $(2m - n)^3$
37. $(3y - y^2 + 2y^3 - 1)/(y + 2)$
38. $(3 + x^3 - x)/(x - 3)$
39. $2\{(x - 3)(x^2 - 2x + 1) - x[3 - x(x - 2)]\}$
40. $-3x\{x[x - x(2 - x)] - (x + 2)(x^2 - 3)\}$
41. $(x - 1)(x - 2)(2x^3 - 3x^2 - 2x - 1)$
42. $(2x - 1)(2x + 1)(3x^3 - 4x + 3)$
43. $(12x^2 - 19x^3 - 4x - 3 + 12x^5)/(4x^2 - 1)$
44. $(9x^3 - x + 2x^5 + 9x^3 - 2 - x)/(2 + x^2 - 3x)$
45. Replace each question mark with an appropriate algebraic expression:
    (A) $w^2 - x + y = w^2 - (?)$
    (B) $s^2 - x + y - z = s^2 + (?)$
    (C) $(y - 1)^2 - y + 1 = (y - 1)^2 - (?)$
    (D) $x^2 - y^2 + 2y - 1 = x^2 - (?)$

46. Replace each question mark with an appropriate algebraic expression:
    (A) $x^2 - y^2 - z^2 = x^2 = (?)$
    (B) $x^2 + y^2 - z^2 = x^2 + (?)$
47. Which of the following algebraic expressions are polynomials?

    (A) $xy - 2x + 3y - 1$ (B) $\sqrt{x} + 5\sqrt{x} - 7$

    (C) $3x^2 - 2x - 4$ (D) $2t^5 - \sqrt{2}t^3 + 5t - 12$

    (E) $5x^2 - 3xy + 7y^2$ (F) $(x^2 - 3x + 7)/(2x^2 - 5)$

    (G) $2x - 3$ (H) $2x + y - \frac{1}{2}$

48. Which of the following algebraic expressions are polynomials?

    (A) $3x^2 - 2x - 9$ (B) $x - \frac{1}{3}$

    (C) $x^2 - 3\sqrt{xy} + 2y^3$ (D) $x^3 - 2xy^2 + y^3$

    (E) $x^2 + (x/y)$ (F) $t^4 + 1$

    (G) $2x - 3y + 5$ (H) $m^2 - 2mn + n^2$

49. In Prob. 47:
    (A) Identify all the first-degree polynomials in one variable.
    (B) Identify all the first-degree polynomials in two variables.
    (C) Identify all the second-degree polynomials in one variable.
    (D) Identify all the second-degree polynomials in two variables.
50. Repeat Prob. 49 for Prob. 48.
51. Subtract the sum of the second two polynomials from the sum of the first two: $(2x^2 - 4xy + y^2)$, $(3xy - y^2)$, $(x^2 - 2xy - y^2)$, and $(-x^2 + 3xy - 2y^2)$.
52. Subtract the sum of the first two polynomials from the sum of the second two: $(3m^3 - 2m + 5)$, $(4m^2 - m)$, $(3m^2 - 3m - 2)$, and $(m^3 + m^2 + 2)$.
53. A pile of coins consists of nickels, dimes, and quarters. There are five fewer dimes than nickels, and two more quarters than dimes. If x equals the number of nickels, write an algebraic expression that represents the value of the pile in cents. Simplify the expression.
54. A coin purse contains dimes and quarters only. There are four more dimes than quarters. If x equals the number of dimes, write an algebraic expression that represents the value of the money in the purse in cents. Simplify the expression.
55. The length of a rectangle is 8 ft more than its width. If y is the length of the rectangle, write an algebraic expression that represents its area. Change the expression to a form without parentheses.
56. The width of a rectangle is 5 in. less than its length. If x is the length of the rectangle, write an algebraic expression that represents the perimeter of the rectangle and simplify the expression.
57. Given $P(x) = x^3 - 6x^2 + 12x - 4$ and $D(x) = x^2 - 3x + 2$, find $Q(x)$ and $R(x)$ such that $P(x) = D(x)Q(x) + R(x)$ and the degree of $R(x)$ is less than the degree of $D(x)$ or $R(x) = 0$.
58. Repeat the preceding problem for $P(x) = x^4 + x^3 - 4x^2 + 7x + 2$ and $D(x) = x^2 - x + 1$.
59. Combine $7x + 5x$ into a single term, justifying each step by a property studied in Chap. 1.
60. Justify each step by a property studied in Chap. 1.
    1. $8x - 3x = 8x + [-(3x)]$

2. $= 8x + (-3)x$
3. $= [8 + (-3)]x$
4. $= 5x$

61. Justify each step by a property studied in Chap. 1.
    1. $(3x + 2y) + (5x + 6y) = (3x + 2y) + (6y + 5x)$
    2. $= 3x + [2y + (6y + 5x)]$
    3. $= 3x + [(2y + 6y) + 5x]$
    4. $= 3x + [(2 + 6)y + 5x]$
    5. $= 3x + (8y + 5x)$
    6. $= 3x + (5x + 8y)$
    7. $= (3x + 5x) + 8y$
    8. $= (3 + 5)x + 8y$
    9. $= 8x + 8y$

62. How is the distributive property used in

$$\begin{array}{r} x - 2 \\ x + 3 \\ \hline x^2 - 2x \\ 3x - 6 \\ \hline x^2 + x - 6 \end{array}$$

63. If you are given two polynomials, one of degree m and another of degree n, $m > n$, then (A) what is the degree of their sum? (B) their product?

64. For each real polynomial $a_n x^n + a_{n-1}x^{n-1} + \cdots + a_1 x + a_0$, what is its additive inverse?

65. In the set of all real polynomials,
    (A) What is the additive identity?
    (B) What is the multiplicative identity?

66. Real polynomials satisfy all field properties except one. Which one?

2.2 FACTORING SPECIAL POLYNOMIALS

By now you should have little trouble multiplying polynomials. In fact, you should be able to multiply many first-degree polynomials mentally. In this section we are interested in the reverse process; that is, given a polynomial $P(x)$, find two or more polynomials of lower degree, called *factors* of $P(x)$, so that their product will be $P(x)$.

To write a natural number in a completely factored form is to write it as a product of prime factors. Thus,

$$60 = 2^2 \cdot 3 \cdot 5$$

is the complete factorization of 60, while $30 \cdot 2$, $4 \cdot 15$, and $80 \cdot \frac{3}{4}$ are not.

What does it mean to write a polynomial in a completely factored form? To answer this, we will extend some of the ideas of prime numbers to polynomials. First, we define a *polynomial over a set S* to be a polynomial whose coefficients are taken out of S. Thus, a polynomial over the set of integers I is a polynomial whose coefficients are integers, a polynomial over the set of real numbers R is a polynomial whose coefficients are real numbers, and so on. In this section we will restrict our attention to polynomials over the integers I. For example,

$$2x^2 - 3x + 2 \qquad 5x^2 - 3xy + y^2$$

A single-term polynomial over I is *prime over* I if its coefficient is an integer. Thus, $9x^4$ and $-3x^2y^3$ are prime polynomials over I. A polynomial over I of two or more terms is said to be *prime over* I if it has no polynomial factors with integers as coefficients other than itself and ± 1. And finally, a polynomial over I is written in *completely factored form* if it is written as a product of prime polynomials over I. For example, $4x^2(2x - 3y)$ is the completely factored form of $8x^3 - 12x^2y$.

In this section we will review procedures involved in factoring certain special types of polynomials. In Chap. 5, the factoring problem will be considered again, but from a more general point of view through the study of the theory of equations. Factoring polynomials is useful in work with algebraic fractions and in solving polynomial equations.

The following special products give special insight into the factoring process of some first-, second-, and third-degree polynomials. These types occur with sufficient frequency to warrant special attention.

Special Products	$u(x + y) = ux + uy$	(distributive property)
	$(x + y)(x - y) = x^2 - y^2$	(difference of two squares)
	$(x + y)^2 = x^2 + 2xy + y^2$	(perfect square)
	$(x - y)^2 = x^2 - 2xy + y^2$	(perfect square)
	$(x + a)(x + b) = x^2 + (a + b)x + ab$	(second degree in one variable)
	$(ax + b)(cx + d) = acx^2 + (ad + bc)x + bd$	(second degree in one variable)
	$(u + v)(x + y) = ux + uy + vx + vy$	(second degree in four variables)
	$(x + y)(x^2 - xy + y^2) = x^3 + y^3$	(sum of two cubes)
	$(x - y)(x^2 + xy + y^2) = x^3 - y^3$	(difference of two cubes)

Of course, we are primarily interested in these special products as read from right to left. Before we consider several examples, it is worth noting that most polynomials over I do not have factors with integers as coefficients, hence are prime to start with. In fact, even for the second-degree polynomials

$$ax^2 + bx + c \qquad \text{or} \qquad ax^2 + bxy + cy^2$$

if a, b, and c are chosen at random from I, the probability of the polynomials not having factors with integers as coefficients is much larger than that of their having such factors.* It is therefore worthwhile knowing if a polynomial over I is prime before we start to look for its factors. The following theorem (which we state without proof) is useful in this regard for certain second-degree polynomials, particularly if the coefficients are not too large.

Theorem 2.
ac Test

Given integers a, b, and c, then there exist integers d, e, f, and g such that

$$ax^2 + bx + c = (dx + e)(fx + g)$$
$$ax^2 + bxy + cy^2 = (dx + ey)(fx + gy)$$

if and only if ac can be written as the product of two integers whose sum is b (that is, if and only if there exist integers m and n such that $ac = mn$ and $m + n = b$).

Example 5.

Write (A) $2x^2 + 3x - 2$, (B) $3x^2 - 2x + 4$, and (C) $3x^3y + 3x^2y - 36xy$ in completely factored form (if they are already prime over I, it should be indicated).

SOLUTION

(A) Use the ac test to test for factorability. Since $ac = (2)(-2) = -4$ has factors, -1 and 4, whose sum is $b = 3$, $2x^2 + 3x - 2$ can be factored. Thus

$$2x^2 + 3x - 2 = (x + 2)(2x - 1)$$

(B) Test $3x^2 - 2x + 4$ for factorability. Since $ac = (3)(4) = 12$ does not have integer factors whose sum is $b = -2$, the polynomial cannot be factored, hence it is prime.

(C) Remove common monomial factors first:

$$3x^3y + 3x^2y - 36xy = 3xy(x^2 + x - 12)$$

and proceed as above. Test $x^2 + x - 12$ for factorability. $ac = (1)(-12) = -12$ has integer factors, 4 and -3, whose sum is $b = -1$, hence is factorable. Thus

$$3x^3y + 3x^2y - 36xy = 3xy(x + 4)(x - 3)$$

* Given $P(x) = ax^2 + bx + c$, $a \in \{x \in I \mid 1 \le x \le 9\}$, b, $c \in \{x \in I \mid -9 \le x \le 9\}$. Factorable cases, 524; nonfactorable cases, 2,725. (See "But What If It Doesn't Factor," L. M. Collister and T. R. McCabe, *Mathematics Teacher*, February 1973, p. 155, for a more complete discussion.)

Problem 5. Write (A) $3x^2 - x + 2$, (B) $2x^2 - 7x - 4$, and (C) $4x^4y - 14x^3y + 6x^2y$ in completely factored forms (if they are already prime over I, it should be indicated).

ANSWER

(A) Prime; (B) $(2x + 1)(x - 4)$; (C) $2x^2y(x - 3)(2x - 1)$.

When factoring a difference of two squares (the sum of two squares is prime), a difference of two cubes, or a sum of two cubes, it is best to memorize the special products as "factoring formulas."

Example 6. Write (A) $16x^2 - 64$, (B) $4x^2 + 1$, (C) $8x^3 - 1$, and (D) $y^3 + 1$ in completely factored forms.

SOLUTION

(A) $16x^2 - 64 = (4x)^2 - 8^2 = (4x + 8)(4x - 8)$
(B)   Prime
(C) $8x^3 - 1 = (2x)^3 - 1^3 = (2x - 1)(4x^2 + 2x + 1)$
(D) $y^3 + 1 = (y + 1)(y^2 - y + 1)$

Problem 6. Write (A) $4u^2 - 9v^2$, (B) $a^2 + b^2$, (C) $x^3 - 8$, and (D) $x^3 + 8y^3$ in completely factored forms.

ANSWER

(A) $(2u - 3v)(2u + 3v)$; (B) prime; (C) $(x - 2)(x^2 + 2x + 4)$;
(D) $(x + 2y)(x^2 - 2xy + 4y^2)$.

Some polynomials can be factored after suitably grouping their terms. The method is effective when it applies, but in practice most polynomials will not yield to the process. The following example illustrates the procedure.

Example 7. $2ax - 3bx + 10ay - 15by = (2ax - 3bx) + (10ay - 15by)$
$$= x(2a - 3b) + 5y(2a - 3b)$$
$$= (x + 5y)(2a - 3b)$$

Problem 7. Write $4ax - 2bx + 6ay - 3by$ in completely factored form.

ANSWER

$(2x + 3y)(2a - b)$.

EXERCISE 8

A *Multiply mentally.*

1. $(b + 10)(b - 8)$
2. $(m - 12)(m + 5)$
3. $(x - 7)(x + 7)$
4. $(x + 12)(x - 12)$
5. $(2x + 3)(x + 3)$
6. $(4t - 3)(t - 2)$
7. $(5x - 7)(3x + 2)$
8. $(4n - 7)(3n + 2)$
9. $(4y - 3)^2$
10. $(3y + 1)^2$
11. $(5m + 3n)(5m - 3n)$
12. $(3x - 2y)(3x + 2y)$
13. $(4m - n)(3m + 5n)$
14. $(4u - v)(2u + 3v)$
15. $(2x - 3y)^2$
16. $(4a + 3b)^2$

Write each polynomial in a completely factored form over I. If the polynomial is prime over I, it should be indicated.

17. $m^2 - 7m + 12$
18. $x^2 - 7x + 10$
19. $z^2 + 3z + 5$
20. $x^2 - 2y + 3$
21. $u^2 + 9uv + 20v^2$
22. $a^2 + 8ab + 15b^2$
23. $t^2 - 36$
24. $y^2 - 25$
25. $x^2 + 36$
26. $x^2 + 25$
27. $y^2 + y - 4$
28. $x^2 - 6x - 3$
29. $4y^2 - 28y + 48$
30. $6m^2 + 48m + 72$
31. $2t^4 - 24t^3 + 40t^2$
32. $x^3 - 11x^2 + 24x$
33. $6x^2 + 11xy + 3y^2$
34. $12x^2 + 17xy + 6y^2$
35. $25x^2 - 16y^2$
36. $a^2b^2 - c^2$
37. $m^2 - 4mn - 12n^2$
38. $m^2 - 4mn - 12n^2$
39. $2a^2 - 3ab - 4b^2$
40. $3u^2 + 2uv - 3v^2$

B
41. $6x^2 - xy - 12y^2$
42. $6x^2 + 7xy - 3y^2$
43. $2y^3 - 2y^2 + 8y$
44. $3m^3 - 6m^2 + 15m$
45. $4x^3y - xy^3$
46. $u^3v - 9uv^3$
47. $4x^2 + 9y^2$
48. $9u^2 + 4v^2$
49. $(a - b)^2 - 4(c - d)^2$
50. $(x + 2)^2 - 9$
51. $3m^3n - 15m^2n^2 + 18mn^3$
52. $4u^3v + 14u^2v^2 + 6uv^3$
53. $y^3 - 1$
54. $x^3 + 1$
55. $a^3b^3 + 8$
56. $54x^3 - 2y^3$
57. $27 - x^3y^3$
58. $4u^3 + 32v^3$
59. $mx + my - 2nx - 2ny$
60. $ax - 2xb - ay + 2by$
61. $2am - 3an + 2bm - 3bn$
62. $15ac - 20ad + 3bc - 4bd$
63. $x^3 - 2x^2 - x + 2$
64. $x^3 - 2x^2 + x - 2$
65. $4y^3 - 12y^2 - 9y + 27$
66. $2x^3 - x^2 - 8x + 4$
67. $r^4 - s^4$
68. $x^4 - 3x^2 - 4$
69. $x^4 - 7x^2 - 18$
70. $16a^4 - b^4$
71. $4(A + B)^2 - 5(A + B) - 6$
72. $2(a^2 - 2ab + b^2) + 5(a - b) - 12$
73. $18a^3 - 8a(x^2 + 8x + 16)$
74. $25(4x^2 - 12xy + 9y^2) - 9a^2b^2$

C
75. $x^6 - 1$
76. $a^6 - 64b^6$
77. $(y - x)^2 - y + x$
78. $x^2(x - 1) - x + 1$
79. $25 - a^2 - 2ab - b^2$
80. $x^2 - 2xy + y^2 - 9$

81. $x^4 - x^2 + 4x - 4$ 82. $16x^4 - x^2 + 6xy - 9y^2$

83. Describe the elements in the set

$$B = \{x \mid -2x^2 + 2x = -2x(x-1), \ x \text{ a real number}\}$$

84. Given $12t^2 - 32t$ and $4t(3t - 8)$, name the same number for (all, two, no) replacements of t by real numbers.

85. Use Theorem 2 to find all positive integers p under 15 such that $x^2 - 7x + p$ can be factored over I.

86. Use Theorem 2 to find all integers p such that $x^2 + px + 12$ can be factored over I.

2.3 ADDING AND SUBTRACTING FRACTIONS

Fractional forms in which the numerator and denominator are polynomials are called *rational expressions*. For example,

$$\frac{1}{x+5} \qquad \frac{u+7}{3u^2 - 2u + 4} \qquad \frac{x^2 - 3xy - 7y^2}{x^3 - y^3}$$

are all rational expressions. (Recall that a nonzero constant is a polynomial of degree zero.) In this section, all polynomials will be real polynomials over I, that is, polynomials with integers as coefficients whose replacement set for the variable(s) is the set of real numbers. Rational forms made up of real polynomials name real numbers for any replacement of the variable(s) by real numbers, except when a denominator is zero; therefore, all the properties of real-number fractions listed in Theorems 7, 8, and 9 in Chap. 1 apply to these forms. Thus, if $P(x)$, $Q(x)$, $R(x)$, and $S(x)$ are real polynomials, then (excluding division by zero)

$$\frac{P(x)R(x)}{Q(x)R(x)} = \frac{P(x)}{Q(x)} \qquad \text{(fundamental property of fractions)} \qquad (1)$$

$$\frac{P(x)}{Q(x)} + \frac{R(x)}{Q(x)} = \frac{P(x) + R(x)}{Q(x)} \qquad\qquad (2)$$

$$\frac{P(x)}{Q(x)} - \frac{R(x)}{Q(x)} = \frac{P(x) - R(x)}{Q(x)} \qquad\qquad (3)$$

$$\frac{P(x)}{Q(x)} \cdot \frac{R(x)}{S(x)} = \frac{P(x) \cdot R(x)}{Q(x) \cdot S(x)} \qquad\qquad (4)$$

$$\frac{P(x)}{Q(x)} \div \frac{R(x)}{S(x)} = \frac{P(x)}{Q(x)} \cdot \frac{S(x)}{R(x)} \qquad\qquad (5)$$

$$\frac{-P(x)}{Q(x)} = \frac{P(x)}{-Q(x)} = -\frac{P(x)}{Q(x)} \tag{6}$$

$$\frac{-P(x)}{-Q(x)} = -\frac{-P(x)}{Q(x)} = -\frac{P(x)}{-Q(x)} = \frac{P(x)}{Q(x)} \tag{7}$$

It is also worth recalling that if a and b are any real numbers, then

$$b - a = -(a - b)$$

The recognition of this relationship is often useful in working with certain kinds of fractional forms.

Reduction to Lowest Terms and Raising to Higher Terms

A rational expression is in *lowest terms* if the numerator and denominator are relatively prime, that is, if after writing the numerator and denominator in completely factored form (over I), they do not share common factors other than ± 1. The fundamental property of fractions [Eq. (1)] is the key to the process of reducing fractions to lowest terms, and the principle behind what is commonly called canceling. Fractions may also be changed to higher terms by using Eq. (1) from right to left. This is useful in the process of obtaining common denominators when adding and subtracting fractions. A few examples should serve to make these ideas clear.

Example 8. Reducing to lowest terms:

(A) $\dfrac{6x^2 y^3}{9xy^5} = \dfrac{2x \overset{1}{\cancel{(3xy^3)}}}{3y^2 \underset{1}{\cancel{(3xy^3)}}} = \dfrac{2x}{3y^2}$

(B) $\dfrac{2x^2 + 5x - 12}{6x^2 - 7x - 3} = \dfrac{(x + 4)\overset{1}{\cancel{(2x - 3)}}}{(3x + 1)\underset{1}{\cancel{(2x - 3)}}} = \dfrac{x + 4}{3x + 1}$

(C) $\dfrac{b - a}{a^2 - b^2} = \dfrac{\overset{-1}{\cancel{-(a - b)}}}{\underset{1}{\cancel{(a - b)}}(a + b)} = \dfrac{-1}{a + b} = -\dfrac{1}{a + b}$

Raising to higher terms:

(D) $\dfrac{2x}{5y} = \dfrac{?}{15xy^2}$

SOLUTION

$$\dfrac{2x}{5y} = \dfrac{2x(3xy)}{5y(3xy)} = \dfrac{6x^2y}{15xy^2}$$

(E) $\dfrac{-2}{2(x+y)} = \dfrac{?}{2(x^2-y^2)}$

SOLUTION

$$\dfrac{-2}{2(x+y)} = \dfrac{-2(x-y)}{2(x+y)(x-y)} = \dfrac{-2x+2y}{2(x^2-y^2)} = \dfrac{2y-2x}{2(x^2-y^2)}$$

(F) $-\dfrac{1}{3x} = \dfrac{?}{3x^2-3x}$

SOLUTION

$$-\dfrac{1}{3x} = \dfrac{(-1)(x-3)}{3x(x-3)} = \dfrac{-x+3}{3x^2-3x} = \dfrac{3-x}{3x^2-3x}$$

Problem 8. Reduce to lowest terms.

(A) $\dfrac{8x^4y^3}{12x^2y^7}$ (B) $\dfrac{3x^3y+12xy}{6xy^2}$ (C) $\dfrac{9-x^2}{2x^2+5x-3}$

Raise to higher terms.

(D) $\dfrac{1}{2y} = \dfrac{?}{4y^2}$ (E) $\dfrac{x}{3y^2} = \dfrac{?}{6xy^2-3y^2}$ (F) $\dfrac{x-2y}{x+y} = \dfrac{?}{x^2+4xy+3y^2}$

ANSWER

(A) $2x^2/3y^4$; (B) $(x^2+4)/2y$; (C) $-(x-3)/(2x-1)$ or $(3-x)/(2x-1)$;
(D) $2y$; (E) $2x^2-x$; (F) $x^2+xy-6y^2$.

Addition and Subtraction

The addition and subtraction properties of rational expressions stated in Eqs. (2) and (3) tell us that we may either add or subtract rational expressions, if their denominators are the same, by adding or subtracting their numerators and placing the result over the common denominator; if the denominators are not the same, we raise the fractions to higher terms, using property (1) to obtain common denominators, and then use either property (2) or (3).

Even though any common denominator will do, the problem will generally become less involved if the least common denominator (LCD) is used. If the LCD is not obvious (often it is), we factor each denominator completely, including numerical coefficients. The LCD should then contain each different prime factor in all denominators to the highest power it occurs in any one denominator.

Example 9. (A) $\dfrac{1}{2y} + \dfrac{1}{4y^2} - 1 = \dfrac{1(2y)}{(2y)(2y)} + \dfrac{1}{4y^2} - \dfrac{4y^2}{4y^2} = \dfrac{2y + 1 - 4y^2}{4y^2} = \dfrac{1 + 2y - 4y^2}{4y^2}$

Note that the LCD is $4y^2$.

(B) $\dfrac{3}{x^2 - 6x + 9} - \dfrac{2}{x^2 - 9} - \dfrac{5}{3 - x} = \dfrac{3}{(x - 3)^2} - \dfrac{2}{(x - 3)(x + 3)} + \dfrac{5}{x - 3}$

NOTE: $-\dfrac{5}{3 - x} = -\dfrac{5}{-(x - 3)} = \dfrac{5}{x - 3}$

The LCD is $(x - 3)^2(x + 3)$. Thus,

$\dfrac{3(x + 3)}{(x - 3)^2(x + 3)} - \dfrac{2(x - 3)}{(x - 3)^2(x + 3)} + \dfrac{5(x - 3)(x + 3)}{(x - 3)^2(x + 3)}$

$$= \dfrac{3(x + 3) - 2(x - 3) + 5(x - 3)(x + 3)}{(x - 3)^2(x + 3)}$$

$$= \dfrac{5x^2 + x - 30}{(x - 3)^2(x + 3)}$$

Problem 9. Perform the indicated operations and simplify.

(A) $\dfrac{1}{4x^2} - \dfrac{2x + 1}{3x^3} + \dfrac{3}{12x}$ (B) $\dfrac{4}{y^2 - 4} + \dfrac{3}{y^2 - 4y + 4} - \dfrac{2}{2 - y}$

ANSWER

(A) $\dfrac{3x^2 - 5x - 4}{12x^3}$; (B) $\dfrac{2y^2 + 7y - 10}{(y-2)^2(y+2)}$.

EXERCISE 9

A *Reduce to lowest terms.*

1. $\dfrac{12x^5y^2}{6x^7y}$

2. $\dfrac{12m^3n^5}{9m^3n^8}$

3. $\dfrac{6x^3y - 6x^2y^2}{8x^3y^2}$

4. $\dfrac{8m^2n^2 + 8mn^3}{4m^3n^3}$

5. $\dfrac{a^2b + ab^2}{ab + b^2}$

6. $\dfrac{m^2 - mn}{m^2n - mn^2}$

7. $\dfrac{2x^2 + 3xy}{4x^2 - 9y^2}$

8. $\dfrac{a^2 - 16b^2}{ab - 4b^2}$

9. $\dfrac{x^2y - 8xy + 15y}{xy - 3y}$

10. $\dfrac{m^3 + 7m^2 + 10m}{m^2 + 5m}$

Replace each question mark with an appropriate polynomial.

11. $\dfrac{5m}{3n} = \dfrac{?}{12mn^2}$

12. $\dfrac{3x}{7y} = \dfrac{?}{14y^2}$

13. $\dfrac{w}{2z^2} = \dfrac{?}{6wz^2 - 2z^3}$

14. $\dfrac{3x}{2y^2} = \dfrac{?}{4xy^2 - 6y^3}$

15. $\dfrac{2m + n}{m - n} = \dfrac{?}{m^2 + mn - 2n^2}$

16. $\dfrac{3x}{2x + 3} = \dfrac{?}{4x^2 - 4x - 3}$

Perform the indicated operations and simplify.

17. $\dfrac{1}{2a^2} - \dfrac{2b - 1}{2a^2}$

18. $\dfrac{5}{3k} - \dfrac{6x - 4}{3k}$

19. $\dfrac{1}{x} - \dfrac{y}{x^2} + \dfrac{y^2}{x^3}$

20. $\dfrac{u}{v^2} - \dfrac{1}{v} + \dfrac{u^2}{v^3}$

21. $\dfrac{2}{x} + 1$

22. $x + \dfrac{1}{x}$

23. $\dfrac{3y + 8}{4y^2} - \dfrac{2y - 1}{y^3} - \dfrac{5}{8y}$

24. $\dfrac{4t - 3}{18t^3} + \dfrac{3}{4t} - \dfrac{2t - 1}{6t^2}$

B 25. $\dfrac{3}{x^2-1}-\dfrac{2}{x^2-2x+1}$

26. $\dfrac{1}{m^2-n^2}+\dfrac{1}{m^2+2mn+n^2}$

27. $2+\dfrac{x+1}{x-3}$

28. $\dfrac{t+1}{t-1}-1$

29. $x-3-\dfrac{x-1}{x-2}$

30. $\dfrac{x^2-2x}{x+2}+x-3$

31. $\dfrac{2x}{x^2-y^2}+\dfrac{1}{x+y}-\dfrac{1}{x-y}$

32. $\dfrac{2}{x+3}-\dfrac{1}{x-3}+\dfrac{2x}{x^2-9}$

33. $5+\dfrac{a}{a+1}-\dfrac{a}{a-1}$

34. $\dfrac{1}{y+2}+3-\dfrac{2}{y-2}$

35. $\dfrac{3}{x-1}+\dfrac{2}{1-x}$

36. $\dfrac{5}{y-3}-\dfrac{2}{3-y}$

37. $\dfrac{1}{5x-5}-\dfrac{1}{3x-3}+\dfrac{1}{1-x}$

38. $\dfrac{x+7}{ax-bx}+\dfrac{y+9}{by-ay}$

39. $\dfrac{m^2}{m^2+2m+1}+\dfrac{1}{3m+3}-\dfrac{1}{6}$

40. $\dfrac{x}{x^2-x-2}-\dfrac{1}{x^2+5x-14}-\dfrac{2}{x^2+8x+7}$

41. $\dfrac{x}{x^2-xy+y^2}-\dfrac{xy}{x^3+y^3}$

42. $\dfrac{xy^2}{x^3-y^3}-\dfrac{y}{x^2+xy+y^2}$

43. $\dfrac{x}{ax+ay+bx+by}-\dfrac{y}{ax-ay+bx-by}$

44. $\dfrac{a}{(a+b)(x+y)}-\dfrac{b}{(a-b)(x+y)}$

C *In Probs. 45 to 48 the equalities hold except for what values of x?*

45 $\dfrac{x^2-1}{x-1}=x+1$

46. $\dfrac{x^2-x-6}{x-3}=x+2$

47. $\dfrac{2x^2-5x-3}{x^2+x-2}=\dfrac{2x-3}{x+2}$

48. $\dfrac{3x^2-11x-4}{x^2-16}=\dfrac{3x+1}{x+4}$

Replace question marks with appropriate expressions.

49. $-\dfrac{1}{3-x}=\dfrac{?}{x-3}$

50. $-\dfrac{-3}{3-x}=-\dfrac{?}{x-3}$

51. $\dfrac{y-x}{3-x}=\dfrac{?}{x-3}$

52. $-\dfrac{a-b}{b-a}=?$

2.4 MULTIPLYING AND DIVIDING FRACTIONS

Properties 4, 5, and 1 listed in the preceding section are the key properties in the operations of multiplying and dividing rational expressions. It is worth noting that in the multiplication process any *factor* of a numerator can cancel a like factor of a denominator, and that the same is true in the division process after inversion of the divisor takes place.

Example 10. (A) $(x^2 - 4) \cdot \dfrac{2x - 3}{x + 2} = \dfrac{\overset{1}{\cancel{(x+2)}}(x - 2)}{1} \cdot \dfrac{(2x - 3)}{\underset{1}{\cancel{(x+2)}}} = (x - 2)(2x - 3)$

(B) $\dfrac{10x^3 y}{3xy + 9y} \div \dfrac{4x^2 - 12x}{x^2 - 9} = \dfrac{10x^3 y}{3y(x + 3)} \cdot \dfrac{(x + 3)(x - 3)}{4x(x - 3)} = \dfrac{5x^2}{6}$

(C) $\dfrac{4 - 2x}{4} \div (x - 2) = \dfrac{2(2 - x)}{4} \cdot \dfrac{1}{x - 2} = \dfrac{2 - x}{2(x - 2)} = \dfrac{-(x - 2)}{2(x - 2)} = -\dfrac{1}{2}$

Problem 10. Perform the indicated operations and reduce to lowest terms.

(A) $(y - 3) \cdot \dfrac{3y + 2}{y^2 - 9}$

(B) $\dfrac{12x^2 y^3}{2xy^2 + 6xy} \div \dfrac{3y^3 + 9y^2}{y^2 + 6y + 9}$

(C) $(4 - x) \div \dfrac{x^2 - 16}{5}$

ANSWER

(A) $(3y + 2)/(y + 3)$; (B) $2x$; (C) $-5/(x + 4)$.

A fractional form with fractions in its numerator, denominator, or both is called a *complex fraction*. It is often necessary to represent a complex fraction as a *simple fraction*, that is (in all cases we will consider), as the quotient of two polynomials. The process does not involve any new concepts. It is a matter of applying old concepts and processes in the right sequence. We will illustrate two approaches to the problem, each with its own merits depending on the particular problem under consideration. One of the methods makes very effective use of the property $a/b = ak/bk$, with $k \neq 0$.

Example 11. Express $\dfrac{1 - (1/4c^2)}{1 + (1/2c)}$ as a simple fraction.

SOLUTION

METHOD 1: Multiply the numerator and denominator by the LCD of all fractions within the numerator and denominator. Thus

$$\frac{1 - (1/4c^2)}{1 + (1/2c)} = \frac{[1 - (1/4c^2)]4c^2}{[1 + (1/2c)]4c^2} = \frac{4c^2 - 1}{4c^2 + 2c} = \frac{(2c + 1)(2c - 1)}{2c(2c + 1)} = \frac{2c - 1}{2c}$$

METHOD 2: Write the numerator and denominator as single fractions. Then treat as a quotient. Thus

$$\frac{1 - (1/4c^2)}{1 + (1/2c)} = \frac{(4c^2 - 1)/4c^2}{(2c + 1)/2c} = \frac{4c^2 - 1}{4c^2} \div \frac{2c + 1}{2c}$$

$$= \frac{(2c - 1)(2c + 1)}{4c^2} \cdot \frac{2c}{2c + 1} = \frac{2c - 1}{2c}$$

Problem 11. Express the following as a simple fraction in lowest terms. Use two methods.

$$\frac{1 - (1/3x)}{1 - (1/9x^2)}$$

ANSWER

$3x/(3x + 1)$.

Example 12. Express $2 - \dfrac{1}{2 - \dfrac{2}{2 + (1/x)}}$ as a simple fraction.

SOLUTION

$$2 - \frac{1}{2 - \dfrac{2}{2 + (1/x)}} = 2 - \frac{1}{2 - \dfrac{2x}{[2 + (1/x)]x}} = 2 - \frac{1}{2 - \dfrac{2x}{2x + 1}}$$

$$= 2 - \frac{1(2x + 1)}{\left(2 - \dfrac{2x}{2x + 1}\right)(2x + 1)}$$

$$= 2 - \frac{2x + 1}{4x + 2 - 2x} = 2 - \frac{2x + 1}{2x + 2} = \frac{4x + 4 - 2x - 1}{2x + 2}$$

$$= \frac{2x + 3}{2x + 2}$$

Problem 12. Express $2 - \dfrac{2}{2 - \dfrac{1}{1 - (1/x)}}$ as a simple fraction in lowest terms.

ANSWER

$-2/(x-2)$ or $2/(2-x)$.

EXERCISE 10

A *Perform the indicated operations and reduce to lowest terms.*

1. $\dfrac{a^2 - a}{a - 1} \cdot \dfrac{a + 1}{a}$

2. $\dfrac{x + 3}{x^3 + 3x^2} \cdot \dfrac{x^3}{x - 3}$

3. $\dfrac{m + n}{m^2 - n^2} \div \dfrac{m^2 - mn}{m^2 - 2mn + n^2}$

4. $\dfrac{x^2 - 6x + 9}{x^2 - x - 6} + \dfrac{x^2 + 2x - 15}{x^2 + 2x}$

5. $(t^2 - t - 12) \div \dfrac{t^2 - 9}{t^2 - 3t}$

6. $\dfrac{2y^2 + 7y + 3}{4y^2 - 1} \div (y + 3)$

7. $\left(\dfrac{-d^5}{3a} \div \dfrac{d^2}{6a^2}\right) \cdot \dfrac{a}{-4d^3}$

8. $\dfrac{-d^5}{3a} \div \left(\dfrac{d^2}{6a^2} \cdot \dfrac{a}{-4d^3}\right)$

9. $\dfrac{1 + (3/x)}{x - (9/x)}$

10. $\dfrac{1 - (y^2/x^2)}{1 - (y/x)}$

11. $\dfrac{(1/x) + (1/y)}{(y/x) - (x/y)}$

12. $\dfrac{b - (a^2/b)}{(1/a) - (1/b)}$

B 13. $\dfrac{2 - m}{2m + m^2} \cdot \dfrac{m^2 + 4m + 4}{m^2 - 4}$

14. $\dfrac{9 - x^2}{x^2 + 5x + 6} \cdot \dfrac{x + 2}{x - 3}$

15. $\dfrac{t^2 - 16}{2t^2 + 10t + 8} \div \dfrac{t^2 - 13t + 36}{t^3 + 1}$

16. $\left[\left(\dfrac{x^3}{y^3} - 1\right)\left(\dfrac{y}{x - y}\right)\right] \div \dfrac{x^2 + xy + y^2}{y^2}$

17. $\dfrac{x^2 - xy}{xy + y^2} \div \left(\dfrac{x^2 - y^2}{x^2 + 2xy + y^2} \div \dfrac{x^2 - 2xy + y^2}{x^2y + xy^2}\right)$

18. $\left(\dfrac{x^2 - xy}{xy + y^2} \div \dfrac{x^2 - y^2}{x^2 + 2xy + y^2}\right) \div \dfrac{x^2 - 2xy + y^2}{x^2y + xy^2}$

19. $\dfrac{(x/y) - 2 + (y/x)}{(x/y) - (y/x)}$

20. $\dfrac{1 + (2/x) - (15/x^2)}{1 + (4/x) - (5/x^2)}$

21. $\dfrac{n - \dfrac{n^2}{n-m}}{1 + \dfrac{m^2}{n^2-m^2}}$

22. $\dfrac{\dfrac{a^2}{a-b} - a}{\dfrac{b^2}{a-b} + b}$

23. $\dfrac{\dfrac{y}{x+y} - \dfrac{x}{x-y}}{\dfrac{x}{x+y} + \dfrac{y}{x-y}}$

24. $\dfrac{\dfrac{m}{m+2} - \dfrac{m}{m-2}}{\dfrac{m+2}{m-2} - \dfrac{m+2}{m-2}}$

25. $1 - \dfrac{1}{1-(1/x)}$

26. $2 - \dfrac{1}{1 - \dfrac{2}{x+2}}$

27. $1 - \dfrac{x-(1/x)}{1-(1/x)}$

28. $\dfrac{t - \dfrac{1}{1+(1/t)}}{t + \dfrac{1}{t-(1/t)}}$

c 29. $1 - \dfrac{1}{1 - \dfrac{1}{1 - \dfrac{1}{1-(1/x)}}}$

30. $1 + \dfrac{1}{1 + \dfrac{1}{1 + [1/(1+x)]}}$

31. A formula for the average rate r for a round trip between two points, where the rate going is r_G and the rate returning is r_R, is given by the complex fraction

$$r = \frac{2}{(1/r_G) + (1/r_R)}$$

Express r as a simple fraction.

32. The air speed indicator on a jet aircraft registers 500 mph. If the plane is traveling with an airstream moving at 100 mph, then the plane's ground speed is 600 mph, or is it? According to Einstein, velocities must be added according to the following formula:

$$v = \frac{v_1 + v_2}{1 + (v_1 v_2/c^2)}$$

where v is the resultant velocity, c is the speed of light, and v_1 and v_2 are the two velocities to be added. Convert the right side of the equation to a simple fraction.

33. Show for any number x, with $x \neq 0$, that if we take it and its reciprocal and add 1 to each the quotient of the two sums will be the number x with which we started.

2.5 INTEGRAL EXPONENTS

In this section we will extend the meaning of exponent so that not only will symbols such as a^3 be defined, but also symbols such as 5^0 and a^{-3}; that is, we will extend the meaning of exponent to include all integers. In extending the concept of exponent beyond natural numbers, we will require that any new exponent symbol be defined so that all five laws of exponents for natural numbers continue to hold.

How should a^0 be defined? If all the exponent laws are to hold even if some of the exponents are zero, a^0 should be defined so that when the first law of exponents is applied,

$$a^0 \cdot a^2 = a^{0+2} = a^2$$

This suggests that a^0 should be defined as the multiplicative identity 1. If, however, we let $a = 0$ and follow the same reasoning, we find

$$0^0 \cdot 0^2 = 0^{0+2} = 0^2 = 0$$

and 0^0 could be any real number, hence is not uniquely determined. For this reason we cannot define 0^0. Thus we formally define a^0 as follows: For a any real number,

---

$$a^0 = 1 \qquad a \neq 0$$

0^0 is not defined

How should a^{-2} be defined? If all the laws of exponents are to continue to hold even if some of the exponents are negative integers, then a^{-2}, $a \neq 0$, should be defined so that when the first law of exponents is applied,

$$a^{-2} \cdot a^2 = a^{-2+2} = a^0 = 1$$

Thus a^{-2} must be the multiplicative inverse of a^2; that is,

$$a^{-2} = \frac{1}{a^2}$$

This kind of reasoning leads to the following formal definition: For n a positive integer and a any real number,

---

$$a^{-n} = \frac{1}{a^n} \qquad a \neq 0$$

Of course, it follows from this definition and properties of equality that

$$a^n = \frac{1}{a^{-n}} \qquad a \neq 0$$

Example 13. (A) $4{,}250^0 = 1$

(B) $(u^3v^2)^0 = 1 \qquad u \neq 0, v \neq 0$

(C) $10^{-3} = \dfrac{1}{10^3} = \dfrac{1}{1{,}000} = 0.001$

(D) $\dfrac{1}{10^{-6}} = 10^6 = 1{,}000{,}000$

(E) $x^{-8} = \dfrac{1}{x^8}$

(F) $\dfrac{x^{-3}}{y^{-5}} = \boxed{\dfrac{x^{-3}}{1} \cdot \dfrac{1}{y^{-5}} = \dfrac{1}{x^3} \cdot \dfrac{y^5}{1}} = \dfrac{y^5}{x^3}$

Problem 13. Write (A) to (D) as decimal fractions, and (E) and (F) with positive exponents.

(A) 635^0 (B) $(x^2)^0, x \neq 0$ (C) 10^{-5}
(D) $1/10^{-3}$ (E) $1/x^{-4}$ (F) u^{-7}/v^{-3}

ANSWER

(A) 1; (B) 1; (C) 0.00001; (D) 1,000; (E) x^4; (F) v^3/u^7.

It is possible, though somewhat difficult, to show that, under the above definitions of zero and negative integral exponent, all exponent laws continue to hold and no contradictions are introduced into our mathematical system. We accept these results without proof, and relist the exponent laws as follows:

Laws of Exponents $n, m \in I; a, b \in R$

1. $a^m a^n = a^{m+n}$
2. $(a^n)^m = a^{mn}$
3. $(ab)^n = a^n b^n$

4. $\left(\dfrac{a}{b}\right)^n = \dfrac{a^n}{b^n} \qquad b \neq 0$

5. $\dfrac{a^m}{a^n} = a^{m-n} = \dfrac{1}{a^{n-m}} \qquad a \neq 0$

These laws allow us to change or simplify algebraic expressions involving integers as exponents, without having to return to basic definitions.

Example 14. Simplify and express answers using positive exponents only.

(A) $a^5 a^{-2} \boxed{= a^{5-2}} = a^3$

(B) $(a^{-3}b^2)^{-2} \boxed{= (a^{-3})^{-2}(b^2)^{-2}} = a^6 b^{-4} = \dfrac{a^6}{b^4}$

(C) $\left(\dfrac{a^{-5}}{a^{-2}}\right)^{-2} \boxed{= \dfrac{(a^{-5})^{-2}}{(a^{-2})^{-2}}} = \dfrac{a^{10}}{a^4} = a^6$

(D) $\dfrac{4x^{-3}y^{-5}}{6x^{-4}y^3} = \dfrac{2x^{-3-(-4)}}{3y^{3-(-5)}} = \dfrac{2x^{-3+4}}{3y^{3+5}} = \dfrac{2x}{3y^8}$

In place of using the fifth law of exponents, we can multiply numerator and denominator by $x^4 y^5$ and use the first law of exponents to obtain the same result:

$$\dfrac{4x^{-3}y^{-5}}{6x^{-4}y^3} = \dfrac{(2x^{-3}y^{-5})(x^4y^5)}{(3x^{-4}y^3)(x^4y^5)} = \dfrac{2xy^0}{3x^0y^8} = \dfrac{2x}{3y^8}$$

(E) $\left(\dfrac{m^{-3}m^3}{n^{-2}}\right)^{-2} = \left(\dfrac{m^{-3+3}}{n^{-2}}\right)^{-2} = \left(\dfrac{m^0}{n^{-2}}\right)^{-2} = \left(\dfrac{1}{n^{-2}}\right)^{-2} = \dfrac{1}{n^4}$

(F) $(a^{-1} - b^{-1})^2 = \left(\dfrac{1}{a} - \dfrac{1}{b}\right)^2 = \left(\dfrac{b-a}{ab}\right)^2 = \dfrac{b^2 - 2ab + a^2}{a^2b^2}$

Problem 14. Simplify, and express the answers using positive exponents only.

(A) $x^{-7}x^3$ (B) $(x^{-2}y^4)^{-3}$ (C) $\left(\dfrac{x^{-6}}{x^{-3}}\right)^{-3}$

(D) $\dfrac{8x^2y^{-2}}{12x^{-3}y^4}$ (E) $\left(\dfrac{y^{-3}}{x^{-5}x^5}\right)^{-3}$ (F) $(x^{-2} + y^{-2})^2$

ANSWER

(A) $1/x^4$; (B) x^6/y^{12}; (C) x^9; (D) $2x^5/3y^6$; (E) y^9; (F) $(x^4 + 2x^2y^2 + y^4)/x^4y^4$.

Scientific Notation

Scientific work often involves the use of very large numbers or very small numbers. For example, the average cell contains about 200,000,000,000,000 molecules, and the diameter of an electron is about 0.0000000000004 cm. It is generally troublesome to write and work with numbers of this type in standard decimal form. However, with exponents defined for all integers, it is possible to express any decimal fraction as a number between 1 and 10 and an integral power of 10, that is, in *scientific notation*. Laws of exponents, of course, can be used to an advantage in computations involving these power forms.

Example 15. Decimal Fractions and Scientific Notation

$$7 = 7 \times 10^0 \qquad\qquad 0.5 = 5 \times 10^{-1}$$
$$720 = 7.2 \times 10^2 \qquad\qquad 0.08 = 8 \times 10^{-2}$$
$$6,430 = 6.43 \times 10^3 \qquad\qquad 0.00032 = 3.2 \times 10^{-4}$$
$$5,350,000 = 5.35 \times 10^6 \qquad 0.0000000738 = 7.38 \times 10^{-8}$$

Can you discover a simple rule relating the number of decimal places that the decimal is moved to the power of 10 that is used?

Problem 15. (A) Write each number in scientific notation: 430, 23,000, 345,000,000, 0.3, 0.0031, 0.000000683.

(B) Write as decimal fractions: 4×10^3, 5.3×10^5, 2.53×10^{-2}, 7.42×10^{-6}.

ANSWER

(A) 4.3×10^2, 2.3×10^4, 3.45×10^8, 3×10^{-1}, 3.1×10^{-3}, 6.83×10^{-7};
(B) 4,000; 530,000; 0.0253; 0.00000742.

Example 16. Evaluation of a Complicated Arithmetic Problem

$$\frac{(0.26)(720)}{(48,000,000)(0.0013)} = \frac{(2.6 \times 10^{-1})(7.2 \times 10^2)}{(4.8 \times 10^7)(1.3 \times 10^{-3})}$$

$$= \frac{(2.6)(7.2)}{(4.8)(1.3)} \cdot \frac{(10^{-1})(10^2)}{(10^7)(10^{-3})} = 3 \times 10^{-3} \text{ or } 0.003$$

Problem 16. Use scientific notation to evaluate $\dfrac{(1,200)(0.048)}{(0.00016)(24,000,000)}$.

ANSWER

1.5×10^{-2} or 0.015.

EXERCISE 11

A
1. $a^9 = a^5 a^?$
2. $y^8 = y^? y^2$
3. $1/n^6 = n^8/n^?$
4. $1/u^2 = u^?/u^9$

Simplify, and write the answer using positive exponents only.

5. $8,732^0$
6. 25^0
7. $y^{-5}y^5$
8. $x^3 x^{-3}$
9. $(2x^2)(3x^3)(x^4)$
10. $(2x^5)(3x^7)(4x^2)$
11. $(p^2 q^5)^3$
12. $(x^2 y^3)^4$
13. a^8/a^{-4}
14. b^{-3}/b^5
15. $(2cd^2)^{-3}$
16. $(3x^3 y^{-2})^2$
17. $(ab^3/c^2 d)^4$
18. $(x^2 y/2w^2)^3$

19. $\dfrac{10^{23} \cdot 10^{-11}}{10^{-3} \cdot 10^{-2}}$
20. $\dfrac{10^{-13} \cdot 10^{-4}}{10^{-21} \cdot 10^3}$

21. $4x^{-2}y^{-3}/2x^{-3}y^{-1}$
22. $2a^6 b^{-2}/16a^{-3}b^2$
23. $(n^{-3}/n^{-2})^{-2}$
24. $(x^{-1}/x^{-8})^{-1}$

25. $\dfrac{8 \times 10^3}{2 \times 10^{-5}}$
26. $\dfrac{18 \times 10^{12}}{6 \times 10^{-4}}$

Write the numbers in Probs. 27 to 38 in scientific notation.

27. 35
28. 72
29. 0.6
30. 0.3
31. 283
32. 340
33. 0.017
34. 0.085
35. 4,930
36. 6,800
37. 0.0000000729
38. 0.000592

In Probs. 39 to 50 write each number as a decimal fraction.

39. 5.72×10
40. 3.7×10
41. 4×10^4
42. 7.1×10^3
43. 9.7×10^{-2}
44. $8.37 \times 10^{-}$
45. 5×10^{-3}
46. 4×10^{-4}
47. 6.5×10^9
48. 2.51×10^9
49. 6.3×10^{-12}
50. 5.9×10^{-7}

B *Simplify, and write the answer using positive exponents only.*

51. $\dfrac{(-x^2)^3}{(x^3)^4(-x)^2}$
52. $\left(\dfrac{3y^2}{x}\right)^2 \left(-\dfrac{x}{y}\right)^3$

53. $\left(\dfrac{2x^{-3}y^2}{4xy^{-1}}\right)^{-2}$

54. $\left(\dfrac{6mn^{-2}}{3m^{-1}n^2}\right)^{-3}$

55. $\dfrac{5(u-v+w)^8}{(u-v+w)^{11}}$

56. $\dfrac{3(x+y)^3(x-y)^4}{(x-y)^26(x+y)^5}$

57. $\left[\left(\dfrac{u^3v^{-1}w^{-2}}{u^{-2}v^{-2}w}\right)^{-2}\right]^2$

58. $\left[\left(\dfrac{x^{-2}y^3t}{x^{-3}y^{-2}t^2}\right)^2\right]^{-1}$

59. $\left(\dfrac{3^3x^0y^{-2}}{2^3x^3y^{-5}}\right)^{-1}\left(\dfrac{3^3x^{-1}y}{2^2x^2y^{-2}}\right)^2$

60. $\left(\dfrac{2^2x^2y^0}{8x^{-1}}\right)^{-2}\left(\dfrac{x^{-3}}{x^{-5}}\right)^3$

61. $(x+y)^{-2}$

62. $(a^2-b^2)^{-1}$

63. $\dfrac{m^{-1}}{n^{-1}}+\dfrac{n^{-1}}{m^{-1}}$

64. $\dfrac{x^{-2}}{y^{-2}}-\dfrac{2}{x^2}$

65. $\dfrac{x^{-1}+y^{-1}}{x+y}$

66. $\dfrac{c-d}{c^{-1}-d^{-1}}$

67. $(x^{-1}+y^{-1})^{-1}$

68. $(x^{-1}+y^{-1})^2$

Convert each of the numbers in Probs. 69 through 72 to scientific notation, simplify, and express the final answer in scientific notation and as a decimal fraction.

69. $\dfrac{(90{,}000)(0.000002)}{0.006}$

70. $\dfrac{(0.0006)(4000)}{0.00012}$

71. $\dfrac{(60{,}000)(0.000003)}{(0.0004)(1{,}500{,}000)}$

72. $\dfrac{(0.000039)(140)}{(130{,}000)(0.00021)}$

73. If the mass of the earth is 6×10^{27} grams and each gram is 1.1×10^{-6} ton, find the mass of the earth in tons.

74. In 1929, Vernadsky, a biologist, estimated that all the free oxygen of the earth weighs 1.5×10^{21} grams, and that it is produced by life alone. If 1 gram is approximately 2.2×10^{-3} lb, what is the amount of free oxygen in pounds?

75. Some designers of high-speed computers are developing single addition times of 10^{-7} sec (100 nanoseconds). How many additions would such a computer be able to perform in 1 sec? In 1 min?

76. If electricity travels in a computer circuit at the speed of light (1.86×10^5 mi per sec), how far will it travel in the time it takes the computer in Prob. 75 to complete a single addition? (The size of circuits is a critical problem in computer design.) Give the answer in miles and in feet.

C 77. $\left[\dfrac{u^{-2}-v^{-2}}{(u^{-1}-v^{-1})^2}\right]^{-1}$

78. $\left(\dfrac{x^{-1}}{x^{-1}-y^{-1}}\right)^{-1}$

79. $y^{2n+2}y^{n-2}$

80. $x^{5-n}x^{n+2}$

81. x^{n+2}/x^n

82. x^{2n}/x^n

83. $(x^{n+1})^n$

84. $(x^{n+1})^2$

85. $\dfrac{(x^n y^{n+1})^2}{x^{2n+1} y^{2n}}$ 86. $\dfrac{u^{n+3} v^n}{u^{n+1} v^{n+4}}$

87. Show that $(x/y)^{-n} = (y/x)^n$.
88. For $n \in I$ and $x \in R$, when does $(-x)^n = -x^n$?

2.6 RATIONAL EXPONENTS

Recall that a square root of a number b is a number a such that $a^2 = b$; a cube root of a number b is a number a such that $a^3 = b$. Thus a square root of 4 is 2 or -2, since $2^2 = 4$ and $(-2)^2 = 4$. A cube root of -8 is -2, since $(-2)^3 = -8$. In general, for n a natural number, we define *an nth root of a number b* to be a number a if and only if a satisfies the equation

$$a^n = b$$

How many real fourth roots of 16 exist? Of -16? How many real fifth roots of 32 exist? Of -32? In general, what can we say about the number of real nth roots of a real number b? The following important theorem (which we state without proof) answers these questions completely.

Theorem 3. Number of Real Roots of a Real Number.

(A) There exist exactly two even real roots of a positive real number; one is the negative of the other.

(B) There are no even real roots of a negative real number.

(C) There exists exactly one odd real root of a real number. It is negative if the real number is negative, and positive if the real number is positive.

If all exponent laws are to continue to hold even if some of the exponents are rational numbers, then how should symbols such as $7^{1/2}$ or $5^{1/3}$ be defined? Applying one of the laws of exponents, we note that

$$(7^{1/2})^2 = 7^{2/2} = 7 \quad \text{and} \quad (5^{1/3})^3 = 5^{3/3} = 5$$

Hence $7^{1/2}$ must name a square root of 7, since $7^{1/2}$ satisfies the equation $a^2 = 7$; and $5^{1/3}$ must name a cube root of 5, since $5^{1/3}$ satisfies the equation $a^3 = 5$. In general, for n a natural number and b not negative when n is even,

$$(b^{1/n})^n = b^{n/n} = b$$

Therefore, $b^{1/n}$ must name an nth root of b, since $b^{1/n}$ satisfies the equation $a^n = b$. But which nth root? We would like $b^{1/n}$ to be uniquely defined.

If n is even and b is positive, then, according to Theorem 3, there are two real nth roots of b, one the negative of the other. We will use $b^{1/n}$ to name only the positive one. The following definition takes care of all cases.

Definition 1. $b^{1/n}$, $n \in N$, $b \in R$

n	b positive	b negative	$b = 0$
Even	$b^{1/n}$ is the positive nth root of b	$b^{1/n}$ is not defined in R	$0^{1/n} = 0$
Odd	$b^{1/n}$ is *the* nth real root of b (positive)	$b^{1/n}$ is *the* nth real root of b (negative)	$0^{1/n} = 0$

Example 17.
(A) $4^{1/2} = 2$
(B) $-4^{1/2} = -2$
(C) $(-4)^{1/2}$ is not defined in R
(D) $8^{1/3} = 2$
(E) $(-8)^{1/3} = -2$
(F) $0^{1/5} = 0$

Problem 17. Find each of the following.

(A) $9^{1/2}$ (B) $-9^{1/2}$ (C) $(-9)^{1/2}$
(D) $27^{1/3}$ (E) $(-27)^{1/3}$ (F) $0^{1/4}$

ANSWER

(A) 3; (B) -3; (C) not defined in R; (D) 3; (E) -3; (F) 0.

How should a symbol such as $5^{2/3}$ be defined? If the laws of exponents are to continue to hold for all rational exponents, then $5^{2/3} = (5^{1/3})^2$; that is, $5^{2/3}$ must represent the cube root of 5 squared. In general, we define

$$b^{m/n} = (b^{1/n})^m$$

where m and n are natural numbers and b is any real number, with the exclusion of b being negative when n is even. Using the same restrictions, we define

$$b^{-m/n} = \frac{1}{b^{m/n}} \qquad b \neq 0$$

We now know what $b^{m/n}$ means for all rational numbers m/n and real numbers b. It can be shown, though we will not, that all five laws of exponents continue to hold for rational exponents as long as we avoid even roots of negative numbers. With the latter restriction in effect, the following useful relationship is an immediate consequence of the exponent laws:

$$b^{m/n} = (b^{1/n})^m = (b^m)^{1/n}$$

Example 18.   (A) $8^{2/3} = (8^{1/3})^2 = 2^2 = 4$ or $8^{2/3} = (8^2)^{1/3} = 64^{1/3} = 4$

(B) $(-8)^{5/3} = [(-8)^{1/3}]^5 = (-2)^5 = -32$

(C) $(3x^{1/3})(2x^{1/2}) = 6x^{1/3+1/2} = 6x^{5/6}$

(D) $(2x^{1/3}y^{-2/3})^3 = 8xy^{-2}$ or $8x/y^2$

(E) $\left(\dfrac{4x^{1/3}}{x^{1/2}}\right)^{1/2} = \dfrac{4^{1/2}x^{1/6}}{x^{1/4}} = \dfrac{2}{x^{1/4-1/6}} = \dfrac{2}{x^{1/12}}$ or $2x^{-1/12}$

(F) $(2a^{1/2} + b^{1/2})(a^{1/2} + 3b^{1/2}) = 2a + 7a^{1/2}b^{1/2} + 3b$

Problem 18.   Simplify, and express the answers using positive exponents only.

(A) $9^{3/2}$ (B) $(-27)^{4/3}$

(C) $(5y^{3/4})(2y^{1/3})$ (D) $(2x^{-3/4}y^{1/4})^4$

(E) $\left(\dfrac{8x^{1/2}}{x^{2/3}}\right)^{1/3}$ (F) $(x^{1/2} - 2y^{1/2})(3x^{1/2} + y^{1/2})$

ANSWER

(A) 27; (B) 81; (C) $10y^{13/12}$; (D)$16\,y/x^3$; (E) $2/x^{1/18}$; (F) $3x - 5x^{1/2}y^{1/2} - 2y$.

The laws of exponents can be used as long as we are dealing with symbols that name real numbers. Can you resolve the following contradiction?

$$-1 = (-1)^{2/2} = [(-1)^2]^{1/2} = 1^{1/2} = 1$$

The second member of the equality chain, $(-1)^{2/2}$, involves the even root of a negative number, which is not real. Thus we see that the laws of exponents do not necessarily hold when we are dealing with nonreal quantities.

EXERCISE 12

A   *Find each of the following.*

1. $16^{1/2}$
2. $8^{1/3}$
3. $8^{2/3}$
4. $16^{3/2}$
5. $(-32)^{3/5}$
6. $32^{3/5}$
7. $(-9)^{1/2}$
8. $-9^{1/2}$
9. $(\frac{8}{27})^{2/3}$
10. $(\frac{4}{27})^{3/2}$
11. $25^{-3/2}$
12. $8^{-2/3}$
13. $(4^{-8})^{3/16}$
14. $(3^6)^{-1/3}$
15. $7^{2/3} \cdot 7^{4/3}$
16. $5^{3/2} \cdot 5^{1/2}$

Simplify, and express the answer using positive exponents only.

17. $y^{1/5}y^{2/5}$
18. $x^{1/4}x^{3/4}$
19. $a^{2/3}/a^{1/3}$
20. $x^{2/5}/x^{3/5}$
21. $x^{1/4}x^{-3/4}$
22. $d^{2/3}/d^{-1/3}$
23. $n^{3/4}n^{-2/3}$
24. $m^{1/2}m^{-1/3}$
25. $(y^{-8})^{1/16}$
26. $(x^{-2/3})^{-6}$
27. $(8x^3y^{-6})^{1/3}$
28. $(4u^{-2}v^4)^{1/2}$
29. $(x^4y^6)^{-1/2}$
30. $(4x^{1/2}y^{3/2})^2$
B 31. $(-16)^{-3/2}$
32. $-16^{-3/2}$
33. $(m^{-3}/n^2)^{-1/6}$
34. $(x^{-2/3}/y^{-1/2})^{-6}$

35. $\left(\dfrac{25x^5y^{-1}}{16x^{-3}y^{-5}}\right)^{1/2}$

36. $\left(\dfrac{8a^{-4}b^3}{27a^2b^{-3}}\right)^{1/3}$

37. $\left(\dfrac{8y^{1/3}y^{-1/4}}{y^{-1/12}}\right)^2$

38. $\left(\dfrac{9x^{1/3}x^{1/2}}{x^{-1/6}}\right)^{1/2}$

39. $(a^{3/n}b^{3/m})^{1/3}, n > 0, m > 0$
40. $(a^{n/2}b^{n/3})^{1/n}, n > 0$

Multiply, and express the answer using positive exponents only.

41. $2x^{1/3}(3x^{2/3} - x^6)$
42. $3m^{3/4}(4m^{1/4} - 2m^8)$
43. $(x^{1/2} + y^{1/2})(x^{1/2} - y^{1/2})$
44. $(2x^{1/2} + y^{1/2})(x^{1/2} + y^{1/2})$
45. $(x^{1/2} - y^{1/2})^2$
46. $(x^{1/2} + y^{1/2})^2$
47. $(x^{-1/2} - y^{-1/2})^2$
48. $(a^{-1/2} + 3b^{-1/2})(2a^{-1/2} - b^{-1/2})$
C 49. $(a^m/a^{m-2})^{1/2}, m > 0$
50. $(x^{m+2}/x^m)^{1/2}, m > 0$
51. $(y^{m^2+1}y^{2m})^{1/(m+1)}, m > 0$
52. $(x^{m/4}x^{m/4})^{-2}, m > 0$
53. (A)   Find a value of $x \in R$ such that $(x^2)^{1/2} \neq x$.
    (B)   Find a value of $x \in R$ and a value of $n \in N$ such that $(x^n)^{1/n} \neq x$.
54. Which of the following statements are true?
    (A) $(x^2)^{1/2} = |x|, x \in R$
    (B) $(x^{2n})^{1/2n} = |x|, n \in N, x \in R$
    (C) $(x^{2n+1})^{1/(2n+1)} = x, n \in N, x \in R$
    (D) $(x^n)^{1/n} = x, n \in N, x \in R^+$
55. Can you resolve the contradiction $-1 = i^2 = i^{4/2} = (i^4)^{1/2} = 1^{1/2} = 1$?

2.7 RADICALS

For n a natural number greater than 1 and b any real number except b negative when n is even, we define

$$\sqrt[n]{b} = b^{1/n}$$

The symbol $\sqrt{}$ is called a *radical*, n is called the *index*, and b is called the *radicand*. (Note that, if $n = 2$, we write $\sqrt{b}$ in place of $\sqrt[2]{b}$.) There are occasions when it is more convenient to work with radicals than with rational exponents, or vice versa. It is often an advantage to be able to shift back and forth between the two forms. The following relationships are useful in this regard:

$$b^{m/n} = (b^m)^{1/n} = \sqrt[n]{b^m}$$
$$b^{m/n} = (b^{1/n})^m = (\sqrt[n]{b})^m$$

where b is not negative for n even. Note what can happen if we relax this last restriction:

$$(-1)^{2/2} = [(-1)^2]^{1/2} = \sqrt{(-1)^2} = \sqrt{1} = 1$$
$$(-1)^{2/2} = [(-1)^{1/2}]^2 = (\sqrt{-1})^2 = i^2 = -1$$

Thus, it appears that $-1 = 1$!

Example 19.   From rational exponent form to radical form.

(A) $x^{1/7} = \sqrt[7]{x}$

(B) $(3u^2v^3)^{3/5} = \sqrt[5]{(3u^2v^3)^3}$ or $(\sqrt[5]{3u^2v^3})^3$ (the first is usually preferred)

(C) $y^{-2/3} = \dfrac{1}{y^{2/3}} = \dfrac{1}{\sqrt[3]{y^2}}$ or $\sqrt[3]{y^{-2}}$ or $\sqrt[3]{\dfrac{1}{y^2}}$

From radical form to rational exponent form.

(D) $\sqrt[5]{6} = 6^{1/5}$

(E) $-\sqrt[3]{x^2} = -x^{2/3}$

(F) $\sqrt{x^2 + y^2} = (x^2 + y^2)^{1/2}$

NOTE: $(x^2 + y^2)^{1/2} \neq x + y$. Why?

Problem 19.   Convert to radical form.

(A) $u^{1/5}$ (B) $(6x^2y^5)^{2/9}$ (C) $(3xy)^{-3/5}$

Convert to rational exponent form.

(D) $\sqrt[4]{9u}$ (E) $-\sqrt[7]{(2x)^4}$ (F) $\sqrt[3]{x^3 + y^3}$

ANSWER

(A) $\sqrt[5]{u}$; (B) $\sqrt[9]{(6x^2y^5)^2}$ or $(\sqrt[9]{6x^2y^5})^2$; (C) $1/\sqrt[5]{(3xy)^3}$; (D) $(9u)^{1/4}$;
(E) $-(2x)^{4/7}$; (F) $(x^3 + y^3)^{1/3}$ (not $x + y$).

Changing and simplifying radical expressions is aided by the introduction of several laws of radicals that follow directly from exponent properties considered earlier.

Laws of n and m are natural numbers ≥ 2.
Radicals x and y are positive real numbers.

1. $\sqrt[n]{x^n} = x$
2. $\sqrt[n]{xy} = \sqrt[n]{x}\,\sqrt[n]{y}$

3. $\sqrt[n]{\dfrac{x}{y}} = \dfrac{\sqrt[n]{x}}{\sqrt[n]{y}}$

4. $\sqrt[kn]{x^{km}} = \sqrt[n]{x^m}, \ k \in N$

The proofs of these laws are left as exercises.

Example 20. $x, y \in R^+$

(A) $\sqrt[5]{(3x^2y)^5} = 3x^2y$
(B) $\sqrt{10}\,\sqrt{5} = \sqrt{50} = \sqrt{25 \cdot 2} = \sqrt{25}\,\sqrt{2} = 5\sqrt{2}$

(C) $\sqrt[3]{\dfrac{x}{27}} = \dfrac{\sqrt[3]{x}}{\sqrt[3]{27}} = \dfrac{\sqrt[3]{x}}{3}$ or $\dfrac{1}{3}\sqrt[3]{x}$

(D) $\sqrt[6]{x^4} = \sqrt[2\cdot3]{x^{2\cdot2}} = \sqrt[3]{x^2}$

Problem 20.   Simplify as in Example 20.

(A) $\sqrt[7]{(u^2 + v^2)^7}$ (B) $\sqrt{6}\,\sqrt{2}$ (C) $\sqrt[3]{x^2/8}$ (D) $\sqrt[8]{y^6}$

ANSWER

(A) $u^2 + v^2$; (B) $2\sqrt{3}$; (C) $\sqrt[3]{x^2}/2$ or $\frac{1}{2}\sqrt[3]{x^2}$; (D) $\sqrt[4]{y^3}$.

The laws of radicals provide us with the means of changing algebraic expressions containing radicals to a variety of equivalent forms. One form often useful is the simplest radical form. An algebraic expression that contains radicals is said to be in the simplest radical form if all four of the following conditions are satisfied:

Simplest Radical Form

1. A radicand (the expression within the radical sign) contains no polynomial factor to a power greater than or equal to the index of the radical.
2. The power of the radicand and the index of the radical have no common factor other than 1.
3. No radical appears in a denominator.
4. No fraction appears within a radical.

It should be understood that forms other than the simplest radical form may be more useful on occasion. The choice depends on the situation.

Example 21.
Radical Expressions Changed to Simplest Radical Forms

The replacement set for all variables is the set of positive real numbers.

(A) $\sqrt[3]{54} = \sqrt[3]{3^3 \cdot 2} = \sqrt[3]{3^3} \cdot \sqrt[3]{2} = 3\sqrt[3]{2}$

(B) $\sqrt{12x^3y^5z^2} = \sqrt{(2^2x^2y^4z^2)(3xy)} = \sqrt{2^2x^2y^4z^2}\sqrt{3xy} = 2xy^2z\sqrt{3xy}$

(C) $\sqrt[6]{16x^4y^2} = \sqrt[6]{(2^2x^2y)^2} = \sqrt[3]{4x^2y}$

(D) $\dfrac{3}{\sqrt{5}} = \dfrac{3\sqrt{5}}{\sqrt{5}\sqrt{5}} = \dfrac{3\sqrt{5}}{5}$ or $\dfrac{3}{5}\sqrt{5}$

(E) $\dfrac{6x^2}{\sqrt[3]{3x}} = \dfrac{6x^2\sqrt[3]{3^2x^2}}{\sqrt[3]{3x}\sqrt[3]{3^2x^2}} = \dfrac{6x^2\sqrt[3]{9x^2}}{\sqrt[3]{3^3x^3}} = \dfrac{6x^2\sqrt[3]{9x^2}}{3x} = 2x\sqrt[3]{9x^2}$

(F) $\sqrt[3]{\dfrac{2a^2}{3b}} = \sqrt[3]{\dfrac{(2a^2)(3^2b^2)}{(3b)(3^2b^2)}} = \sqrt[3]{\dfrac{18a^2b^2}{3^3b^3}} = \dfrac{\sqrt[3]{18a^2b^2}}{\sqrt[3]{3^3b^3}} = \dfrac{\sqrt[3]{18a^2b^2}}{3b}$

Problem 21. Reduce to simplest radical form.

(A) $\sqrt[3]{16}$ (B) $\sqrt{18x^5y^2z^3}$ (C) $\sqrt[9]{8x^6y^3}$

(D) $\dfrac{6}{\sqrt{2x}}$ (E) $\dfrac{10x^3}{\sqrt[3]{2x^2}}$ (F) $\sqrt[3]{\dfrac{3y^2}{2x^4}}$

ANSWER

(A) $2\sqrt[3]{2}$; (B) $3x^2yz\sqrt{2xz}$; (C) $\sqrt[3]{2x^2y}$; (D) $3\sqrt{2x}/x$; (E) $5x^2\sqrt[3]{4x}$; (F) $\sqrt[3]{12x^2y^2}/2x^2$.

EXERCISE 13

A *Change to radical form.* (*Do not simplify.*)

1. $7^{1/2}$
2. $5^{1/3}$
3. $x^{3/4}$
4. $u^{3/5}$
5. $5m^{2/3}$
6. $4y^{3/7}$
7. $(4ab^3)^{2/5}$
8. $(7x^2y)^{2/3}$
9. $(a+b)^{1/2}$
10. $a^{1/2}+b^{1/2}$
11. $(a^2+b^2)^{1/2}$
12. $(a^3+b^3)^{2/3}$

Change to rational exponent form. (*Do not simplify.*)

13. $\sqrt[7]{x}$
14. $\sqrt[4]{m}$
15. $\sqrt[3]{a^2}$
16. $\sqrt[5]{y^3}$
17. $\sqrt[4]{(2xy)^3}$
18. $\sqrt[3]{(a+b)^2}$
19. $3/\sqrt[3]{y}$
20. $1/\sqrt{x}$

Simplify, and write in simplest radical form.

21. $\sqrt[3]{-27}$
22. $\sqrt[3]{-8}$
23. $\sqrt{4a^4b^8}$
24. $\sqrt{16x^2y^4}$
25. $\sqrt[5]{32m^5n^{15}}$
26. $\sqrt[4]{16x^8y^4}$
27. $\sqrt{18}$
28. $\sqrt{8}$
29. $\sqrt{27m^2n^7}$
30. $\sqrt{8x^3y^5}$
31. $\sqrt[4]{2^4a^5b^8}$
32. $\sqrt[3]{x^4x^4y^7}$
33. $\sqrt[10]{x^6}$
34. $\sqrt[4]{x^2}$
35. $\sqrt[3]{3}\sqrt[3]{9}$
36. $\sqrt{2}\sqrt{8}$
37. $\sqrt[3]{9x^2y}\sqrt[3]{3xy^2}$
38. $\sqrt{18m^3n^4}\sqrt{2m^3n^2}$
39. $1/\sqrt{7}$
40. $1/\sqrt{3}$
41. $2/\sqrt[3]{2}$
42. $6/\sqrt[3]{3}$
43. $\sqrt{9m^5}/\sqrt{2n}$
44. $\sqrt{4a^3}/\sqrt{3b}$
45. $\sqrt{6x/7y}$
46. $\sqrt{3m/2n}$
47. $\sqrt[3]{x^3+y^3}$
48. $\sqrt{a^2+b^2}$

B *Change to radical form.* (*Do not simplify.*)

49. $-3x^{1/2}$
50. $-5y^{2/5}$
51. $(3m^2n^3)^{-3/5}$
52. $(2xy)^{-2/3}$
53. $(x^{1/2}+y^{-1/2})^{1/3}$
54. $x^{-1/2}+y^{-1/2}$

Change to rational exponent form. (Do not simplify.)

55. $-3x\sqrt[4]{a^3b}$

56. $-5\sqrt[3]{2x^2y^2}$

57. $\sqrt[3]{m^2} - \sqrt{n}$

58. $-5u^2/(\sqrt{u} + \sqrt[5]{v^3})$

59. $(3/\sqrt{x}) + (2/\sqrt{y})$

60. $-2x/\sqrt{x^2 + y^2}$

Simplify, and write in simplest radical form.

61. $\sqrt[4]{a^8b^4/16c^{12}}$

62. $\sqrt[3]{8x^2/27y^6}$

63. $-2x\sqrt[3]{8x^8y^{13}}$

64. $-m\sqrt[5]{3^6m^7n^{11}}$

65. $\sqrt[8]{2^6(x+y)^6}$

66. $\sqrt[6]{x^4(x-y)^2}$

67. $\sqrt[4]{6u^3v^4}\ \sqrt[4]{4u^5v}$

68. $\sqrt[3]{2x^2v^3}\ \sqrt[3]{3x^5y}$

69. $\dfrac{8u^3v^5}{\sqrt[3]{4u^2v^2}}$

70. $\dfrac{4x^3y^2}{\sqrt[3]{2xy^2}}$

71. $\dfrac{1}{\sqrt[3]{(x-y)^2}}$

72. $\dfrac{x-y}{\sqrt[3]{x-y}}$

73. $\dfrac{\sqrt{6}\ \sqrt{8x}}{\sqrt{18x}}$

74. $\dfrac{\sqrt{2x}\ \sqrt{5}}{\sqrt{20x}}$

75. $6c\sqrt[3]{\dfrac{2ab}{9c^2}}$

76. $-3x\sqrt[3]{\dfrac{3y^2}{4x}}$

77. $\sqrt[5]{4n^2/16m^3}$

78. $\sqrt[4]{3y^3/4x}$

79. $\sqrt[4]{m^4 + 4m^6}$

80. $-\sqrt{x^4 + 2x^2}$

c *Simplify Probs. 81 to 88, and express the results in simplest radical form.*

81. $\sqrt[3]{8\sqrt{16x^6y^4}}$

82. $\sqrt[4]{16x^4\sqrt[3]{16x^{24}y^4}}$

83. $\sqrt{2x^5y^3}\ \sqrt[3]{16x^7y^7}$

84. $\sqrt[3]{3m^2n^2}\ \sqrt[4]{3m^3n^2}$

85. $\dfrac{\sqrt{2x}}{\sqrt[3]{x}}$

86. $\dfrac{\sqrt[3]{4m^2n^2}}{\sqrt{2mn}}$

87. $\sqrt[n]{x^{2n}y^{n^2+n}}$

88. $\sqrt[3]{x^{3n}(x+y)^{3n+6}}$

89. Use the exponent laws to prove the first and second radical laws:

(A) $\sqrt[n]{x^n} = x,\ x \in R^+,\ n \in N,\ n \geq 2$

(B) $\sqrt[n]{xy} = \sqrt[n]{x}\ \sqrt[n]{y},\ x \in R^+,\ n \in N,\ n \geq 2$

90. Use the exponent laws to prove the third and fourth radical laws:

(A) $\sqrt[n]{x/y} = \sqrt[n]{x}/\sqrt[n]{y},\ x, y \in R^+,\ n \in N,\ n \geq 2$

(B) $\sqrt[kn]{x^{km}} = \sqrt[n]{x^m},\ x \in R^+,\ k, n \in N,\ n \geq 2$

91. (A) Find a value of $x \in R$ such that $\sqrt{x^2} \neq x$.

(B) Find a value of $x \in R$ and a value of $n \in N$ such that $\sqrt[n]{x^n} \neq x$.

92. Which of the following statements are true?

    (A) $\sqrt{x^2} = |x|,\ x \in R$

    (B) $\sqrt[2n]{x^{2n}} = |x|,\ n \in N,\ x \in R$

    (C) $\sqrt[(2n+1)]{x^{2n+1}} = x,\ n \in N,\ x \in R$

    (D) $\sqrt[n]{x^n} = x,\ n \in N,\ x \in R^+$

93. Resolve the following contradiction.

    $$\sqrt{-3}\sqrt{-3} = \sqrt{(-3)(-3)} = \sqrt{9} = 3$$
    $$\sqrt{-3}\sqrt{-3} = i\sqrt{3}\,i\sqrt{3} = i^2(\sqrt{3})^2 = (-1)3 = -3$$

94. Show that $\sqrt[n]{a^n + b^n} \neq a + b$ by a suitable counterexample.

2.8 SUMS, DIFFERENCES, PRODUCTS, AND QUOTIENTS INVOLVING RADICALS

Sums and Differences of Radicals

Algebraic expressions involving radicals can often be simplified by adding or subtracting terms that contain exactly the same radical expression. We proceed in essentially the same way as when we combine like terms in polynomials. You will recall that the distributive property of real numbers played a central role in this process.

Example 22. (A) $5\sqrt{3} + 4\sqrt{3}\ \boxed{= (5+4)\sqrt{3}} = 9\sqrt{3}$

(B) $2\sqrt[3]{xy^2} - 7\sqrt[3]{xy^2}\ \boxed{= (2-7)\sqrt[3]{xy^2}} = -5\sqrt[3]{xy^2}$

(C) $3\sqrt{xy} - 2\sqrt[3]{xy} + 4\sqrt{xy} - 7\sqrt[3]{xy} = 3\sqrt{xy} + 4\sqrt{xy} - 2\sqrt[3]{xy} - 7\sqrt[3]{xy}$
$$= 7\sqrt{xy} - 9\sqrt[3]{xy}$$

Problem 22. Combine as many terms as possible.

(A) $6\sqrt{2} + 2\sqrt{2}$ (B) $3\sqrt[5]{2x^2y^3} - 8\sqrt[5]{2x^2y^3}$

(C) $5\sqrt[3]{mn^2} - 3\sqrt{mn} - 2\sqrt[3]{mn^2} + 7\sqrt{mn}$

ANSWER

(A) $8\sqrt{2}$; (B) $-5\sqrt[5]{2x^2y^3}$; (C) $3\sqrt[3]{mn^2} + 4\sqrt{mn}$.

Thus we see that if two terms contain exactly the same radical (the same index and the same radicand), then they can be combined into a single term. Occasionally, terms containing radicals can be combined after they have been expressed in simplest radical form.

Example 23. (A) $4\sqrt{8} - 2\sqrt{18} = 4\sqrt{4\cdot 2} - 2\sqrt{9\cdot 2}$
$$= 8\sqrt{2} - 6\sqrt{2}$$
$$= 2\sqrt{2}$$

(B) $\sqrt[3]{81} - \sqrt[3]{\frac{1}{9}} = \sqrt[3]{3^3\cdot 3} - \sqrt[3]{\frac{3}{3^3}} = 3\sqrt[3]{3} - \frac{1}{3}\sqrt[3]{3}$
$$= \left(3 - \frac{1}{3}\right)\sqrt[3]{3} = \frac{8}{3}\sqrt[3]{3}$$

Problem 23. Express terms in simplest radical form and combine where possible.

(A) $\sqrt{12} - \sqrt{48}$ (B) $\sqrt[3]{1/4} - \sqrt[3]{16}$

ANSWER

(A) $-2\sqrt{3}$; (B) $-\frac{3}{2}\sqrt[3]{2}$.

Products and Quotients Involving Radicals

We conclude this section by considering several special types of products and quotients that involve radicals. The distributive law will play a central role in our approach to these problems. In the examples that follow, all variables represent positive real numbers, hence all quantities involved represent real numbers, and the properties of real numbers discussed in Chap. 1 apply.

Example 24. Multiply and simplify.

(A) $\sqrt{2}(\sqrt{10} - 3) = \sqrt{20} - 3\sqrt{2} = 2\sqrt{5} - 3\sqrt{2}$

(B) $(\sqrt{2} - 3)(\sqrt{2} + 5) = \sqrt{2}\sqrt{2} - 3\sqrt{2} + 5\sqrt{2} - 15$
$$= 2 + 2\sqrt{2} - 15$$
$$= 2\sqrt{2} - 13$$

(C) $(\sqrt{x} - 3)(\sqrt{x} + 5) = \sqrt{x}\sqrt{x} - 3\sqrt{x} + 5\sqrt{x} - 15$
$$= x + 2\sqrt{x} - 15$$

(D) $(\sqrt[3]{m} + \sqrt[3]{n^2})(\sqrt[3]{m^2} - \sqrt[3]{n}) = \sqrt[3]{m^3} - \sqrt[3]{mn} + \sqrt[3]{m^2 n^2} - \sqrt[3]{n^3}$
$$= m - \sqrt[3]{mn} + \sqrt[3]{m^2 n^2} - n$$

Problem 24.   Multiply and simplify.

(A) $\sqrt{3}(\sqrt{6} - 4)$ (B) $(\sqrt{3} - 2)(\sqrt{3} + 4)$ (C) $(\sqrt{y} - 2)(\sqrt{y} + 4)$

(D) $(\sqrt[3]{x^2} - \sqrt[3]{y^2})(\sqrt[3]{x} + \sqrt[3]{y})$

ANSWER

(A) $3\sqrt{2} - 4\sqrt{3}$; (B) $2\sqrt{3} - 5$; (C) $y + 2\sqrt{y} - 8$;
(D) $x + \sqrt[3]{x^2 y} - \sqrt[3]{xy^2} - y$.

Recall that to express $\sqrt{2}/\sqrt{3}$ in simplest radical form, we multiplied the numerator and denominator by $\sqrt{3}$ to clear the denominator of the radical; thus

$$\frac{\sqrt{2}}{\sqrt{3}} = \frac{\sqrt{2}}{\sqrt{3}} \cdot \frac{\sqrt{3}}{\sqrt{3}} = \frac{\sqrt{6}}{3}$$

The process of converting an irrational denominator to a rational form is called *rationalizing a denominator*.

How can we rationalize the binomial denominator in $1/(\sqrt{5} - \sqrt{2})$? Multiplying the numerator and denominator by $\sqrt{5}$ or $\sqrt{2}$ does not help. Try it. Recalling the special product $(a - b)(a + b) = a^2 - b^2$ suggests that if we multiply the numerator and denominator by $\sqrt{5} + \sqrt{2}$ we will obtain $(\sqrt{5})^2 - (\sqrt{2})^2 = 5 - 2 = 3$, a rational number, in the denominator. Thus

$$\frac{1}{\sqrt{5} - \sqrt{2}} = \frac{1(\sqrt{5} + \sqrt{2})}{(\sqrt{5} - \sqrt{2})(\sqrt{5} + \sqrt{2})} = \frac{\sqrt{5} + \sqrt{2}}{5 - 2} = \frac{\sqrt{5} + \sqrt{2}}{3}$$

Example 25.   Rationalize denominators and simplify.

(A) $\dfrac{\sqrt{2}}{\sqrt{6} - 2} = \dfrac{\sqrt{2}(\sqrt{6} + 2)}{(\sqrt{6} - 2)(\sqrt{6} + 2)} = \dfrac{\sqrt{12} + 2\sqrt{2}}{6 - 4}$

$= \dfrac{2\sqrt{3} + 2\sqrt{2}}{2} = \dfrac{2(\sqrt{3} + \sqrt{2})}{2} = \sqrt{3} + \sqrt{2}$

(B) $\dfrac{\sqrt{x} - \sqrt{y}}{\sqrt{x} + \sqrt{y}} = \dfrac{(\sqrt{x} - \sqrt{y})(\sqrt{x} - \sqrt{y})}{(\sqrt{x} + \sqrt{y})(\sqrt{x} - \sqrt{y})} = \dfrac{x - 2\sqrt{xy} + y}{x - y}$

Problem 25. Rationalize denominators and simplify.

(A) $\dfrac{\sqrt{2}}{\sqrt{8}+2}$ (B) $\dfrac{\sqrt{m}+\sqrt{n}}{\sqrt{m}-\sqrt{n}}$

ANSWER

(A) $1-\dfrac{\sqrt{2}}{2}$; (B) $\dfrac{m+2\sqrt{mn}+n}{m-n}$.

EXERCISE 14

Unless otherwise stated, the replacement set for all variables is the set of positive real numbers.

A *Simplify by combining as many terms as possible.*

1. $6\sqrt{x}-10\sqrt{x}$
2. $2\sqrt{m}-7\sqrt{m}$
3. $3\sqrt[3]{u}-2\sqrt[3]{u}-2\sqrt[3]{u}$
4. $\sqrt[5]{a}-4\sqrt[5]{a}+2\sqrt[5]{a}$
5. $3\sqrt{2}-2\sqrt{3}-\sqrt{2}$
6. $\sqrt{5}-2\sqrt{3}+3\sqrt{5}$
7. $5\sqrt[5]{y}-2\sqrt[5]{y}+3\sqrt[4]{y}$
8. $2\sqrt[3]{x}+3\sqrt[3]{x}-\sqrt{x}$
9. $\sqrt{12}+\sqrt{3}$
10. $\sqrt{8}-\sqrt{2}$
11. $\sqrt{8}+2\sqrt{27}$
12. $2\sqrt{12}+3\sqrt{18}$

Multiply and simplify.

13. $\sqrt{5}(\sqrt{5}-2)$
14. $\sqrt{7}(2-\sqrt{7})$
15. $\sqrt{5}(\sqrt{10}+\sqrt{5})$
16. $\sqrt{3}(\sqrt{3}+\sqrt{6})$
17. $\sqrt{m}(3\sqrt{m}-\sqrt{n})$
18. $\sqrt{x}(5-2\sqrt{x})$
19. $(\sqrt{2}-1)(\sqrt{2}+3)$
20. $(2-\sqrt{3})(3+\sqrt{3})$
21. $(\sqrt{5}+2)^2$
22. $(\sqrt{3}-3)^2$
23. $(2\sqrt{7}-\sqrt{3})(2\sqrt{7}+\sqrt{3})$
24. $(\sqrt{5}-\sqrt{2})(\sqrt{5}+\sqrt{2})$
25. $(2\sqrt{x}+3)(2\sqrt{x}-3)$
26. $(\sqrt{x}-\sqrt{y})(\sqrt{x}+\sqrt{y})$

Rationalize denominators and simplify.

27. $\dfrac{1}{\sqrt{5}+2}$
28. $\dfrac{1}{\sqrt{11}-3}$

29. $\dfrac{4}{\sqrt{6}-2}$
30. $\dfrac{2}{\sqrt{5}+1}$

31. $\dfrac{\sqrt{2}}{\sqrt{6}+2}$
32. $\dfrac{\sqrt{2}}{\sqrt{10}-2}$

33. $\dfrac{\sqrt{x}}{\sqrt{x}-2}$

34. $\dfrac{\sqrt{y}}{\sqrt{y}+3}$

35. $\dfrac{\sqrt{2}-1}{\sqrt{2}+1}$

36. $\dfrac{\sqrt{3}+2}{\sqrt{3}-2}$

B *Simplify by combining as many terms as possible.*

37. $\sqrt{24}-\sqrt{12}+3\sqrt{3}$

38. $\sqrt{8}-\sqrt{20}+4\sqrt{2}$

39. $\sqrt{\dfrac{1}{2}}+\dfrac{\sqrt{2}}{2}+\sqrt{8}$

40. $\dfrac{\sqrt{3}}{3}+2\sqrt{\dfrac{1}{3}}+\sqrt{12}$

41. $\sqrt[4]{32}-4\sqrt{\dfrac{1}{8}}$

42. $\sqrt[3]{\dfrac{1}{3}}+\sqrt[3]{3^5}$

43. $\sqrt{\dfrac{xy}{2}}+\sqrt{8xy}$

44. $\sqrt{\dfrac{3uv}{2}}-\sqrt{24uv}$

Multiply and simplify.

45. $(5\sqrt{m}+2)(2\sqrt{m}-3)$

46. $(3\sqrt{u}-2)(2\sqrt{u}+4)$

47. $(\sqrt[5]{u^2}-\sqrt[5]{v^3})(\sqrt[5]{u^3}+\sqrt[5]{v^2})$

48. $(\sqrt[3]{x}-\sqrt[3]{y^2})(\sqrt[3]{x^2}+2\sqrt[3]{y})$

49. $(3-\sqrt{3}\,i)^2$

50. $(2+\sqrt{2}\,i)^2$

51. $\sqrt{3-\sqrt{8}}\ \sqrt{3+\sqrt{8}}$

52. $\sqrt{4+\sqrt{10}}\ \sqrt{4-\sqrt{10}}$

53. Is $3-\sqrt{2}$ a solution of the equation $x^2-6x+3=0$?

54. Is $2+\sqrt{3}$ a solution of the equation $x^2-4x+1=0$?

55. Evaluate x^2-2x+2 for $x=1-\sqrt{2}\,i$.

56. Evaluate x^2-2x+2 for $x=1+\sqrt{2}\,i$.

Rationalize denominators and simplify.

57. $\dfrac{\sqrt{2}+\sqrt{3}}{\sqrt{3}-\sqrt{2}}$

58. $\dfrac{\sqrt{5}-\sqrt{2}}{\sqrt{5}+\sqrt{2}}$

59. $\dfrac{2+\sqrt{x}}{\sqrt{x}-3}$

60. $\dfrac{3-\sqrt{a}}{\sqrt{a}-2}$

61. $\dfrac{5\sqrt{a}}{3-2\sqrt{a}}$

62. $\dfrac{3\sqrt{x}}{2\sqrt{x}-3}$

63. $\dfrac{3\sqrt{2}+2\sqrt{3}}{2\sqrt{2}-3\sqrt{3}}$

64. $\dfrac{2\sqrt{5}-3\sqrt{2}}{5\sqrt{5}+2\sqrt{2}}$

65. $\dfrac{1+\sqrt{3}\,i}{2-\sqrt{3}\,i}$

66. $\dfrac{2-\sqrt{2}\,i}{3+\sqrt{2}\,i}$

C *Multiply and simplify.*

67. $\left(-\dfrac{1}{2} - \dfrac{\sqrt{3}}{2}i\right)^3$

68. $\left(-\dfrac{1}{2} + \dfrac{\sqrt{3}}{2}i\right)^3$

Rationalize denominators.

69. $\dfrac{1}{\sqrt[3]{x} - \sqrt[3]{y}}$

70. $\dfrac{1}{\sqrt[3]{x} + \sqrt[3]{y}}$

71. $\dfrac{1}{\sqrt[3]{x^2} + \sqrt[3]{xy} + \sqrt[3]{y^2}}$

72. $\dfrac{1}{\sqrt[3]{x^2} - \sqrt[3]{xy} + \sqrt[3]{y^2}}$

73. $\dfrac{1}{\sqrt{x} - \sqrt{y} + \sqrt{z}}$

74. $\dfrac{1}{\sqrt{x} + \sqrt{y} - \sqrt{z}}$

EXERCISE 15 CHAPTER REVIEW EXERCISES

A

1. Given the polynomials $3x - 4$, $x + 2$, $3x^2 + x - 8$, and $x^3 + 8$:
   - (A) Add all four.
   - (B) Subtract the sum of the first and third from the sum of the second and fourth.
   - (C) Multiply the third and fourth.
   - (D) Divide the last by the second.
   - (E) Factor the third.
2. Simplify $8x^2 - [2x - x(3x - 2)]$.
3. Write each polynomial in a completely factored form over *I*. If the polynomial is prime over *I*, it should be indicated.
   - (A) $9x^2 - 12x + 4$
   - (B) $t^2 + 4t - 6$
   - (C) $6n^3 - 9n^2 - 15n$
4. Simplify $(3x^2y + 2xy^2)/(9x^2 - 4y^2)$

Perform the indicated operations and simplify.

5. $\dfrac{2}{5b} - \dfrac{4}{3a^3} - \dfrac{1}{6a^2b^2}$

6. $\dfrac{3s}{3s^2 - 12s} + \dfrac{1}{2s + 4s}$

7. $\dfrac{y - 2}{y^2 - 4y + 4} \div \dfrac{y^2 + 2y}{y^2 + 4y + 4}$

8. $\dfrac{x - (1/x)}{1 - (1/x^2)}$

Simplify, and write the answers using positive exponents only. The replacement set for all variables is the set of positive real numbers.

9. $6(xy^3)^5$

10. $(c^2/d^5)^3$

11. $9u^8v^6/3u^4v^8$

12. $(2 \cdot 10^5)(3 \cdot 10^{-3})$

13. $(x^{-3}y^2)^{-2}$

14. $u^{5/3}/u^{2/3}$

15. $(9a^4b^{-2})^{1/2}$

16. Change to radical form:
    (A) $(2mn)^{2/3}$ (B) $3x^{2/5}$
    Change to rational exponent form:
    (C) $\sqrt[5]{x^5}$ (D) $-3\sqrt[3]{(xy)^2}$

Express in simplest radical form. The replacement set for all variables is the set of positive real numbers.

17. $\sqrt[3]{(2x^2y)^3}$

18. $3x\sqrt[3]{x^5y^4}$

19. $\sqrt{2x^2y^5}\,\sqrt{18x^3y^2}$

20. $6ab/\sqrt{3a}$

21. $\sqrt{y/2x}$

22. $\sqrt{7}+2\sqrt{3}-4\sqrt{3}$

23. $\sqrt{5}/(3-\sqrt{5})$

24. $\sqrt[8]{y^6}$

B 25. Given the algebraic expressions
    (a) $2x^2-3x+5$ (b) $(x-3)/(x^2-2x+3)$
    (c) $2x-\sqrt{5}$ (d) $x^2-3xy-y^2$
    (e) $x^2-\sqrt{x-3}$ (f) $x^3-(1/x)$
    (A) Identify all polynomials.
    (B) Identify all second-degree polynomials.
26. Divide $20x-14x^2+2x^4+4$ by $2x+6$ and check.
27. Simplify $-2x\{(x^2+2)(x-3)-x[x-x(3-x)]\}$.
28. Write each polynomial in a completely factored form over *I*. If the polynomial is prime over *I*, it should be indicated.
    (A) $(x-y)^2-x^2$
    (B) $3x^3-24y^3$
    (C) $(y-b)^2-y+b$

Perform the indicated operations and simplify.

29. $\dfrac{4}{s^2-4}+\dfrac{1}{2-s}$

30. $\dfrac{y}{x^2}\div\left(\dfrac{x^2+3x}{2x^2-5x-3}\div\dfrac{x^3y-x^2y}{2x^2-3x+1}\right)$

31. $\dfrac{1-\dfrac{1}{1+(x/y)}}{1-\dfrac{1}{1-(x/y)}}$

Simplify and write answers using positive exponents only. The replacement set for all variables is the positive real numbers.

32. $(p^4q^4)=(pq)^?$

33. $(-a^2b/c)^2(c/b^2)^3(1/a^3)^2$

34. $\left(\dfrac{8u^{-1}}{2^2u^2v^0}\right)^{-2}\left(\dfrac{u^{-5}}{u^{-3}}\right)^3$

35. $\dfrac{5^0}{3^2}+\dfrac{3^{-2}}{2^{-2}}$

36. $(27x^2y^{-3}/8x^{-4}y^3)^{1/3}$

37. $(x^{1/2}+y^{1/2})^2$

38. Convert to power-of-10 notation and simplify $\dfrac{0.000052}{(130)(0.0002)}$.

39. Change to radical form:
    (A) $-3x^{2/3}$ (B) $2(xy)^{-3/4}$
    Change to rational exponent form:

    (C) $\dfrac{x}{\sqrt[5]{x^3}}$ (D) $\sqrt[6]{\sqrt[3]{x^4}}$

Express in simplest radical form. The replacement set for all variables is the set of positive real numbers.

40. $-2x\sqrt[5]{3^6 x^7 y^{11}}$

41. $2x^2/\sqrt[3]{4x}$

42. $\sqrt[5]{\dfrac{3y^2}{8x^2}}$

43. $\sqrt[9]{8x^6 y^{12}}$

44. $\sqrt{9m^4 + 9m^2 n^2}$

45. $\sqrt[3]{3} - \dfrac{6}{\sqrt[3]{9}} + \sqrt[3]{\dfrac{1}{9}}$

46. $(2\sqrt{x} - 5\sqrt{y})(\sqrt{x} + \sqrt{y})$

47. $3\sqrt{x}/(2\sqrt{x} - \sqrt{y})$

C 48. $(x^2 - x - 6)/(x - 3) = x + 2$, except for what values of x?

49. Given $P(x) = 4x^3 - 8x^2 + 8x - 2$ and $D(x) = 2x^2 - x + 2$, find $Q(x)$ and $R(x)$ such that $P(x) = D(x)Q(x) + R(x)$, where the degree of $R(x)$ is less than the degree of $D(x)$ or $R(x) = 0$.

50. Justify each step by a property studied in Chap. 1.
    1. $9m - 2m = 9m + [-(2m)]$
    2. $ = 9m + (-2)m$
    3. $ = [9 + (-2)]m$
    4. $ = 7m$

51. Describe the elements in the set

$$A = \{x \mid -3x^3 - 6x = -3x(x^2 + 2), x \text{ a real number}\}$$

52. Find all positive integers p under 10 so that $x^2 - 5x + p$ can be factored over I.

53. $-\dfrac{1}{a - b} = \dfrac{?}{b - a}$

54. Simplify $\left[x - \dfrac{1}{1 - (1/x)} \right] \div \left(\dfrac{x}{x + 1} - \dfrac{x}{1 - x} \right)$

Simplify, and express the answers using positive exponents only. The replacement set for all variables is the set of positive real numbers.

55. $\left(\dfrac{x^{m^2}}{x^{2m-1}} \right)^{1/(m-1)}, \; m > 1$

56. $\left(\dfrac{a^{-2}}{b^{-1}} + \dfrac{b^{-2}}{a^{-1}} \right)^{-1}$

57. For what real values of x does

   (A) $\sqrt{x^2} = x$ (B) $\sqrt{x^2} = |x|$ (C) $\sqrt[3]{x^3} = x$

Express in simplest radical form. The replacement set for all variables is the set of positive real numbers.

58. $\sqrt{2xy}\,\sqrt[3]{4x^2y^2}$

59. $\sqrt[3]{8\sqrt{64\sqrt{xy}}}$

60. $\sqrt[(n+1)]{x^{n^2}x^{2n+1}}$

61. $1/(\sqrt[3]{x^2} - \sqrt[3]{y^2})$

Chapter

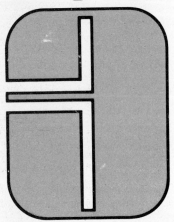

First- and Second-Degree Equations and Inequalities in One Variable

3.1 FIRST-DEGREE EQUATIONS IN ONE VARIABLE

Recall that we defined a *constant* as a symbol that names a single thing, and a *variable* as a symbol that is a placeholder for constants. (In this course, constants will generally name numbers.) The *replacement set* for a variable was defined to be the set of constants that are permitted to replace the variable. Since we use variables in equations as placeholders for constants, an equation is neither true nor false until the variables are replaced with constants. For this reason equations are frequently referred to as *open statements*. The *solution set* for an equation is defined to be the set of elements from its replacement set that makes the equation a true statement. Any element of the solution set is called a solution or a root of the equation. To *solve an equation* is to find the solution set for the equation.

For example, if the replacement set for the variable x is the set of integers, then the solution set for the equation

$$x^2 - \tfrac{1}{9} = 0$$

is the empty set. If, on the other hand, the replacement set is the set of rational numbers, then the solution set is $\{-\tfrac{1}{3}, \tfrac{1}{3}\}$, and we call $-\tfrac{1}{3}$ and $\tfrac{1}{3}$ solutions or roots of the equation. What is the solution set for the equation $x^2 - 4 = 0$ if the replacement set for the variable x is the set of natural numbers? The set of integers? (*Answer:* $\{2\}$, $\{-2, 2\}$.)

Knowing what we mean by the solution set of an equation is one thing; finding it is another. To this end we introduce the idea of equivalent equations. Two equations are said to be *equivalent* if they both have the same solution set. A basic technique for solving equations is to perform operations on equations that produce simpler equivalent equations, and to continue the process until an equation is reached whose solution is obvious.

The following theorem is fundamental to the equation-solving process.

Theorem 1. If $f(x)$, $g(x)$, and $h(x)$ are open statements that represent real numbers for each replacement of x out of some chosen replacement set, then the following equations are equivalent:

$$f(x) = g(x)$$
$$f(x) + h(x) = g(x) + h(x)$$
$$f(x) - h(x) = g(x) - h(x)$$
$$h(x) \cdot f(x) = h(x) \cdot g(x) \qquad h(x) \neq 0$$
$$\frac{f(x)}{h(x)} = \frac{g(x)}{h(x)} \qquad h(x) \neq 0$$

This theorem follows directly from the properties of equalities listed in Theorem 3 in Chap 1. Its proof is left as an exercise. In addition, equivalent equations can be obtained by suitable use of the substitution principle.

Now we will use Theorem 1 to help us solve first-degree equations in one variable. In subsequent sections and chapters we will use the same theorem to help us solve other types of equations.

First-Degree Equations in one Variable

Any equation that can be written in the form

$$ax + b = 0 \qquad a \neq 0 \tag{1}$$

---

where a and b are constants and x is a variable, is called a *first-degree equation* in one variable.

Does Eq. (1) always have a solution? If it has a solution, is it unique? We can use Theorem 1 in the last section to answer both of these questions.

$$ax + b = 0 \qquad a \neq 0 \qquad a, b \in R$$
$$(ax + b) - b = 0 - b \qquad \text{(Theorem 1)}$$
$$ax = -b$$

$$\frac{ax}{a} = \frac{-b}{a} \qquad \text{(Theorem 1)}$$

$$x = -\frac{b}{a}$$

All these equations are equivalent by Theorem 1. The last equation has one and only one solution, namely, $-b/a$; hence the first equation has the same unique solution.

Example 1. Solve $3x - 2(2x - 5) = 2(x + 3) - 8$.

SOLUTION

$$3x - 2(2x - 5) = 2(x + 3) - 8$$
$$3x - 4x + 10 = 2x + 6 - 8$$
$$-x + 10 = 2x - 2$$
$$-x = 2x - 12$$
$$-3x = -12$$
$$x = 4$$

The check is left as an exercise.

Problem 1. Solve and check: $2(3 - x) - (3x + 1) = 8 - 2(x + 2)$.

ANSWER

$x = \frac{1}{3}$.

Example 2. Solve

$$\frac{x+1}{3} - \frac{x}{4} = \frac{1}{2}$$

SOLUTION

If we could find a number that is exactly divisible by each denominator, then we could use the multiplication property in Theorem 1 to clear the equation of fractions. A number that is exactly divisible by a set of integers is called the *least common multiple* (LCM) of the set. In this case, the LCM of 3, 4, and 2 is 12. Thus,

$$\frac{x+1}{3} - \frac{x}{4} = \frac{1}{2}$$

$$12\frac{x+1}{3} - 12\frac{x}{4} = 12 \cdot \frac{1}{2}$$

$$4(x+1) - 3x = 6$$

$$4x + 4 - 3x = 6$$

$$x = 2$$

The check is left as an exercise.

Problem 2. Solve and check.

$$\frac{x}{5} - \frac{x-2}{2} = \frac{3}{4}$$

ANSWER

$x = \frac{5}{6}$.

Some equations involving variables in a denominator can be transformed into linear equations. We may proceed in essentially the same way as in the preceding example; however, the replacement set of the equation must exclude any value of the variable that will make a denominator zero. As long as we use the replacement set of the original equation, we may multiply through by the LCM of the denominators even though it contains a variable, and, according to Theorem 1, the new equation will be equivalent to the old.

Example 3. Solve and check.

$$\frac{x}{2x-4} - \frac{2}{3} = \frac{7-2x}{3x-6}$$

SOLUTION

$$\frac{x}{2x-4} - \frac{2}{3} = \frac{7-2x}{3x-6} \qquad x \neq 2$$

$$\frac{x}{2(x-2)} - \frac{2}{3} = \frac{7-2x}{3(x-2)}$$

$$6(x-2)\frac{x}{2(x-2)} - 6(x-2)\frac{2}{3} = 6(x-2)\frac{7-2x}{3(x-2)}$$

$$3x - 4x + 8 = 14 - 4x$$

$$3x = 6$$

$$x = 2 \qquad \text{(no solution)}$$

Since 2 is not in the replacement set of the original equation, the original equation has no solution. Note that when $x = 2$ is replaced in the left and right members of the original equation, neither is defined.

Problem 3. Solve and check.

$$\frac{x-3}{2x-2} = \frac{1}{6} - \frac{1-x}{3x-3}$$

ANSWER

No solution.

Example 4. Solve $A = P + Prt$ for P.

SOLUTION

$$A = P + Prt$$

$$P + Prt = A \qquad \text{(symmetric law of equality)}$$

$$P(1 + rt) = A \qquad \text{(distributive property)}$$

$$P = \frac{A}{1 + rt} \qquad \text{(division property, Theorem 1)}$$

Problem 4. Solve $C = \frac{5}{9}(F - 32)$ for F.

ANSWER

$F = \frac{9}{5}C + 32$.

EXERCISE 16

A *Solve each equation.*

1. $3(x + 2) = 5(x - 6)$
2. $5x + 10(x - 2) = 40$
3. $5 + 4(t - 2) = 2(t + 7) + 1$
4. $5x - (7x - 4) - 2 = 5 - (3x + 2)$
5. $x(x + 2) = x(x + 4) - 12$
6. $x(x + 4) - 2 = x^2 - 4(x + 3)$

7. $3 - \dfrac{2x - 3}{3} = \dfrac{5 - x}{2}$

8. $\dfrac{x - 2}{3} + 1 = \dfrac{x}{7}$

9. $0.1(x - 7) + 0.05x = 0.8$

10. $0.4(x + 5) - 0.3x = 17$

11. $\dfrac{3x}{24} - \dfrac{2 - x}{10} = \dfrac{5 + x}{40} - \dfrac{1}{15}$

12. $\dfrac{2x - 3}{9} - \dfrac{x + 5}{6} = \dfrac{3 - x}{2} + 1$

13. $\dfrac{1}{m} - \dfrac{1}{9} = \dfrac{4}{9} - \dfrac{2}{3m}$

14. $\dfrac{2}{3x} + \dfrac{1}{2} = \dfrac{4}{x} + \dfrac{4}{3}$

15. $\dfrac{5x}{x + 5} = 2 - \dfrac{25}{x + 5}$

16. $\dfrac{3}{2x - 1} + 4 = \dfrac{6x}{2x - 1}$

B *Solve each equation.*

17. $\dfrac{2x}{10} - \dfrac{3 - x}{14} = \dfrac{2 + x}{5} - \dfrac{1}{2}$

18. $\dfrac{3x}{24} - \dfrac{2 - x}{10} = \dfrac{5 + x}{40} - \dfrac{1}{15}$

19. $\dfrac{1}{3} - \dfrac{s - 2}{2s + 4} = \dfrac{s + 2}{3s + 6}$

20. $\dfrac{n - 5}{6n - 6} = \dfrac{1}{9} - \dfrac{n - 3}{4n - 4}$

21. $\dfrac{3x}{2 - x} + \dfrac{6}{x - 2} = 3$

22. $5 - \dfrac{2x}{3 - x} = \dfrac{6}{x - 3}$

23. $\dfrac{5t - 22}{t^2 - 6t + 9} - \dfrac{11}{t^2 - 3t} - \dfrac{5}{t} = 0$

24. $\dfrac{5}{x - 3} = \dfrac{33 - x}{x^2 - 6x + 9}$

25. $\dfrac{1}{x^2 - x - 2} - \dfrac{3}{x^2 - 2x - 3} = \dfrac{1}{x^2 - 5x + 6}$

26. $\dfrac{5x - 22}{x^2 - 6x + 9} - \dfrac{11}{x^2 - 3x} - \dfrac{5}{x} = 0$

27. Which of the following are true?
    (A) $\{x \mid 2x - 5 = 11,\ x \text{ an integer}\} = \{3\}$
    (B) $3z - 7 = 7$, $3z = 0$, and $z = 0$ are equivalent equations.

28. Which of the following are true?
    (A) $2t + 5 = t - 3$, $2t = t - 8$, and $t = -8$ are equivalent equations.
    (B) $\{m \mid 3m + 11 = 5,\ m$ a positive integer$\} = \emptyset$.

Solve for the indicated letter.

29. $a_n = a_1 + (n - 1)d$ for d (arithmetic progressions)
30. $F = \frac{9}{5}C + 32$ for C (temperature scale)
31. $1/f = (1/d_1) + (1/d_2)$ for f (simple lens formula)
32. $1/R = (1/R_1) + (1/R_2)$ for R_1 (electric circuit)
33. $A = 2ab + 2ac + 2bc$ for a (area of a rectangular solid)
34. $A = 2ab + 2ac + 2bc$ for c
35. $P_1 V_1 / T_1 = P_2 V_2 / T_2$ for T_2 (gas law)
36. $P_1 V_1 / T_1 = P_2 V_2 / T_2$ for V_2

37. $y = \dfrac{2x - 3}{3x + 5}$ for x 38. $x = \dfrac{3y + 2}{y - 3}$ for y

C   39. Solve for x: $\dfrac{x - x^2}{\dfrac{x}{x+1} - x} = x^2 - 1$

40. Solve $\dfrac{y}{1 - y} = \left(\dfrac{x}{1 - x}\right)^3$ for y in terms of x.

41. Solve $y = \dfrac{a}{1 + \dfrac{b}{x + c}}$ for x in terms of y.

42. Let m and n be real numbers with $m > n$. Then there exists a positive real number p such that $m = n + p$. Find the fallacy in the following argument:

$$m = n + p$$
$$(m - n)m = (m - n)(n + p)$$
$$m^2 - mn = mn + mp - n^2 - np$$
$$m^2 - mn - mp = mn - n^2 - np$$
$$m(m - n - p) = n(m - n - p)$$
$$m = n$$

43. Answer the "whys" in the following proof of the addition property in Theorem 1: Let r be a number such that $f(r) = g(r)$, then $f(r) + h(r) = g(r) + h(r)$ (why?). Thus, any solution of $f(x) = g(x)$ is a solution of $f(x) + h(x) = g(x) + h(x)$. Also, if r is a number such that $f(r) + h(r) = g(r) + h(r)$, then $f(r) = g(r)$ (why?). Hence, any solution of $f(x) + h(x) = g(x) + h(x)$ is a solution of $f(x) = g(x)$. Thus $f(x) = g(x)$ and $f(x) + h(x) = g(x) + h(x)$ are equivalent (why?).

44. Prove the multiplication property in Theorem 1.
45. Prove the subtraction property in Theorem 1.
46. Prove the division property in Theorem 1.

Applications

There are many different types of algebraic applications that lead to linear equations—so many, in fact, that no single approach will apply to all. The following suggestions, however, may be of help to you:

1. Read the problem very carefully—a second and a third time, if necessary.
2. Write down important facts and relationships on a piece of paper.
3. Identify unknown quantities in terms of a single variable if possible.
4. Write an equation that relates these unknown quantities and the facts in the problem.
5. Solve the equation.
6. Answer all the questions in the original problem.
7. Check the solution(s) in the original problem.

Example 5. Find four consecutive even integers such that the sum of the first three exceeds the fourth by 8.

SOLUTION

Let x = the first integer
$x + 2$ = the second integer
$x + 4$ = the third integer
$x + 6$ = the fourth integer
Now form an equation and solve it:

$$x + (x + 2) + (x + 4) = (x + 6) + 8$$
$$3x + 6 = x + 14$$
$$2x = 8$$
$$x = 4$$

The four consecutive even integers are 4, 6, 8, 10.
CHECK: $(4 + 6 + 8) - 10 = 18 - 10 = 8$.

Problem 5. Find three consecutive odd numbers such that three times their sum is five more than eight times the middle one.

ANSWER

3, 5, 7.

Example 6. In a pile of coins containing only quarters and dimes, there are three less quarters than dimes. If the total value of the pile is $2.75, how many of each type of coin is in the pile?

SOLUTION

Let x = the number of dimes in the pile
$x - 3$ = the number of quarters in the pile

$$\begin{pmatrix} \text{value of} \\ \text{dimes} \\ \text{in cents} \end{pmatrix} + \begin{pmatrix} \text{value of} \\ \text{quarters} \\ \text{in cents} \end{pmatrix} = \begin{pmatrix} \text{value of} \\ \text{pile} \\ \text{in cents} \end{pmatrix}$$

$$10x + 25(x - 3) = 275 \quad \text{(not 2.75)}$$
$$10x + 25x - 75 = 275$$
$$35x = 350$$
$$x = 10 \text{ dimes}$$
$$x - 3 = 7 \text{ quarters}$$

CHECK: There are three more dimes than quarters, and the total value of both is $10 \cdot 10 + 7 \cdot 25 = 275$ cents or $2.75.

Problem 6. If you have 20 dimes and nickels in your pocket worth $1.40, how many of each do you have?

ANSWER

8 dimes and 12 nickels.

Example 7. How many gallons of a mixture containing 80% alcohol should be added to 5 gal of a 20% solution to give a 30% solution?

SOLUTION

Let x = amount of 80% solution added to the 5 gal of 20% solution

$$\begin{pmatrix} \text{amount of} \\ \text{pure alcohol} \\ \text{in 80\% solution} \end{pmatrix} + \begin{pmatrix} \text{amount of} \\ \text{pure alcohol} \\ \text{in 20\% solution} \end{pmatrix} = \begin{pmatrix} \text{amount of} \\ \text{pure alcohol} \\ \text{in new 30\% solution} \end{pmatrix}$$

$$0.8x + 0.2(5) = 0.3(x + 5)$$
$$8x + 2(5) = 3(x + 5)$$
$$8x + 10 = 3x + 15$$
$$5x = 5$$
$$x = 1 \text{ gal}$$

CHECK: $0.8(1) + 0.2(5) \underset{?}{=} 0.3(1 + 5)$
$$1.8 = 1.8$$

Problem 7. How much 90% acid solution must be added to 20 cc of a 40% acid solution to increase it to a 50% solution?

ANSWER

5 cc.

Example 8. In an electronic computer center a card-sorter operator is given the job of alphabetizing a given quantity of IBM cards. He knows that an older sorter can do the job by itself in 6 hr. With the help of a newer machine the job is completed in 2 hr. How long would it take the new machine to do the job alone?

SOLUTION

Let x = time for new machine to do job alone
Quantity of work = rate × time
Rate of old machine = $\frac{1}{6}$ job per hour
Rate of new machine = $1/x$ job per hour

$$\left(\begin{array}{c}\text{quantity of}\\\text{work done by}\\\text{first machine}\\\text{in 2 hr}\end{array}\right) + \left(\begin{array}{c}\text{quantity of}\\\text{work done by}\\\text{second machine}\\\text{in 2 hr}\end{array}\right) = 1 \text{ whole job}$$

$$\text{(rate)(time)} \quad + \quad \text{(rate)(time)} \quad = 1$$

$$\frac{1}{6}(2) \quad + \quad \frac{1}{x}(2) \quad = 1$$

$$\frac{1}{3} + \frac{2}{x} = 1$$

$$x + 6 = 3x$$

$$2x = 6$$

$$x = 3 \text{ hr}$$

CHECK: $\frac{1}{6}(2) + \frac{1}{3}(2) = \frac{1}{3} + \frac{2}{3} = 1$ whole job

Problem 8. At a family cabin water is pumped and stored in a large water tank. Two pumps are used for this purpose. One can fill the tank by itself in 6 hr, and the other can do the job in 9 hr. How long will it take both pumps operating together to fill the tank?

ANSWER

$3\frac{3}{5}$ hr.

EXERCISE 17

These problems are not grouped from easy (A) to difficult or theoretical (C). They are grouped according to type. Some are easy and some are difficult.

Number

1. Find three consecutive even numbers so that the first plus twice the second is twice the third.
2. Find four consecutive even numbers so that the sum of the first and last is the same as the sum of the second and third.

Geometry

3. The area of a rectangle 64 ft long is the same as the area of a 16-ft square. Find the width of the rectangle.
4. Find the dimensions of a rectangle with a perimeter of 52 in., if its length is 5 in. more than twice its width.

Puzzle

5. In crossing the Grand Canyon in Arizona, a man went one-third of the way by foot, 10 mi by boat, and one-sixth of the way by mule. How long was the trip.
6. A pole is located in a pond. One-fifth of the pole is in the sand, 10 ft of it is in the water, and two-thirds of it is in the air. How long is the pole?

Business

7. If a stock you bought on Monday went up 10 percent on Tuesday and fell 10 percent on Wednesday, how much did you pay for the stock on Monday if you sold it on Wednesday for $99?
8. A friend of yours paid $72 for a pair of skis after receiving a discount of 20 percent. What was the list price for the skis?
9. Five individuals formed a glider club and decided to share equally the cost of a glider. They found, however, that if they let three more join the club the share for each of the original five would be reduced by $120. What was the total cost of the glider?
10. A travel agent, arranging a round-trip charter flight from New York to

Europe, tells 100 signed-up members of a group that they can save $120 each if they can find 50 more people to sign up for the trip to fill the plane. What is the total round-trip charter cost of the jet transport? What is the cost per person if 100 go? What is the cost per person if 150 go?

11. A research chemist charges $20 per hr for his services and $8 per hr for his assistant. On a given job a customer received a bill for $1,040. If the chemist worked 10 hr more on the job than his assistant, how much time did each spend?

12. A mechanic charges $6 per hr for his labor and $4 per hr for his assistant. On a repair job his bill was $190, with $92 for labor and $98 for parts. If the assistant worked 2 hr less than the mechanic, how many hours did each work?

Music

13. The three major chords in music are composed of notes whose frequencies are in the ratio $4:5:6$. If the first note of a chord has a frequency of 264 hertz (middle C on the piano), find the frequencies of the other two notes. (*Hint:* Set up two proportions using $4:5$ and $4:6$.)

14. The three minor chords are composed of notes whose frequencies are in the ratio $10:12:15$. If the first note of a minor chord is A, with a frequency of 220 hertz, what are the frequencies of the other two notes?

Life Science

15. A naturalist for a fish and game department estimated the total number of rainbow trout in a certain lake using the popular capture-mark-recapture technique. He netted, marked, and released 200 rainbow trout. A week later, after thorough mixing, he netted 200 more and found 8 marked ones among them. Assuming that the proportion of marked fish in the second sample was the same as the proportion of all marked fish in the total population, estimate the number of rainbow trout in the lake.

16. In biology there is an approximate rule, called the bioclimatic rule for temperate climates, which states that in spring and early summer periodic phenomena, such as blossoming for a given species, appearance of certain insects, and ripening of fruit, usually occur about 4 days later for each 500 ft of altitude increase or $1°$ latitude increase from any given base. In terms of formulas we have

$$d = 4\left(\frac{h}{500}\right) \quad \text{and} \quad d = 4L$$

where d = days, h = change in altitude in feet, and L = change in latitude in degrees.

What change in altitude would delay pear trees from blossoming for 16 days? What change in latitude would accomplish the same thing?

17. Gregor Mendel (1822), a Bavarian monk and biologist whose name is known to almost everyone, made discoveries which revolutionized the science of heredity. Out of many experiments in which he crossed peas of one characteristic with those of another, Mendel evolved his now-famous laws of heredity. In one experiment he crossed dihybrid yellow round peas (which contained green and wrinkled as recessive genes) and obtained 560 peas of the following types: 319 yellow round, 101 yellow wrinkled, 108 green round, and 32 green wrinkled. From his laws of heredity he predicted the ratio $9:3:3:1$. Using the ratio, calculate the theoretical expected number of each type of pea from this cross, and compare it with the experimental results.

18. If an adult with pure brown eyes marries an adult with blue eyes, their children, because of the dominance of brown, will all have brown eyes but will be carriers of the gene for blue. If the children marry individuals with the same type of parents, then according to Mendel's laws of heredity, we would expect the third generation (the children's children) to include three times as many with brown eyes as with blue. Out of a sample of 1,748 third-generation children with second-generation parents as described, how many brown-eyed children and blue-eyed children would be expected?

Psychology

19. In 1948, Professor Brown, a psychologist, trained a group of rats (in an experiment on motivation) to run down a narrow passage in a cage to receive food in a goal box. He then put a harness on each rat and connected it to an overhead wire attached to a scale. In this way he could place the rat different distances from the food and measure the pull (in grams) of the rat toward the food. He found that the relation between motivation (pull) and position was given approximately by the equation

$$p = -\tfrac{1}{5}d + 70 \qquad 30 \le d \le 175$$

where pull p is measured in grams, and distance d is measured in centimeters. When the pull registered was 40 grams, how far was the rat from the goal box?

20. Professor Brown performed the same kind of experiment as described in Prob. 19, except that he replaced the food in the goal box with a mild electric shock. With the same kind of apparatus, he was able to measure the avoidance strength relative to the distance from the object to be avoided. He found that the avoidance strength a (measured in grams) was related to the distance d that the rat was from the shock (measured in centimeters) approximately by the equation

$$a = -\tfrac{4}{3}d + 230 \qquad 30 \le d \le 175$$

If the same rat were trained as described in this problem and in Prob. 19, at what distance (to one decimal place) from the goal box would the approach and avoidance strengths be the same? (What do you think the rat would do at this point?)

21. The intelligence quotient (IQ) is found by dividing the mental age, as indicated by standard tests, by the chronological age and multiplying by 100. For example, if a child has a mental age of 12 and a chronological age of 10, his IQ is 120. If an 11-year-old has an IQ of 132 (superior intelligence), compute his mental age.

Economics

22. Henry Schultz, an economist, formulated a price-demand equation for sugar in the United States as follows: $q = 70.62 - 2.26p$, where p = wholesale price in cents of 1 lb of sugar, and q = per-capita consumption in pounds of sugar in the United States for any year. At what price per pound would the per-capita consumption per year be 25.42 lb?

Earth Science

23. Pressure in sea water increases by 1 atmosphere (15 lb per ft^2) for each 33 ft of depth; it is 15 lb per ft^2 at the surface. Thus, $p = 15 + 15(d/33)$, where p is the pressure in pounds per square foot at a depth of d feet below the surface. How deep is a diver if he observes that the pressure is 165 lb per ft^2?

24. As dry air moves upward, it expands and in so doing cools at the rate of about 5.5°F for each 1,000-ft rise. This ascent is known as the *adiabatic process*. If the ground temperature is 80°F, write an equation that relates temperature T with altitude h (in thousands of feet). How high is an airplane if the pilot observes that the temperature is 25°F?

25. An earthquake emits a primary wave and a secondary wave. Near the surface of the earth the primary wave travels at about 5 mi per sec, and the secondary wave at about 3 mi per sec. From the time lag between the two waves arriving at a given seismic station, it is possible to estimate the distance to the quake. (The *epicenter* can be located by obtaining distance bearings at three or more stations.) Suppose a station measures a time difference of 12 sec between the arrival of the two waves. How far is the earthquake from the station?

26. A ship using sound-sensing devices above and below water recorded a surface explosion 39 sec sooner on its underwater device than on its above-water device. If sound travels in air at about 1,100 fps, and in water at about 5,000 fps, how far away was the explosion?

Chemistry

27. A chemist has 3 kg (3,000 grams) of 20% hydrochloric acid. He wishes to increase its strength to 25% by draining off some and replacing it with an 80% solution. How many grams must be drained and replaced with the 80% solution?

28. How many gallons of pure alcohol must be added to 3 gal of a 20% solution to obtain a 40% solution?

Rate –Time

29. A skydiver free-falls (because of air resistance) at about 176 fps, or 120 mph; with his parachute open he falls at about 22 fps, or 15 mph. If the skydiver opened his chute halfway down, and the total time for the descent was 6 min, how high was the plane when he jumped?

30. Two ocean liners leave San Francisco at the same time for a round trip to Hawaii. The first averaged 25 mph each way, while the second averaged 20 mph going and 30 mph returning. Which ship returned to San Francisco first? (*Hint:* Find the average rate of each for the round trip.)

31. A contractor has just finished constructing a swimming pool in your back-yard, and you have turned on a large water valve to fill it. The large valve lets water into the pool at a rate of 60 gal per min. After 2 hr you become impatient and turn on the garden hose, which lets water in at 15 gal per min. If the swimming pool holds 30,000 gal of water, what will be the total time required to fill it?

32. In a computer center two electronic card sorters are used to sort 52,000 IBM cards. If the first sorter operates at 225 cards per min and the second sorter operates at 175 cards per min, how long will it take both sorters together to sort all the cards?

33. You are at a river resort and rent a motor boat for 5 hr at 7 A.M. You are told that the boat will travel at 8 mph upstream and 12 mph returning. You decide that you would like to go as far up the river as you can, and still be back at noon. At what time should you turn back, and how far from the resort will you be at that time?

34. The cruising speed of an airplane is 150 mph (relative to ground). You wish to hire the plane for a 3-hr sightseeing trip. You instruct the pilot to fly north as far as he can and still return to the airport at the end of the allotted time.
    (A) How far north should the pilot fly if there is a 30-mph wind blowing from the north?
    (B) How far north should the pilot fly if there is no wind blowing?

Puzzle

35. A purse with $4.50 in it contains half as many dimes as quarters, and three times as many nickels as dimes. How many of each type of coin are in the purse?

36. A friend of yours came out of a post office having spent $1.32 on thirty 4- and 5-cent stamps. How many of each type did he buy?

37. A water reed sticks 1 ft out of the water. If it were pulled over to the side until the top just reached the surface, it would be at a point 3 ft from where it originally protruded. How deep is the water? (*Hint:* Recall the Pythagorean theorem.)

38. Diophantus, an early Greek algebraist (A.D. 280), was the subject for a famous ancient puzzle. See if you can find Diophantus' age at death from the following information. Diophantus was a boy for one-sixth of his life; after one-twelfth more he grew a beard; after one-seventh more he married, and after 5 years of marriage he produced a son; the son lived half as long as his father, and Diophantus died 4 years after his son's death.

39. A classic problem is the courier problem. If a column of men 3 mi long is marching at 5 mph, how long will it take a courier on a motorcycle traveling at 25 mph to deliver a message from the end of the column to the front and then return?

40. After exactly 12 o'clock noon, what time will the hands of a clock be together again?

3.2 FIRST-DEGREE INEQUALITIES IN ONE VARIABLE

Equivalent Inequalities

In Chap. 1 recall that we defined $a > b$ and $b < a$ for real numbers a and b, and stated several properties for these relations in Theorem 10. The symbols $<$ and $>$ and $\leq$ and $\geq$ are called *inequality symbols*, and two algebraic expressions joined by any of these symbols, such as

$$3(x + 2) \geq 3x - \tfrac{4}{5}$$

form an *inequality statement*, or simply an *inequality*.

Since we use variables in inequalities as placeholders for constants, an inequality is neither true nor false until the variables are replaced with constants. For this reason inequalities are often referred to as *open statements*. The *solution set* for an inequality is defined as the set of elements from the replacement set that make the inequality a true statement. Any element of the solution set is called a *solution* of the inequality. To *solve an inequality* is to find the solution set for the inequality.

As with equations, we are interested in performing operations on inequalities that will produce simpler *equivalent inequalities* (inequalities that have the same solution set), leading eventually to an inequality whose solution is obvious. The following theorem is fundamental to the inequality-solving process.

Theorem 2. If $f(x)$, $g(x)$, and $h(x)$ are open statements that represent real numbers for each replacement of x out of some chosen replacement set, then the following inequalities are equivalent:

$$f(x) > g(x)$$

$$f(x) + h(x) > g(x) + h(x)$$

$$f(x) - h(x) > g(x) - h(x)$$

$$h(x) \cdot f(x) > h(x) \cdot g(x) \qquad \text{[for } x \text{ such that } h(x) > 0]$$

$$h(x) \cdot f(x) < h(x) \cdot g(x) \qquad \text{[for } x \text{ such that } h(x) < 0]$$

$$\frac{f(x)}{h(x)} > \frac{g(x)}{h(x)} \qquad \text{[for } x \text{ such that } h(x) > 0]$$

$$\frac{f(x)}{h(x)} < \frac{g(x)}{h(x)} \qquad \text{[for } x \text{ such that } h(x) < 0]$$

The same theorem holds if $>$ is replaced with $\geq$, and $<$ with $\leq$. In comparing Theorem 2 with Theorem 1 we see that the only difference is in the multiplication and division properties. In these two cases, the sign reverses if the inequality is multiplied or divided by a negative quantity. The proof of the theorem will be left as an exercise. As with equations, equivalent inequalities can also be obtained by suitable use of the substitution principle.

Solutions and Applications

Example 9. Solve and graph.

$$\frac{2x - 3}{4} + 6 > 2 + \frac{4x}{3}$$

SOLUTION

$$\frac{2x - 3}{4} + 6 > 2 + \frac{4x}{3}$$

$$12 \frac{2x - 3}{4} + 12 \cdot 6 > 12 \cdot 2 + 12 \frac{4x}{3}$$

$$6x - 9 + 72 > 24 + 16x$$

$$6x + 63 > 24 + 16x$$

$$-10x > -39$$

$$x < 3.9$$

Solution set $= \{x \in R \mid x < 3.9\}$, or less formally, simply $x < 3.9$.
Graph:

Problem 9.   Solve and graph.

$$\frac{4x - 3}{3} + 8 > 6 + \frac{3x}{2}$$

ANSWER

$x < 6$

Double-inequality statements of the type $a < x < b$, $a \leq x < b$, etc., are very useful and are encountered frequently. Formally

---

$$\{x \in R \mid a < x < b\} = \{x \in R \mid a < x \text{ and } x < b\}$$

To solve a double inequality, we can always split it up as indicated on the right, and then proceed as above; however, it is easier to keep it in the form on the left and proceed as indicated in the next example. The justification for the process should be clear.

Example 10.   In a chemistry experiment a solution of hydrochloric acid is to be kept between 30 and 35°C, that is, $30 \leq C \leq 35$. What is the range temperature in degrees Fahrenheit? $[C = \frac{5}{9}(F - 32)]$

SOLUTION

$$30 \leq C \leq 35$$
$$30 \leq \tfrac{5}{9}(F - 32) \leq 35$$
$$\tfrac{9}{5} \cdot 30 \leq \tfrac{9}{5} \cdot \tfrac{5}{9}(F - 32) \leq \tfrac{9}{5} \cdot 35$$
$$54 \leq F - 32 \leq 63$$
$$54 + 32 \leq F - 32 + 32 \leq 63 + 32$$
$$86 \leq F \leq 95$$

Problem 10.   A film developer is to be kept between 68 and 77°F, that is, $68 \leq F \leq 77$. What is the range in temperature in degrees Celsius? $(F = \frac{9}{5}C + 32.)$

ANSWER

$20 \leq C \leq 25$.

EXERCISE 18

A *Solve and graph.*

1. $4x + 8 \geq x - 1$
2. $7x - 8 < 4x + 7$
3. $2(x - 3) + 5 < 5 - x$
4. $3 - x \geq 5(3 - x)$
5. $(M/-3) \leq -2$
6. $(N/-2) > 4$
7. $-7n \geq 21$
8. $-5t < -10$
9. $2(1 - u) \geq 5u$
10. $3 - m < 4(m - 3)$

11. $\dfrac{y - 3}{4} - 1 > \dfrac{y}{2}$

12. $-2 - \dfrac{B}{4} \leq \dfrac{1 + B}{3}$

13. $2 \leq 3m - 7 < 14$

14. $-4 < 5t + 6 \leq 21$

B 15. $\dfrac{p}{3} - \dfrac{p - 2}{2} \leq \dfrac{p}{4} - 4$

16. $\dfrac{q}{7} - 3 > \dfrac{q - 4}{3} + 1$

17. $\dfrac{2}{3}(x + 7) - \dfrac{x}{4} > \dfrac{1}{2}(3 - x) + \dfrac{x}{6}$

18. $\dfrac{2x}{5} - \dfrac{1}{2}(x - 3) \leq \dfrac{2x}{3} - \dfrac{3}{10}(x + 2)$

19. $-1 \leq \frac{2}{3}A + 5 \leq 11$
20. $-4 \leq \frac{9}{5}x + 32 \leq 68$
21. $24 \leq \frac{2}{3}(x - 5) < 36$
22. $-12 < \frac{3}{4}(2 - x) \leq 24$

23. If the perimeter of a rectangle with a length of 10 in. must be smaller than 30 in., what values may be used for the width?

24. If the area of a rectangle of length 10 in. must be less than 65 in.^{2}, what values may be used for the width?

25. As dry air moves upward it expands, and in so doing cools at a rate of about 5.5°F for each 1,000-ft rise up to about 40,000 ft. If the ground temperature is 70°F, then the temperature T at height h is given approximately by $T = 70 - 0.0055h$. For what range in altitude will the temperature be between 26 and −40°F?

26. It is known that temperature has a small but measurable effect upon the velocity of sound. For each Celsius degree rise in temperature in the air, the velocity of sound increases about 2 fps. If at 0°C sound travels at 1,087 fps, its speed at other temperatures is given by

$$V = 1,087 + 2T$$

(A) What temperature range corresponds to a velocity range of $1,097 \leq V \leq 1,137$?

(B) What is the corresponding temperature range in Fahrenheit degrees $[C = \frac{5}{9}(F - 32)]$?

27. A student received grades of 62, 75, and 85 on three tests. How high must he score on a fourth test to have an average of 80 or more?

28. For a business to make a profit it is clear that revenue R must be greater than cost C; in short, a profit will result only if $R > C$. If a company

manufactures records and its cost equation for a week is $C = 300 + 1.5x$ and its revenue equation is $R = 2x$, where x is the number of records sold in a week, how many records must be sold for the company to realize a profit?

29. In a 110-volt electrical house circuit a 30-ampere fuse is used. In order to keep the fuse from "blowing," the total wattage in all the appliances on the circuit must be kept below what figure? ($W = EI$, where $W = $ power in watts, $E = $ pressure in volts, and $I = $ current in amperes.) (*Hint: $I = W/E$ and $I \leq 30$.*)

30. If the power demands in a 110-volt electrical circuit in a home vary between 220 and 2,750 watts, what is the range of current flowing through the circuit? ($W = EI$, where $W = $ power in watts, $E = $ pressure in volts, and $I = $ current in amperes.)

c 31. If both a and b are negative numbers and b/a is greater than 1, then is $a - b$ positive or negative?

32. If both a and b are positive numbers and b/a is greater than 1, then is $a - b$ positive or negative?

33. Which of the following are true?
 (A) $p > q, m > 0 \Rightarrow mp < mq$
 (B) $p < q, m < 0 \Rightarrow mp > mq$
 (C) $p > 0, q < 0 \Rightarrow p + q > q$

34. Which of the following are true?
 (A) $x > 0, y < 0 \Rightarrow y - x < y$
 (B) $x < 0, y < 0 \Rightarrow x/y < 0$
 (C) $x/y > 1 \Rightarrow x > y$

35. Answer the "whys" in the following proof of the multiplication property in Theorem 2. Let r be a number such that $f(r) > g(r)$; then if $h(r) > 0$, we can conclude that $h(r)f(r) > h(r)g(r)$ (why?). If $h(r) < 0$, then $h(r)f(r) < h(r)g(r)$ (why?). On the other hand, if r is a number such that $h(r) > 0$ and $h(r)f(r) > h(r)g(r)$, then $f(r) > g(r)$ (why?). Or if $h(r) < 0$ and $h(r)f(r) < h(r)g(r)$, then $f(r) > g(r)$ (why?). Thus, $f(x) > g(x)$ is equivalent to $h(x)f(x) > h(x)g(x)$ if $h(x) > 0$, and to $h(x)f(x) < h(x)g(x)$ if $h(x) < 0$ (why?).

36. Prove the addition property in Theorem 2.
37. Prove the subtraction property in Theorem 2.
38. Prove the division property in Theorem 2.
39. Assume that $m, n \in R^+$ and that $m > n$, then

$$mn > n^2$$
$$mn - m^2 > n^2 - m^2$$
$$m(n - m) > (n + m)(n - m)$$
$$m > n + m$$
$$0 > n$$

But n was assumed positive. Can you find the error?

3.3 ABSOLUTE VALUE IN FIRST-DEGREE EQUATIONS AND INEQUALITIES

Absolute Value

One is often interested in the distance from the origin to a point, or the distance between two arbitrary points on a number line. Related to these distances is the notion of absolute value. We can formally define the distance between the origin 0 and an arbitrary point x to be the *absolute value* of x, denoted by $|x|$. Thus, $|7| = 7$, $|-7| = 7$, and $|0| = 0$. Notice that the absolute value of a number gives only the distance from the origin and not the direction; that is, it is not a directed distance. If $|x| = 5$, then x could equal 5 or -5. Equivalently, the absolute value of x can be defined in a purely algebraic way without relying on geometric notions:

$$|x| = \begin{cases} x & \text{if } x \geq 0 \\ -x & \text{if } x < 0 \end{cases}$$

Both the geometric and nongeometric interpretations of absolute value are useful, as you will see in the material that follows. The first important property of absolute value that we observe is: *The absolute value of a number is never negative.* The following theorem lists several other useful properties of absolute value.

Theorem 3. If $x, y \in R$, then

(A) $|-x| = |x|$

(B) $|xy| = |x||y|$

(C) $\left|\dfrac{x}{y}\right| = \dfrac{|x|}{|y|}$

(D) $|x|^2 = x^2$

We will prove part (B), and leave the other three parts as exercises. To prove part (B), we consider several cases, each of which is based on the definition of absolute value and sign properties of real numbers.

Case 1. Assume $x = 0$ or $y = 0$, then $|xy|$ and $|x||y|$ are both zero, hence are equal.

Case 2. Assume $x > 0$ and $y > 0$, then $|xy| = xy = |x||y|$.

Case 3. Assume $x < 0$ and $y > 0$, then $|xy| = -(xy = (-x)(y) = |x||y|$.

Case 4. Assume $x > 0$ and $y < 0$, then $|xy| = -(xy) = (x)(-y) = |x||y|$.

Case 5. Assume $x < 0$ and $y < 0$, then $|xy| = xy = (-x)(-y) = |x||y|$.

Example 11. (A) $|-7| = |7|$

(B) $|-x-5| = |-(x+5)| = |x+5|$

(C) $|(-3)(4)| = |-3||4|$

(D) $|x^2 - x - 6| = |(x-3)(x+2)|$
$$= |x-3||x+2|$$

(E) $\left|\dfrac{-12}{2}\right| = \dfrac{|-12|}{|2|}$

(F) $\left|\dfrac{x+5}{x-3}\right| = \dfrac{|x+5|}{|x-3|}$

(G) $|-3|^2 = (-3)^2$

(H) $|x-3|^2 = (x-3)^2$

Problem 11. Which of the following are true?

(A) $|-9| = |9|$

(B) $|-(x-3)| = |x+3|$

(C) $|(6)(-4)| = |6||-4|$

(D) $|(-x)y| = -|x||y|$

(E) $\left|\dfrac{2}{-18}\right| = \dfrac{|2|}{|-18|}$

(F) $\left|\dfrac{x}{y}\right| = \dfrac{|x|}{|y|}$

(G) $|-12|^2 = (-12)^2$

(H) $|x-x_1|^2 = (x-x_1)^2$

ANSWER

(A) T; (B) F; (C) T; (D) F; (E) T; (F) T; (G) T; (H) T.

First-Degree Equations and Inequalities Involving Absolute Value

The absolute value is frequently encountered in equations, formulas, and inequalities. The following theorems give us useful information in this regard. In all cases $ax + b$ is assumed to be a real polynomial with $a \neq 0$.

Theorem 4.

$$|ax + b| = \begin{cases} ax + b & \text{(for } ax + b \geq 0, \text{ that is, for } x \geq -b/a) \\ -(ax + b) & \text{(for } ax + b < 0, \text{ that is, for } x < -b/a) \end{cases}$$

This theorem is an immediate consequence of the definition of absolute value.

Example 12. (A) $|2x + 3| = 2x + 3$ if $2x + 3 \geq 0$, that is, if $x \geq -\frac{3}{2}$

(B) $|2x + 3| = -(2x + 3)$ if $2x + 3 < 0$, that is, if $x < -\frac{3}{2}$

Problem 12. For what values of x does

(A) $|3x - 4| = 3x - 4$

(B) $|3x - 4| = -(3x - 4)$

ANSWER

(A) $x \geq \frac{4}{3}$; (B) $x < \frac{4}{3}$.

Theorem 5. If $p > 0$, then

$$|ax + b| = p \Leftrightarrow ax + b = \pm p$$

The proof of this theorem is left as an exercise. We will prove the next theorem to illustrate some of the special techniques used in proofs involving absolute value.

Example 13. For what values of x does $|3x + 5| = 4$?

SOLUTION

$|3x + 5| = 4$ if and only if

$$3x + 5 = \pm 4$$
$$3x = -5 \pm 4$$
$$x = \frac{-5 \pm 4}{3}$$
$$x = -3, -\tfrac{1}{3}$$

Problem 13. For what values of x does $|4x - 8| = 6$?

ANSWER

$\tfrac{7}{2}, \tfrac{1}{2}$.

Theorem 6. If $p > 0$, then

$$|ax + b| < p \Leftrightarrow -p < ax + b < p$$

PROOF

PART I: Show that $|ax + b| < p$ implies $-p < ax + b < p$.
Case 1. If $ax + b \geq 0$, then by Theorem 4 $|ax + b| = ax + b$, and the inequality becomes $ax + b < p$; hence, for this case, the solution set is $\{x \mid 0 \leq ax + b < p\}$.

Case 2. If $ax + b < 0$, then by Theorem 4 $|ax + b| = -(ax + b)$, and the inequality becomes $-(ax + b) < p$ or $ax + b > -p$; hence, for this case, the solution set is $\{x \,|\, -p < ax + b < 0\}$.

The solution set for $|ax + b| < p$ is the union of these two sets; thus

$$\{x \,|\, |ax + b| < p\} = \{x \,|\, -p < ax + b < 0\} \cup \{x \,|\, 0 \le ax + b < p\},$$

or less formally, $-p < ax + b < p$.

PART II: Show that $-p < ax + b < p$ implies $|ax + b| < p$.
The steps in Part I are reversible with suitable grammatical changes.

Example 14.   Solve and graph.

(A) $|x| < 5$
(B) $|x - 3| < 4$
(C) $|2x + 5| < 3$

SOLUTION

(A) $|x| < 5$
$-5 < x < 5$

(B) $|x - 3| < 4$
$-4 < x - 3 < 4$
$-1 < x < 7$

(C) $|2x + 5| < 3$
$-3 < 2x + 5 < 3$
$-8 < 2x < -2$
$-4 < x < -1$

Problem 14.   Solve and graph.

(A) $|x| < 3$ (B) $|x + 2| < 4$ (C) $|3x - 4| < 2$

ANSWER

(A) $-3 < x < 3$; (B) $-6 < x < 2$

(C) $\frac{2}{3} < x < 2$

The proof of the next and last theorem we leave as an exercise.

Theorem 7. If $p > 0$, then

$$|ax + b| > p \Leftrightarrow ax + b < -p \quad \text{or} \quad ax + b > p$$

Example 15. Solve and graph.

(A) $|x| > 5$
(B) $|x - 3| > 4$
(C) $|2x + 5| > 3$

SOLUTION

(A) $|x| > 5$ if and only if

$x < -5 \quad \text{or} \quad x > 5$

(B) $|x - 3| > 4$ if and only if

$x - 3 < -4 \text{ or } x - 3 > 4$
$x < -1 \quad \text{or} \quad x > 7$

(C) $|2x + 5| > 3$ if and only if

$2x + 5 < -3 \text{ or } 2x + 5 > 3$
$2x < -8 \quad \text{or} \quad 2x > -2$
$x < -4 \quad \text{or} \quad x > -1$

Problem 15. Solve and check.

(A) $|x| > 3$ (B) $|x + 2| > 4$ (C) $|3x - 4| > 2$

ANSWER

(A) $x < -3$ or $x > 3$;   (B) $x < -6$ or $x >$;

(C) $x < \frac{2}{3}$ or $x > 2$.

It should be clear that Theorems 6 and 7 remain valid if $>$ is replaced with $\geq$, and $<$ is replaced with $\leq$. The only difference in the graphs in the examples resulting from these changes would be solid dots in place of open dots.

We return for a moment to geometric considerations. The absolute value of the difference of any two numbers $|x - y|$ is the *distance between these two numbers*. The distance between -3 and 8, for example, is $|8 - (-3)| = |11| = 11$ or $|(-3) - 8| = |-11| = 11$. We can take the difference in either order since by Theorem 3A $|x - y| = |y - x|$. Thus one can think of solving the inequality $|x - 3| < 4$ in terms of finding all points no farther away from 3 than four units. What absolute-value inequality statement represents a set of points within two units of 5 on either side? (*Answer:* $|x - 5| < 2$.) Within three units of -2? (*Answer:* $|x + 2| < 3$.)

EXERCISE 19

A *Solve and graph.*

1. $|x| = 7$
2. $|x| = 5$
3. $|x| \leq 7$
4. $|t| \leq 5$
5. $|x| \geq 7$
6. $|x| \geq 5$
7. $|y - 5| = 3$
8. $|t - 3| = 4$
9. $|y - 5| < 3$
10. $|t - 3| < 4$
11. $|y - 5| > 3$
12. $|t - 3| > 4$
13. $|u + 8| = 3$
14. $|x + 1| = 5$
15. $|u + 8| \leq 3$
16. $|x + 1| \leq 5$
17. $|u + 8| \geq 3$
18. $|x + 1| \geq 5$

B
19. $|3x + 4| = 8$
20. $|2x - 3| = 5$
21. $|5x - 3| \leq 12$
22. $|2x - 3| \leq 5$
23. $|2y - 8| > 2$
24. $|3u + 4| > 3$
25. $|5t - 7| = 11$
26. $|6m + 9| = 13$
27. $|7u + 9| < 14$
28. $|9M - 7| < 15$
29. $|\frac{2}{3}x - 1| \geq 5$
30. $|\frac{3}{4}x + 3| \geq 9$
31. $|\frac{9}{5}C + 32| < 31$
32. $|\frac{5}{9}(F - 32)| < 40$

Replace the question marks with the appropriate symbols.

33. $-17 \leq x \leq 17 \Leftrightarrow |?| \leq ?$
34. $-8 < x < 8 \Leftrightarrow |?| < ?$
35. $3 < x < 7 \Leftrightarrow |?| < ?$
36. $-4 < x < 10 \Leftrightarrow |?| < ?$
37. $-7 \leq y \leq 3 \Leftrightarrow |?| \leq ?$
38. $-8 \leq u \leq -2 \Leftrightarrow |?| \leq ?$

For what values of x does each of the following hold?

39. $|x - 5| = x - 5$
40. $|x + 7| = x + 7$
41. $|x + 8| = -(x + 8)$
42. $|x - 11| = -(x - 11)$
43. $|4x + 3| = 4x + 3$
44. $|5x - 9| = (5x - 9)$
45. $|5x - 2| = -(5x - 2)$
46. $|3x + 7| = -(3x + 7)$

C 47. Answer the "whys" in the following proof of Theorem 3A: *Case 1:* If $x > 0$, then $|-x| = x$ (why?) and $|x| = x$ (why?); therefore $|-x| = |x|$. *Case 2:* If $x = 0$, then $|-x| = |0| = 0$ and $|x| = |0| = 0$; therefore $|-x| = |x|$. *Case 3:* If $x < 0$, then $|-x| = -x$ (why?) and $|x| = -x$ (why?); therefore $|-x| = |x|$.

48. Prove Theorem 3C: If $x, y \in R$, then $|x/y| = |x|/|y|$.
49. Prove Theorem 3D: If $x \in R$, then $|x|^2 = x^2$.
50. Prove Theorem 5 from left to right: If $p > 0$, then $|ax + b| = p$ implies $ax + b = \pm p$.
51. For $e \in R^+$, what conditions must $|x - 2|$ satisfy for $|2x - 4| < e$?
52. For $e \in R^+$, what condition must $|x - 3|$ satisfy for $|(x/2) - (3/2)| < e$?
53. For $x, y \in R$, prove that $|x + y| \le |x| + |y|$.
54. For $x, y \in R$, prove that $|x - y| \ge |x| - |y|$.

3.4 QUADRATIC EQUATIONS

The next class of equations we will consider are the second-degree polynomial equations in one variable, called quadratic equations. A *quadratic equation* in one variable is any equation that can be written in the form

$$ax^2 + bx + c = 0 \qquad a \ne 0$$

where x is a variable, and a, b, and c are constants. We will refer to this form as the *standard form* for the quadratic equation.

Solution by Factoring

If the coefficients a, b, and c are integers, and are such that $ax^2 + bx + c$ can be written as the product of two first-degree factors with integral coefficients, then the quadratic equation can be quickly and easily solved. The method of solution by factoring rests on the following property of real numbers: *If m and n are real numbers, then*

$$mn = 0 \text{ if and only if } m = 0 \text{ or } n = 0 \text{ (or both)}$$

Example 16. Solve by factoring if possible.

(A) $6x^2 - 19x - 7 = 0$
(B) $2x^2 - 8x + 3 = 0$
(C) $2x^2 = 3x$

SOLUTION

(A) $\qquad 6x^2 - 19x - 7 = 0$
$\qquad (2x - 7)(3x + 1) = 0$
$\qquad 2x - 7 = 0 \qquad$ or $\qquad 3x + 1 = 0$
$\qquad\qquad x = \tfrac{7}{2} \qquad\qquad\qquad x = -\tfrac{1}{3}$

(B) Does ac have factors whose sum is b? No. Hence, $2x^2 - 8x + 3$ cannot be factored over I. Another method must be used to solve this equation.

(C) $\quad\quad 2x^2 = 3x \quad\quad$ Why shouldn't both members be divided by x?
$$2x^2 - 3x = 0$$
$$x(2x - 3) = 0$$
$$x = 0 \quad\quad \text{or} \quad\quad 2x - 3 = 0$$
$$2x = 3$$
$$x = \tfrac{3}{2}$$

Problem 16. Solve by factoring if possible.

(A) $3x^2 + 7x - 20 = 0$ (B) $2x^2 - 3x - 3 = 0$ (C) $4x^2 = 5x$

ANSWER

(A) $-4, \tfrac{5}{3}$; (B) does not factor over I; (C) $0, \tfrac{5}{4}$.

Solution by Square Root

The easiest type of quadratic equation to solve is an equation of the form

$$ax^2 + c = 0 \quad\quad a \neq 0$$

The method of solution makes direct use of the definition of a square root of a number. The process is illustrated in the following example.

Example 17. Solve by the square-root method.

(A) $2x^2 - 3 = 0$
(B) $3x^2 + 27 = 0$
(C) $(x + \tfrac{1}{2})^2 = \tfrac{5}{4}$

SOLUTION

(A) $\quad 2x^2 - 3 = 0$
$$x^2 = \tfrac{3}{2} \quad\quad \text{What number squared is } \tfrac{3}{2}?$$
$$x = \pm\sqrt{\frac{3}{2}} \quad \text{or} \quad \pm\frac{\sqrt{6}}{2}$$

(B) $3x^2 + 27 = 0$

$$x^2 = -9 \qquad \text{What number squared is } -9?$$

$$x = \pm\sqrt{-9} \quad \text{or} \quad \pm 3i$$

(C) $(x + \frac{1}{2})^2 = \frac{5}{4}$

$$x + \frac{1}{2} = \pm\sqrt{\frac{5}{4}}$$

$$x = -\frac{1}{2} \pm \frac{\sqrt{5}}{2}$$

$$x = \frac{-1 \pm \sqrt{5}}{2}$$

Problem 17. Solve by the square-root method.

(A) $3x^2 - 5 = 0$ (B) $2x^2 + 8 = 0$ (C) $(x + \frac{1}{3})^2 = \frac{2}{9}$

ANSWER

(A) $\pm\sqrt{\frac{5}{3}}$ or $\pm\sqrt{15}/3$; (B) $\pm 2i$; (C) $(-1 \pm \sqrt{2})/3$.

Solution by Completing the Square and Quadratic Formula

The methods of square root and factoring are fast and easy to use when they apply; however, there are equations, as we found in Example 16 and Prob. 16, that cannot be solved by these methods. A more general method must be developed to take care of this type of equation. The method of completing the square is such a method. This method is based on the process of transforming the standard quadratic equation

$$ax^2 + bx + c = 0$$

into the form

$$(x + A)^2 = B$$

where A and B are constants. The last equation can be easily solved by the square-root method just discussed. But how do we transform the first equation into the second? The following brief discussion provides the key to the process.

What number must be added to $x^2 + bx$ so that the result is the square of a first-degree polynomial? There is an easy mechanical rule for finding this number, based on the square of the following binomials:

$$(x + m)^2 = x^2 + 2mx + m^2$$
$$(x - m)^2 = x^2 - 2mx + m^2$$

In either case, we see that the third term on the right is the square of one-half of the coefficient of x in the second term on the right. This observation leads directly to the rule: *To complete the square of a quadratic of the form $x^2 + bx$, add the square of one-half the coefficient of x [that is, add $(b/2)^2$].*

Example 18. (A) To complete the square of $x^2 + 6x$, add $(\frac{6}{2})^2$, that is, 9; thus $x^2 + 6x + 9 = (x + 3)^2$.

(B) To complete the square of $x^2 - 3x$, add $(-\frac{3}{2})^2$, that is, $\frac{9}{4}$; thus $x^2 - 3x + \frac{9}{4} = (x - \frac{3}{2})^2$.

(C) To complete the square of $x^2 + bx$, add $(b/2)^2$, that is, $b^2/4$; thus $x^2 + bx + b^2/4 = (x + b/2)^2$.

Problem 18. Complete the square of each of the following.

(A) $x^2 + 10x$ (B) $x^2 - 5x$ (C) $x^2 + mx$

ANSWER

(A) $x^2 + 10x + 5^2 = (x + 5)^2$; (B) $x^2 - 5x + (-\frac{5}{2})^2 = (x - \frac{5}{2})^2$;
(C) $x^2 + mx + (m/2)^2 = (x + m/2)^2$.

It is important to note that the rule about completing the square applies only to quadratic forms in which the coefficient of the second-degree term is 1. This causes little trouble, however, as you will see. We now solve a few problems by the method of completing the square.

Example 19. Solve by completing the square.

(A) $x^2 + 6x - 2 = 0$
(B) $2x^2 - 4x + 3 = 0$

SOLUTION

(A) $x^2 + 6x - 2 = 0$
$$x^2 + 6x = 2$$
$$x^2 + 6x + 9 = 2 + 9 \qquad \text{Complete the square on the left by adding}$$
$$\text{9 to both members of the equation.}$$
$$(x + 3)^2 = 11$$
$$x + 3 = \pm\sqrt{11}$$
$$x = -3 \pm \sqrt{11}$$

(B) $2x^2 - 4x + 3 = 0$

$\quad\quad x^2 - 2x + \frac{3}{2} = 0$ Make the leading coefficient 1 by dividing by 2.

$\quad\quad x^2 - 2x = -\frac{3}{2}$

$\quad x^2 - 2x + 1 = -\frac{3}{2} + 1$ Complete the square.

$\quad\quad (x - 1)^2 = -\frac{1}{2}$

$$x - 1 = \pm \sqrt{-\frac{1}{2}}$$

$$x = 1 \pm \frac{\sqrt{2}}{2} i$$

Problem 19. Solve by completing the square.

(A) $x^2 + 8x - 3 = 0$ (B) $3x^2 - 12x + 13 = 0$

ANSWER

(A) $-4 \pm \sqrt{19}$; (B) $2 \pm \sqrt{3}\,i/3$.

Let us now consider the general quadratic equation, with unspecified coefficients,

$$ax^2 + bx + c = 0 \quad\quad a \neq 0$$

and solve it by completing the square exactly as we did in the above examples in which the coefficients were specified. To make the leading coefficient 1, multiply both members of the equation by $1/a$. Thus

$$x^2 + \frac{b}{a} x + \frac{c}{a} = 0$$

Adding $-c/a$ to both members and then completing the square of the left member, we have

$$x^2 + \frac{b}{a} x + \frac{b^2}{4a^2} = \frac{b^2}{4a^2} - \frac{c}{a}$$

We now factor the left member and solve by the square-root method.

$$\left(x + \frac{b}{2a}\right)^2 = \frac{b^2 - 4ac}{4a^2}$$

$$x + \frac{b}{2a} = \pm\sqrt{\frac{b^2 - 4ac}{4a^2}}$$

$$x = -\frac{b}{2a} \pm \frac{\sqrt{b^2 - 4ac}}{2a}$$

$$x = \frac{-b \pm \sqrt{b^2 - 4ac}}{2a} \qquad a \neq 0$$

The last equation is called the *quadratic formula*. It should be memorized and used to solve quadratic equations when simpler methods fail. Note that $b^2 - 4ac$, called the *discriminant*, gives us the following useful information about roots.

$$b^2 - 4ac > 0 \Rightarrow ax^2 + bx + c = 0 \text{ has two real solutions}$$
$$b^2 - 4ac = 0 \Rightarrow ax^2 + bx + c = 0 \text{ has one real solution}$$
$$b^2 - 4ac < 0 \Rightarrow ax^2 + bx + c = 0 \text{ has two complex solutions}$$

Example 20. Solve $2x + \frac{3}{2} = x^2$ by use of the quadratic formula.

SOLUTION

$$2x + \tfrac{3}{2} = x^2$$
$$2x^2 - 4x - 3 = 0$$

$$x = \frac{-(-4) \pm \sqrt{(-4)^2 - 4(2)(-3)}}{2(2)}$$

$$x = \frac{4 \pm 2\sqrt{10}}{4} = \frac{2 \pm \sqrt{10}}{2}$$

$\{(2 + \sqrt{10})/2, (2 - \sqrt{10})/2\}$ is the solution set for the given equation.

Problem 20. Solve $x^2 - \frac{5}{2} = -3x$ by use of the quadratic formula.

ANSWER

$(-3 \pm \sqrt{19})/2$.

EXERCISE 20

A *Solve by factoring.*

1. $v^2 - 3v = 0$
2. $u^2 + 5u = 0$
3. $4u^2 = 8u$
4. $3A^2 = -12A$
5. $y^2 - 6y + 5 = 0$
6. $x^2 - 4x - 12 = 0$
7. $2d^2 + 15d - 8 = 0$
8. $3Q^2 - 10Q - 8 = 0$
9. $A^2/2 = A + 4$
10. $(m/4)(m + 1) = 3$

Solve by square-root method.

11. $x^2 - 25 = 0$
12. $x^2 - 16 = 0$
13. $x^2 + 25 = 0$
14. $x^2 + 16 = 0$
15. $m^2 - 12 = 0$
16. $y^2 - 45 = 0$
17. $9y^2 - 16 = 0$
18. $4x^2 - 9 = 0$
19. $4x^2 + 25 = 0$
20. $16a^2 + 9 = 0$
21. $(n + 5)^2 = 9$
22. $(m - 3)^2 = 25$
23. $(d - 3)^2 = -4$
24. $(t + 1)^2 = -9$

Solve using the quadratic formula.

25. $x^2 - 10x - 3 = 0$
26. $x^2 - 6x - 3 = 0$
27. $t^2 = 1 - t$
28. $u^2 = 1 - 3u$
29. $x^2 + 8 = 4x$
30. $y^2 + 3 = 2y$
31. $2x^2 + 1 = 4x$
32. $2m^2 + 3 = 6m$
33. $3q + 2q^2 = 1$
34. $p = 1 - 3p^2$

B *Solve by completing the square.*

35. $x^2 - 6x - 3 = 0$
36. $y^2 - 10y - 3 = 0$
37. $2y^2 - 6y + 3 = 0$
38. $2d^2 - 4d + 1 = 0$
39. $3x^2 - 2x - 2 = 0$
40. $3x^2 + 5x - 4 = 0$
41. $x^2 + mx + n = 0$
42. $ax^2 + bx + c = 0, a \neq 0$

Solve each of the following equations by any method excluding completing the square.

43. $m^2 + 2m = 15$
44. $u^2 = 2u + 3$
45. $(y + 4)^2 = 11$
46. $(x - 5)^2 = 7$
47. $x^2 - 1 = 3x$
48. $x^2 + 2x = 2$
49. $2n^2 = 4n$
50. $2u^2 + 3u = 0$
51. $x^2 + 15 = 2 - 6x$
52. $x^2 - 4x + 13 = 0$
53. $2y = (2/y) + 3$
54. $L = 15/(L - 2)$
55. $1 + (8/x^2) = 4/x$
56. $2/u = (3/u^2) + 1$

57. $\dfrac{24}{10 + m} + 1 = \dfrac{24}{10 - m}$

58. $\dfrac{1.2}{y - 1} + \dfrac{1.2}{y} = 1$

Solve for the indicated letters in terms of the other letters. Use positive square roots only.

59. $s = \frac{1}{2}gt^2$ (solve for t)   60. $a^2 + b^2 = c^2$ (solve for a)

61. $P = EI - RI^2$ (solve for I)   62. $A = P(1+r)^2$ (solve for r)

C 63. Show that if r_1 and r_2 are the two roots of $ax^2 + bx + c = 0$, then $r_1 r_2 = c/a$.

64. For r_1 and r_2 in Prob. 63, show that $r_1 + r_2 = -b/a$.

65. Show that if r_1 and r_2 are any nonzero numbers such that $r_1 r_2 = c/a$ and $r_1 + r_2 = -b/a$, then they are roots of $ax^2 + bx + c = 0$.

66. Use the results of Probs. 63, 64, and 65 to check which of the following are roots of $2x^2 - 2x + 5 = 0$: (A) -1, 2; (B) $2 + \sqrt{3}$, $2 - \sqrt{3}$; (C) $\frac{1}{2} - \frac{3}{2}i$, $\frac{1}{2} + \frac{3}{2}i$.

67. In one stage of the derivation of the quadratic formula, we replaced $\pm\sqrt{(b^2 - 4ac)/4a^2}$ with $\pm\sqrt{b^2 - 4ac}/2a$. What justifies using $2a$ in place of $|2a|$?

68. Find the fallacy:

$$(n+1)^2 = n^2 + 2n + 1$$

$$(n+1)^2 - (2n+1) = n^2$$

$$(n+1)^2 - (2n+1) - n(2n+1) = n^2 - n(2n+1)$$

$$(n+1)^2 - (2n+1) - n(2n+1) + \frac{(2n+1)^2}{4} = n^2 - n(2n+1) + \frac{(2n+1)^2}{4}$$

$$\left[(n+1) - \left(\frac{2n+1}{2}\right)\right]^2 = \left(n - \frac{2n+1}{2}\right)^2$$

$$(n+1) - \frac{2n+1}{2} = n - \frac{2n+1}{2}$$

$$n + 1 = n$$

Applications

Example 21. A tank can be filled in 4 hr by two pipes when both are used. How many hours are required for each pipe to fill the tank alone if the smaller pipe requires 3 hours more than the larger one?

SOLUTION

Quantity of work = rate × time
Let x = time for the larger pipe to fill tank alone
$x + 3$ = time for the smaller pipe to fill tank alone

Then

$1/x$ = rate for larger pipe ($1/x$ of the tank per hour)

$1/(x + 3)$ = rate for smaller pipe [$1/(x + 3)$ of the tank per hour]

Thus

$$\frac{4}{x} + \frac{4}{x + 3} = 1 \qquad \text{whole tank}$$

$$4x + 12 + 4x = x^2 + 3x$$

$$x^2 - 5x - 12 = 0$$

$$x = \frac{5 \pm \sqrt{73}}{2} \qquad \text{Why should we discard the negative answer?}$$

$$x = \frac{5 + \sqrt{73}}{2} \approx 6.78 \text{ hr} \qquad \text{(larger pipe)}$$

$$x + 3 \approx 9.78 \text{ hr} \qquad \text{(smaller pipe)}$$

Problem 21. Two pipes can fill a tank in 3 hr when used together. Alone, one can fill the tank 2 hr faster than the other. How long will it take each pipe to fill the tank alone? Compute the answers to two decimal places, using the square-root table in the end of the book.

ANSWER

5.16 hr and 7.16 hr.

EXERCISE 21

These problems are not grouped from easy (A) to difficult or theoretical (C). They are grouped according to type.

Number

1. Separate 21 into two parts whose product is 104.
2. Find two consecutive positive even integers whose product is 168.
3. Find all numbers with the property that when the number is added to itself the sum is the same as when the number is multiplied by itself.
4. The sum of a number and its reciprocal is $\frac{10}{3}$. Find the number.

Geometry

5. Approximately how far is the horizon from an airplane 2 mi high? Assume the radius of the earth is 4,000 mi and use a square-root table to estimate the answer to the nearest mile.

6. Find the base and height of a triangle with area 2 ft² if its base is 3 ft longer than its height. ($A = \frac{1}{2}bh$.)

7. If the length and width of a 4 × 2 in. rectangle are each increased by the same amount, the area of the new rectangle will be twice the old. What are the dimensions to two decimal places of the new rectangle?

8. The width of a rectangle is 2 in. less than its length. Find its dimensions to two decimal places if its area is 12 in.².

9. A golden rectangle is defined as one that has the property that, when a square with sides equal to the shorter side of the rectangle is removed from one end, the ratio of the sides of the remaining rectangle is the same as the ratio of the sides of the original rectangle. If the shorter side of the original rectangle is 1, find the shorter side of the remaining rectangle after the square has been removed. This number is called the golden ratio, and it turns up frequently in the history of mathematics.

10. Two circles have diameters d_1 and d_2. Show that a circle with diameter $d = \sqrt{d_1{}^2 + d_2^2}$ has the same area as the two circles together.

11. A flag has a white cross of uniform width on a red background. If the cross extends from edge to edge on a 4 × 3 ft flag, find its width if it takes up exactly half the total area of the flag.

Physics—Engineering

12. The pressure p in pounds per square foot of wind blowing at v miles per hour is $p = 0.003v^2$. If a pressure gage on a bridge registers a wind pressure of 14.7 lb per ft², what is the velocity of the wind?

13. In physics it is found that the illumination I in foot-candles on a surface d feet from a light source of c candlepower is given by the formula $I = c/d^2$. How far should a light of 20 candlepower be placed from a surface to produce the same illumination as a light of 10 candlepower at 10 ft? Write the answer in its simplest radical form, and approximate it to two decimal places.

14. One method of measuring the velocity of water in a stream or river is to use an L-shaped tube. Torricelli's law in physics tells us that the height (in feet) that water is pushed up into the tube above the surface is related to the water's velocity (in feet per second) by the formula $v^2 = 2gh$, where g is approximately 32 ft per sec per sec. (*Note:* The device can also be used as a simple speedometer for a boat.) How fast is a stream flowing if $h = 0.5$ ft? Find the answer to two decimal places.

15. At 20 mph a car collides with a stationary object with the same force it would have if it had been dropped 13½ ft, that is, if it had been pushed off the roof of an average 1-story house. In general, a car moving at r miles per hour hits a stationary object with a force of impact equivalent to the force with which it would hit the ground when falling from a certain height h given by the formula $h = 0.0336r^2$. Approximately how fast would a car have to be moving if it crashed as hard as if it had been pushed off the top of a 12-story building 121 ft high?

16. For a car traveling at a speed of v miles per hour, the least number of feet d under the best possible conditions necessary to stop it (including reaction time) is given by the empirical formula $d = 0.044v^2 + 1.1v$. Estimate the speed of a car requiring 165 feet to stop after the danger is realized.

17. If an arrow is shot vertically into the air (from the ground) with an initial velocity of 176 fps, its distance y above the ground t seconds after it is released (neglecting air resistance) is given by $y = 176t - 16t^2$.
    (A) Find the times when y is zero, and interpret the results physically.
    (B) Find the times when the arrow is 16 ft off the ground. Compute the answers to two decimal places.

18. A barrel 2 ft in diameter and 4 ft in height has a 1-in.-diameter drainpipe in the bottom. It can be shown that the height h of the surface of the water above the bottom of the barrel at time t minutes after the drain has been opened is given by the formula $h = [\sqrt{h_0} - (t/240)]^2$, where h_0 is the water level above the drain at time $t = 0$. If the barrel is full and the drain opened, how long will it take to empty half the contents? (*Hint:* The problem is very easily solved if the right side of the equation is not squared.)

Rate—Time

19. One pipe can fill a tank in 5 hr less than another; together they fill the tank in 5 hr. How long would it take each alone to fill the tank? Compute the answer to two decimal places.

20. A new printing press can do a job in 1 hr less than an older press. Together they can do the same job in 1.2 hr. How long would it take each to do the job alone?

21. Two boats travel at right angles to each other after leaving the same dock at the same time. One hour later they are 13 miles apart. If one travels 7 mph faster than the other, what is the rate of each?

22. A speedboat takes 1 hr longer to go 24 miles up a river than to return. If the boat cruises at 10 mph in still water, what is the rate of the current?

Economics—Business

23. If P dollars is invested at r percent compounded annually, at the end of 2 years it will amount to $A = P(1 + r)^2$. At what interest rate will $100 increase to $144 in 2 years? (*Note:* $A = 144$ and $P = 100$.)

24. In a certain city the demand equation for popular records is $q_d = 3,000/p$, where q_d is the quantity of records demanded on a given day if the selling price is p dollars per record. (Notice that, as the price goes up, the number of records people are willing to buy goes down, and vice versa.) On the other hand, the supply equation is $q_s = 1,000p - 500$, where q_s is the quantity of records a supplier is willing to supply at p dollars per record. (Notice that, as the price goes up, the number of records a supplier is willing to sell goes

up, and vice versa.) At what price will supply equal demand; that is, at what price will $q_d = q_s$? In economic theory the price at which supply equals demand is called the equilibrium point, the point at which the price ceases to change.

3.5 EQUATIONS REDUCIBLE TO QUADRATIC FORM

In solving an equation such as

$$\sqrt{x - 1} = -5$$

our first inclination might be to square both members to obtain

$$x - 1 = 25$$
$$x = 26$$

which is not a solution to the original equation since $5 \neq -5$. In addition, we note that the solution set for $x = 5$ is a subset of the equation we obtain by squaring both members, $x^2 = 25$. In general, we can show that:

Theorem 8.   The solution set of $f(x) = g(x)$ is a subset of the solution set of $[f(x)]^n = [g(x)]^n$ for n a positive integer.

This theorem provides us with a method of solving some equations involving radicals. It is important to remember that any new equation obtained by raising both members of an equation to the same power may have solutions (called *extraneous solutions*) that are not solutions of the original equation. On the other hand, any solution of the original equation must be among those of the new equation. Thus, every solution of the new equation must be checked in the original equation to eliminate so-called extraneous solutions.

Example 22.   Solve.

(A) $x + \sqrt{x - 4} = 4$

(B) $\sqrt{2x + 3} - \sqrt{x - 2} = 2$

SOLUTION

(A) $x + \sqrt{x - 4} = 4$

$\qquad\quad \sqrt{x - 4} = 4 - x$ Isolate radical on one side.

$\qquad\quad\ \ x - 4 = 16 - 8x + x^2$ Square both members.

$\quad x^2 - 9x + 20 = 0$

$\quad (x - 5)(x - 4) = 0$

$\qquad\qquad\qquad x = 5, 4$

Checking shows that 4 is good and 5 is extraneous, thus

$$\{x \mid x + \sqrt{x - 4} = 4\} = \{4\}$$

(B) $\sqrt{2x + 3} - \sqrt{x - 2} = 2$

$$\sqrt{2x + 3} = \sqrt{x - 2} + 2$$
$$2x + 3 = x - 2 + 4\sqrt{x - 2} + 4$$
$$x + 1 = 4\sqrt{x - 2}$$
$$x^2 + 2x + 1 = 16(x - 2)$$
$$x^2 - 14x + 33 = 0$$
$$(x - 11)(x - 3) = 0$$
$$x = 3, 11$$

Both solutions check; hence

$$\{x \mid \sqrt{2x + 3} - \sqrt{x - 2} = 2\} = \{3, 11\}.$$

Problem 22. Solve.

(A) $x - 5 = \sqrt{x - 3}$ (B) $\sqrt{2x + 5} + \sqrt{x + 2} = 5$

ANSWER

(A) 7; (B) 2.

If asked to solve the equation

$$x^{2/3} - x^{1/3} - 6 = 0$$

you might at first have trouble. But if you recognize that the equation is quadratic in $x^{1/3}$, you can solve for $x^{1/3}$ first and then solve for x. It may be convenient to make the substitution $u = x^{1/3}$, and then solve the equation

$$u^2 - u - 6 = 0$$
$$(u - 3)(u + 2) = 0$$
$$u = 3, -2$$

Replacing u with $x^{1/3}$, we obtain

$$x^{1/3} = 3 \qquad x^{1/3} = -2$$
$$x = 27 \qquad x = -8$$

In general, if an equation that is not quadratic can be transformed to the form

$$au^2 + bu + c = 0$$

where u is an expression in some other variable, then the equation is said to be in quadratic form. Once recognized as a quadratic form, an equation can often be solved using quadratic methods.

Example 23. Solve $x^6 + 6x^3 - 16 = 0$.

SOLUTION

Let $u = x^3$ and solve:

$$u^2 + 6u - 16 = 0$$
$$(u + 8)(u - 2) = 0$$
$$u = -8, 2$$
$$x^3 = -8 \qquad x^3 = 2$$
$$x = -2 \qquad x = \sqrt[3]{2}$$

Problem 23. Solve.

(A) $x^{2/3} - x^{1/3} - 12 = 0$ (B) $x^4 - 5x^2 + 4 = 0$

ANSWER

(A) $64, -27$; (B) $\pm 1, \pm 2$.

EXERCISE 22

A *Solve.*

1. $\sqrt[3]{x + 5} = 3$
2. $\sqrt[4]{x - 3} = 2$
3. $\sqrt{5n + 9} = n - 1$
4. $m - 13 = \sqrt{m + 7}$
5. $\sqrt{x + 5} + 7 = 0$
6. $3 + \sqrt{2x - 1} = 0$
7. $\sqrt{3x + 4} = 2 + \sqrt{x}$
8. $\sqrt{3w - 2} - \sqrt{w} = 2$
9. $y^4 - 2y^2 - 8 = 0$
10. $x^4 - 7x^2 - 18 = 0$
11. $x^6 + 3x^3 - 10 = 0$
12. $x^6 - 7x^3 - 8 = 0$
13. $2x^{2/3} + 3x^{1/3} - 2 = 0$
14. $x^{2/3} - 3x^{1/3} - 10 = 0$
15. $(m^2 - m)^2 - 4(m^2 - m) = 12$
16. $(x^2 + 2x)^2 - (x^2 + 2x) = 6$

B
17. $\sqrt{u - 2} = 2 + \sqrt{2u + 3}$
18. $\sqrt{3t + 4} + \sqrt{t} = -3$
19. $\sqrt{3y - 2} = 3 - \sqrt{3y + 1}$
20. $\sqrt{2x - 1} - \sqrt{x - 4} = 2$
21. $\sqrt{7x - 2} - \sqrt{x + 1} = \sqrt{3}$
22. $\sqrt{3x + 6} - \sqrt{x + 4} = \sqrt{2}$
23. $3n^{-2} - 11n^{-1} - 20 = 0$
24. $6x^{-2} - 5x^{-1} - 6 = 0$
25. $9y^{-4} - 10y^{-2} + 1 = 0$
26. $4x^{-4} - 17x^{-2} + 4 = 0$
27. $y^{1/2} - 3y^{1/4} + 2 = 0$
28. $4x^{-1} - 9x^{-1/2} + 2 = 0$

29. $(m-5)^4 + 36 = 13(m-5)^2$ 30. $(x-3)^4 + 3(x-3)^2 = 4$

c 31. $\sqrt{5-2x} - \sqrt{x+6} = \sqrt{x+3}$ 32. $\sqrt{2x+3} - \sqrt{x-2} = \sqrt{x+1}$

Solve Probs. 33 to 36 two ways: by squaring and by substitution.

33. $m - 7\sqrt{m} + 12 = 0$ 34. $y - 6 + \sqrt{y} = 0$

35. $t - 11\sqrt{t} + 18 = 0$ 36. $x = 15 - 2\sqrt{x}$

37. Prove Theorem 8.

3.6 QUADRATIC INEQUALITIES IN ONE VARIABLE

In solving quadratic inequalities, we will use the properties of inequalities discussed in Chap. 1 and in the first part of this chapter; however, we will need additional procedures to complete the task. A simple example will illustrate the basic process. To solve

$$x^2 + 2x < 8$$

first write it in the equivalent form

$$x^2 + 2x - 8 < 0$$

and then factor the left member. (Below we will show that factoring can always be accomplished for quadratic polynomials if complex coefficients are allowed.)

$$(x+4)(x-2) < 0$$

The solution set for this inequality will be those values of x for which the factors $(x+4)$ and $(x-2)$ are opposite in sign. Thus, using set ideas,

$$
\begin{aligned}
\{x \mid (x+4)(x-2) < 0\} &= \{x \mid (x+4) > 0 \text{ and } (x-2) < 0\} \\
&\cup \{x \mid (x+4) < 0 \text{ and } (x-2) > 0\} \\
&= \{x \mid x > -4 \text{ and } x < 2\} \\
&\cup \{x \mid x < -4 \text{ and } x > 2\} \\
&= \{x \mid -4 < x < 2\} \cup \varnothing \\
&= \{x \mid -4 < x < 2\}
\end{aligned}
$$

We can obtain the same result with a little less effort by using a geometric approach. If we indicate the sign of each factor relative to a real-number line, we can easily observe intervals over which the two factors have opposite signs. Thus,

From the figure, it is easy to see that

$$\{x \mid (x+4)(x-2) < 0\} = \{x \mid -4 < x < 2\}$$

and conclude that the graph of the solution set of $x^2 + 2x < 8$ looks like

The key to solving quadratic inequalities is the factoring. Can every quadratic polynomial be factored? The answer is yes. In fact, if r_1 and r_2 are solutions of the quadratic equation $ax^2 + bx + c = 0$ with arbitrary complex coefficients, $a \neq 0$, then

$$ax^2 + bx + c = a(x - r_1)(x - r_2)$$

The proof is left as an exercise. (*Hint:* Use r_1 and r_2 from the quadratic formula and multiply the right member of the equation to obtain the left member.)

Example 24.   Solve and graph $x^2 + 2 \geq 4x$.

SOLUTION

$$x^2 + 2 \geq 4x$$
$$x^2 - 4x + 2 \geq 0 \qquad \text{Factor the left member using}$$
$$[x - (2 - \sqrt{2})][x - (2 + \sqrt{2})] \geq 0 \qquad \text{the quadratic formula.}$$

Thus the solution set of $x^2 + 2 \geq 4x$ is

$$\{x \mid x \leq 2 - \sqrt{2} \text{ or } x \geq 2 + \sqrt{2}\}$$

Problem 24.   Solve and graph.

(A) $x^2 - 6 < x$ (B) $x^2 + 7 \geq 6x$

ANSWER

(A) $-2 < x < 3$,

(B) $x \le 3 - \sqrt{2}$ or $x \ge 3 + \sqrt{2}$,

If $ax^2 + bx + c = 0$, $a, b, c \in R$, $a \neq 0$ has only complex roots, then $ax^2 + bx + c$ is either positive for all real x or negative for all real x. This follows from a theorem from calculus, and the reasoning is something like this. Assume the contrary; that is, assume $ax^2 + bx + c$ has only two complex roots, and that $ax^2 + bx + c$ is positive for some values of x and negative for others. Then, by this theorem from calculus, $ax^2 + bx + c$ must equal zero for some real value of x. A contradiction.

Some inequality statements that are not in quadratic form can be solved using the same techniques as above.

Example 25. Solve and graph.

$$\frac{x^2 - x + 1}{2 - x} \ge 1$$

SOLUTION

$$\frac{x^2 - x + 1}{2 - x} \ge 1$$

If we multiply both members by $2 - x$, then we have to consider two cases. Why?

$$\frac{x^2 - x + 1}{2 - x} - 1 \ge 0$$

$$\frac{x^2 - 1}{2 - x} \ge 0$$

$$\frac{(x - 1)(x + 1)}{2 - x} \ge 0$$

We must have an even number of factors with negative signs. From the graph it is easy to see that the solution set for the original inequality is

$$\{x \mid x \le -1 \text{ or } 1 \le x < 2\}$$

Problem 25. Solve and graph.

$$\frac{3}{2-x} \le \frac{1}{x+4}.$$

ANSWER

$-4 \le x < -\frac{5}{2}$ or $x > 2$,

EXERCISE 23

A *Solve and graph.*

1. $(x+2)(x-4) < 0$
2. $(x-3)(x+4) < 0$
3. $x^2 < 10 - 3x$
4. $x^2 + x < 12$
5. $x^2 + 7x + 10 > 0$
6. $x^2 + 21 > 10x$
7. $x(x-8) \le 0$
8. $x(x+6) \ge 0$
9. $x^2 + 5x \ge 0$
10. $x^2 \le 4x$
11. $x^2 \le 9$
12. $x^2 > 4$
13. $x^2 + 4 \ge 4x$
14. $6x \le x^2 + 9$
15. $x^2 + 4 < 4x$
16. $x^2 + 9 < 6x$

B
17. $x^2 < 2$
18. $x^2 \ge 3$
19. $x^2 + 1 \ge 4x$
20. $x^2 \le 2x + 1$
21. $x^2 + 3 \ge 2x$
22. $x < x^2 + 1$
23. $(1/x) < 4$
24. $(5/x) > 3$

25. $\dfrac{2}{x-3} \le -2$
26. $\dfrac{2x}{x+3} \ge 1$

27. $\dfrac{5x-8}{x-5} \ge 2$
28. $\dfrac{3x+1}{x+4} \le 1$

29. $\dfrac{x(x+5)}{x-3} \ge 0$
30. $\dfrac{x-4}{x(x+2)} \le 0$

31. $\dfrac{2}{x+1} \ge \dfrac{1}{x-2}$
32. $\dfrac{3}{x-3} - \dfrac{2}{x+2} \le 0$

33. $x^4 + 36 \ge 13x^2$
34. $4x^4 + 4 \le 17x^2$
35. For what values of x will $\sqrt{(x-3)/(x+5)}$ be a real number?
36. For what values of x will $\sqrt{x^2 - 3x + 2}$ be a real number?
37. If an object is shot straight up from the ground with an initial velocity of 160 fps, its distance d in feet above the ground at the end of t seconds (neglecting air resistance) is given by $d = 160t - 16t^2$. Find the duration of time for which $d \ge 256$.
38. Repeat the preceding problem for $d \ge 0$.

C 39. Show that if r_1 and r_2 are roots of $ax^2 + bx + c = 0$, then $ax^2 + bx + c = a(x - r_1)(x - r_2)$.
  40. Show that $x^2 + bx + c \geq 0$ for $x \in R$ if $c = (b/2)^2$ and $b, c \in R$.
  41. Prove that $x^2 + y^2 \geq 2xy$ for $x, y \in R$.
  42. Prove that if $a > 0$, $b > 0$, and $a^2 > b^2$, then $a > b$.

Solve.

43. $\left|\dfrac{x+1}{x}\right| > 2$ 44. $\left|\dfrac{x+3}{x}\right| \geq 1$

45. $|x^2 - 1| \leq 3$ 46. $|x^2 - x - 5| \leq 1$
47. $\sqrt{2x - 3} > \sqrt{2 - x}$ (*Hint:* $\sqrt{2x - 3} > \sqrt{2 - x}$ if and only if $2x - 3 > 0$, $2 - x > 0$, and $2x - 3 > 2 - x$.)
48. $\sqrt{x^2 + 1} > \sqrt{3 - x}$

EXERCISE 24 CHAPTER-REVIEW EXERCISES

A *Solve.*

1. $x(x - 4) - 4 = x^2 - 4(x - 3)$ 2. $\dfrac{5x}{3} - \dfrac{4 + x}{2} = \dfrac{x - 2}{4} + 1$

Solve and graph.

3. $3(2 - x) - 2 \leq 2x - 1$ 4. $|y + 9| < 5$
5. $|x - 2| > 3$

Solve.

6. $x^2 - 7 = 0$ 7. $2x^2 = 4x$
8. $2x^2 - 7x + 3 = 0$ 9. $m^2 + m - 1 = 0$
10. $y^2 = \frac{3}{2}(y + 1)$ 11. $\sqrt{5x - 6} - x = 0$
12. $m^4 + 5m^2 - 36 = 0$
13. The difference between a number and its reciprocal is $\frac{16}{15}$. Find the number.
14. Find all numbers with the property that when the number is added to itself the sum is the same as when the number is multiplied by itself.

Solve and graph.

15. $x^2 + x < 20$ 16. $x^2 \geq 4x + 21$
17. $x^2 + 16 \geq 8x$

B *Solve.*

18. $\dfrac{u - 3}{2u - 2} = \dfrac{1}{6} - \dfrac{1 - u}{3u - 3}$ 19. $\dfrac{7}{2 - x} = \dfrac{10 - 4x}{x^2 + 3x - 10}$

20. A chemist has 1,200 grams of 60% pure acid. How much should he drain off and replace with 100% pure acid to obtain a solution that is 75% pure?
21. Solve for n: $a_n = a_1 + (n - 1)d$.

Solve and graph.

22. $\dfrac{x+3}{8} \le 5 - \dfrac{2-x}{3}$

23. $|4x - 7| \le 5$

24. $|3x - 8| > 2$

Solve.

25. $(e + \frac{1}{2})^2 = \frac{5}{4}$

26. $u + \dfrac{3}{u} = 2$

27. $\dfrac{x}{x^2 - x - 6} - \dfrac{2}{x - 3} = 3$

28. $2x^{2/3} - 5x^{1/3} - 12 = 0$

29. $y^8 - 17y^4 + 16 = 0$

30. $\sqrt{y - 2} - \sqrt{5y + 1} = -3$

31. Cost equations for manufacturing companies are often quadratic in nature. (At very high or very low outputs the costs are more per unit because of inefficiency of plant operation at these extremes.) If the cost equation for manufacturing transistor radios is $C = x^2 - 10x + 31$, where C is the cost of manufacturing x units per week (both in thousands), find (A) the output for a $15,000 weekly cost and (B) the output for a $6,000 weekly cost.

32. The manufacturing company in the preceding problem sells its transistor radios for $3 each. Thus its revenue equation is $R = 3x$, where R is revenue and x is the number of units sold per week (both in thousands). Find the breakeven points for the company, that is, the output at which revenue equals cost.

Solve and graph.

33. $10x > x^2 + 25$

34. $x^2 + 2x < 1$

35. $\dfrac{1}{x} < 2$

36. $\dfrac{3}{x - 4} \le \dfrac{2}{x - 3}$

C 37. Solve $\dfrac{x}{1 - [1/(1 - x)]} = x - \dfrac{3}{x} + 1$

38. Prove Theorem 7 from left to right: If $p > 0$, then $|ax + b| > p$ implies $ax + b < -p$ or $ax + b > p$.

39. Assuming $|a + b| \le |a| + |b|$, show that $|x + y + z| \le |x| + |y| + |z|$.

40. For $e \in R^+$, what condition must $|x - 3|$ satisfy for $|3x - 9| < e$.

41. Solve for y in terms of x: $3y^2 - 3xy - 2x^2 = 0$.

42. Solve by substitution and also by squaring: $x - 8\sqrt{x} + 15 = 0$.

43. Solve $|x - (1/x)| > 2$.

44. Solve $\sqrt{x - 2} < \sqrt{2x + 1}$.

Chapter

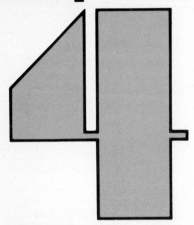

Relations and Functions

Establishing and working with sets of ordered pairs of numbers—whether through tables, graphs, or equations—are common procedures in almost all fields of pure and applied science. This pairing activity is so broad and so fundamental in the activities of man in his attempt to understand and control his environment that he has found it necessary to describe it in the precise language of mathematics. The result has been the extensive development of a subject—the theory and application of relations and functions—that stands among the most important mathematical concepts.

4.1 CARTESIAN PRODUCTS AND COORDINATE SYSTEMS; RELATIONS AND MAPPINGS

Cartesian Products and Coordinate Systems

In the preceding chapters we considered many different kinds of sets. In this chapter we will concentrate on particular sets whose elements are ordered pairs of numbers. If (a, b) is an ordered pair of real numbers, then a is called the *first component* of the ordered pair, and b the *second component*. In general, $(a, b) \neq (b, a)$ unless $a = b$; or stated more directly, $(a, b) = (c, d)$ if and only if $a = c$ and $b = d$.

Sets of ordered pairs can be generated from two given sets A and B by forming the *Cartesian product of A and B* as follows:

$$A \times B = \{(x, y) \mid x \in A \text{ and } y \in B\}$$

Example 1. If $A = \{2, 3\}$ and $B = \{2, 5, 6\}$, find $A \times B$.

SOLUTION

$$A \times B = \{(2, 2), (2, 5), (2, 6), (3, 2), (3, 5), (3, 6)\}$$

Problem 1. If $A = \{-1, 2\}$ and $B = \{3, 5, 7\}$, find $A \times B$.

ANSWER

$\{(-1, 3), (-1, 5), (-1, 7), (2, 3), (2, 5), (2, 7)\}$.

In this course the most important Cartesian product will be $R \times R$ or R^2, where R is the set of real numbers. In short, $R \times R$ (or R^2) is the set of all ordered pairs of real numbers. Just as we formed a real line by establishing a one-to-one correspondence between the points on a line and the elements of R, we can form a real plane by establishing a one-to-one correspondence between the points in a plane and the elements of R^2. This is done, of course, using a Cartesian coordinate system. Recall that a *Cartesian coordinate system* is formed by taking two mutually perpendicular real lines (coordinate axes) through their respective origins in a plane, one horizontal and the other vertical, and then assigning unique ordered pairs of numbers to each point P, called coordinates of P. The first coordinate (abscissa) is the directed distance of P from the vertical axis measured on the horizontal axis, and the second coordinate (ordinate) is the directed distance of P from the horizontal axis measured on the vertical axis. (See Fig. 1.) By reversing this process we can associate each element of R^2

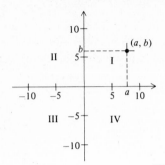

FIGURE 1

with a unique point in a plane. Thus there is a one-to-one correspondence between the points in a plane and the elements of R^2. This result is often referred to as the fundamental theorem of analytic geometry. The coordinate axes divide the plane into four parts called *quadrants* and these are numbered from I to IV in a counterclockwise direction.

Relations

To be able to discuss with precision relationships specified by sets of ordered pairs of elements, it is useful to introduce two new technical terms, *relation* and *function*. We start by defining a relation. A relation is any set of ordered pairs of elements (generally subsets of R^2 in this course). The choice of the word relation for this definition is quite natural, since any set of ordered pairs of numbers establishes a relationship between two sets of numbers, the set of first components of the ordered pairs and the set of second components. The set of first components of the ordered pairs of the set is called the *domain* of the relation, and the set of second components is called the *range* of the relation. The *graph of a relation in R^2* (i.e., the graph of a subset of R^2) is the set of all points in a Cartesian coordinate system that have the elements of the relation as coordinates.

We emphasize the fact that *any* set of ordered pairs of elements is a relation; whether or not it has physical meaning is entirely beside the point. The concept is purely mathematical in nature, and as such it is completely free to be applied to a variety of practical and theoretical problems.

Example 2. Graph each relation and state its domain and range. (I = set of integers.)

(A) $\{(x, y) \mid 0 \le x \le 2, 0 \le y \le 2; x, y \in I\}$

(B) $\{(x, y) \mid y \le |x|, -3 \le x \le 3, y \ge 0; x, y \in I\}$

SOLUTION

(A) Domain: $\{0, 1, 2\}$
Range: $\{0, 1, 2\}$

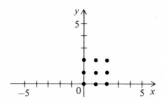

(B) Domain: $\{-3, -2, -1, 0, 1, 2, 3\}$
Range: $\{0, 1, 2, 3\}$

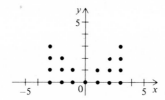

Problem 2. Graph each relation and state its domain and range.

(A) $\{(x, y) \mid -2 \le x \le 2, 0 \le y \le 1; x, y \in I\}$

(B) $\{(x, y) \mid |y| \le x, 0 \le x \le 3; x, y \in I\}$

ANSWER

(A) Domain: $\{-2, -1, 0, 1, 2\}$
Range: $\{0, 1\}$

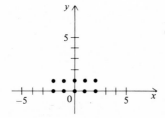

(B)   Domain: $\{0, 1, 2, 3\}$
     Range: $\{-3, -2, -1, 0, 1, 2, 3\}$

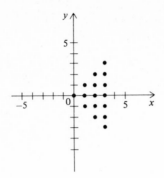

Relations as Mappings

In addition to graphing, we can also look at relations as mappings. For example, if we let f represent the relation

$$\{(x, y) \mid y = x^2, x \in \{-1, 0, 1, 2\}\}$$

then we can think of f as a mapping of elements from the domain of f into elements of the range of f. That is, -1 is mapped into 1, 0 into 0, 1 into 1, and 2 into 4. Thus

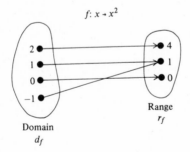

If each element in the domain of a relation f is mapped into a unique element in the range of f, then f is called a *single-valued mapping*. If certain elements in the domain of f are mapped into two or more elements in the range of f, then f is called a *multivalued mapping*. And, finally, if each element in the domain of f is mapped into exactly one element in the range of f, and if each element in the range of f is the image of exactly one element in the domain of f, then the mapping f is said to be *one-to-one*. All one-to-one mappings are single-valued, but some single-valued mappings are not one-to-one. Relations that are single-valued mappings are called *functions*, and we will have much more to say about functions later in the chapter.

Example 3. (A) $g = \{(x, y)\,|\,y = |x|,\ x \in \{-2,\ -1,\ 0,\ 1,\ 2\}\}$

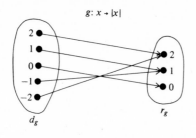

(single-valued but not one-to-one)

(B) $h = \{(x, y)\,|\,|y| = x,\ x \in \{0,\ 1,\ 2\}\}$

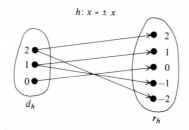

(multivalued)

(C) $m = \{(x, y)\,|\,y = x^3,\ x \in \{0,\ 1,\ 2\}\}$

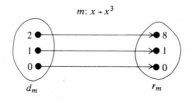

(single-valued and one-to-one)

Problem 3. Express each of the following relations as mappings (as in Example 3), and indicate if the mapping is single-valued, multivalued, or one-to-one.

(A) $f = \{(x, y)\,|\,y = x^2,\ x \in \{-2,\ -1,\ 0,\ 1\}\}$
(B) $g = \{(x, y)\,|\,y^2 = x,\ x \in \{0,\ 1,\ 4\}\}$
(C) $h = \{(x, y)\,|\,y = \sqrt{x},\ x \in \{0,\ 1,\ 4\}\}$

ANSWER

(A)
$f: x \to x^2$

(B)
$g: x \to \pm\sqrt{x}$

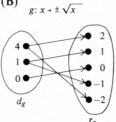

(C)
$h: x \to \sqrt{x}$

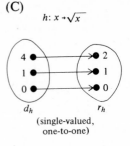

d_f r_f
(single-valued)

d_g r_g
(multivalued)

d_h r_h
(single-valued,
one-to-one)

EXERCISE 25

A   *Given the sets $A = \{-1, -2\}$, $B = \{3, 4, 5\}$, and $C = \{7, 8\}$, find the following Cartesian products.*

1. $A \times B$ 2. $A \times C$ 3. $B \times A$
4. $C \times A$ 5. $B \times C$ 6. $C \times B$

Graph each relation, and state its domain and range.

7. $F = \{(1, 1), (2, 1), (3, 2), (3, 3)\}$
8. $G = \{(-1, -2), (0, -1), (1, 0), (2, 1), (3, 2), (4, 1)\}$
9. $g = \{(-2, 0), (0, 2), (2, 0)\}$
10. $f = \{(2, 4), (4, 2), (2, 0), (4, -2)\}$
11. $h = \{(x, y) | y = x + 3, x \in \{-3, -1, 0, 2\}\}$

12. $H = \left\{(x, y) \,\middle|\, y = \dfrac{x}{2}, x \in \{-4, -1, 0, 2, 4\}\right\}$

Express each of the following relations as mappings (see Example 3), and indicate if the mapping is single-valued, multivalued, or one-to-one.

13. The relation in Prob. 7   14. The relation in Prob. 8
15. The relation in Prob. 9   16. The relation in Prob. 10
17. The relation in Prob. 11   18. The relation in Prob. 12

B   *Describe each of the following Cartesian products using set-builder notation, and give two examples of elements of the set.*

19. $N \times N$ 20. $I \times I$ 21. $N \times I$
22. $I \times N$ 23. $R \times R$ 24. R^2

Graph each relation, and state its domain and range.

25. $f = \{(x, y) \in I \times I | 0 \leq y \leq x, 0 \leq x \leq 3\}$
26. $g = \{(x, y) \in I \times I | 0 \leq y \leq |x|, -2 \leq x \leq 2\}$
27. $F = \{(x, y) \in I \times I | \, |y| \leq x, 2 \leq x \leq 4\}$
28. $G = \{(x, y) \in I \times I | \, |y| \leq |x|, -2 \leq x \leq 2\}$

Express each of the following relations as mappings (see Example 3), and indicate if the mapping is single-valued, multivalued, or one-to-one.

29. $F = \{(x, y) \mid y = x^2 + 1, \ x \in \{-2, -1, 0, 1, 2\}\}$
30. $G = \{(x, y) \mid y = x^4 - 1, \ x \in \{-1, 0, 1, 2\}\}$
31. $h = \{(x, y) \mid y = x^3 + x, \ x \in \{-2, -1, 0, 1, 2\}\}$
32. $H = \{(x, y) \mid y = 2x^3 - 3, \ x \in \{-1, 0, 1, 2\}\}$
33. The relation in Prob. 25
34. The relation in Prob. 26
35. In selecting a teacher for a given subject you are likely to be interested in one who has a good grasp of the subject matter and who also is a good teacher (in the sense of putting across or selling his subject). To clarify the problem even further, let us form the sets

$$U = \{\text{good grasp of subject, poor grasp of subject}\} = \{\text{H, L}\}$$
$$V = \{\text{good teacher, poor teacher}\} = \{\text{G, P}\}$$

and write down all the elements of $U \times V$. If each element of $U \times V$ characterizes a certain type teacher, which one is likely to do you the most good? Which one the most harm?

36. Repeat Prob. 35, but this time think of yourself as a member of a management selection team whose business it is to select management for industry or business. Replace sets U and V with

$$U = \{\text{intelligent, stupid}\} = \{\text{I, S}\}$$
$$V = \{\text{aggressive, passive}\} = \{\text{A, P}\}$$

C *Problems 37 to 42 refer to the following relations:*

$A = \{(x, y) \mid x = y; \ x, y \in R\}$
$B = \{(x, y) \mid x \leq y; \ x, y \in R\}$
$C = \{(x, y) \mid x \text{ is a brother of } y; \ x, y \in \text{ the set of all people}\}$
$D = \{(x, y) \mid x \text{ is a father of } y; \ x, y \in \text{ the set of all people}\}$
$E = \{(x, y) \mid x \text{ is perpendicular to } y; \ x, y \in \text{ the set of all lines}\}$
$F = \{(x, y) \mid x \text{ is parallel to } y; \ x, y \in \text{ the set of all lines}\}$

Note: Allow a line to be parallel to itself.

37. A relation M is said to be *reflexive* if $(x, x) \in M$ for every x in the domain of M. Which of the above relations are reflexive?
38. A relation M is said to be *symmetric* if whenever $(x, y) \in M$, then $(y, x) \in M$. Which of the above relations are symmetric?
39. A relation is said to be *transitive* if whenever $(x, y) \in M$ and $(y, z) \in M$, then $(x, z) \in M$. Which of the above relations are transitive?
40. If a relation is reflexive, symmetric, and transitive, it is called an *equivalence relation*. Which of the above relations are equivalence relations?
41. Which of the following relations are equivalence relations (see Prob. 40)?
(A) "In the same room as" (relative to people)
(B) "Is similar to" (relative to triangles)

42. Give an example of a relation that is transitive and symmetric but not reflexive.
43. Give an example of a relation that is transitive and reflexive but not symmetric.
44. Give an example of a relation that is symmetric and reflexive but not transitive.

4.2 THE STRAIGHT LINE

In this and the next section we will be primarily interested in the graphs of relations specified by equations in two variables. The function concept will be returned to in Sec. 4.4.

Distance Formula and the Straight Line

We start by defining the *distance between two points* $P_1(x_1, y_1)$ and $P_2(x_2, y_2)$ in a Cartesian coordinate system to be

$$d = \overline{P_1 P_2} = \sqrt{(x_2 - x_1)^2 + (y_2 - y_1)^2}$$

This definition is motivated by the Pythagorean theorem (see Fig. 2), but we introduce it by definition so that we can use it to define a straight line.

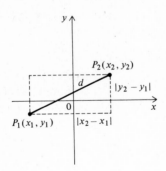

FIGURE 2

Example 4. Find the distance between $(-3, 5)$ and $(-2, -8)$.

SOLUTION

$$d = \sqrt{[-3 - (-2)]^2 + [5 - (-8)]^2} = \sqrt{170}$$

Problem 4. Find the distance between $(6, -3)$ and $(-7, -5)$.

ANSWER

$\sqrt{173}$.

Definition 1. Given two distinct points P_1 and P_2, then the set of all points P, such that the sum of two of the distances $\overline{P_1P}$, $\overline{PP_2}$, and $\overline{P_1P_2}$ is equal to the third, is a *straight line* through P_1 and P_2.

Any equation that can be transformed into the equivalent form

---

$$Ax + By = C$$

---

where A, B, and C are constants (A and B not both zero) and x and y are variables, is called a *linear* (*or first-degree polynomial*) *equation in two variables*. Restricting our attention to real polynomials, the graph of the equation is the graph of its solution set, that is, of the relation

$$\{(x, y) \in R^2 \,|\, Ax + By = C\}$$

The next theorem suggests why we call $Ax + By = C$ a linear equation.

Theorem 1. The graph of the equation $Ax + By = C$, where A, B, and C are constants (A and B not both zero) and x and y are variables, is a straight line. Every straight line in a Cartesian coordinate system is the graph of an equation of this form.

There are two parts to prove in this theorem: *Part I:* Show that the graph of the solution set of $Ax + By = C$ is a straight line. *Part II:* Show that any straight line in a Cartesian coordinate system has an equation of the form $Ax + By = C$. We will prove one case of Part I and leave other cases and Part II as exercises.

PARTIAL PROOF OF PART I

Let $P_1(x_1, y_1)$ and $P_2(x_2, y_2)$ be any two distinct points that satisfy $Ax + By = C$, and let $P_3(x_3, y_3)$ be an arbitrary third point that satisfies the same equation. Assume $B \neq 0$ and $x_1 < x_3 < x_2$, then solving $Ax + By = C$ for y, we obtain

$$y = mx + b \qquad \left(\text{where } m = -\frac{A}{B} \text{ and } b = \frac{C}{B}\right)$$

and, since P_1, P_2, and P_3 satisfy this equation,

$$P_1 = (x_1, mx_1 + b)$$
$$P_2 = (x_2, mx_2 + b)$$
$$P_3 = (x_3, mx_3 + b)$$

Thus

$$\overline{P_1 P_2} = \sqrt{(x_2 - x_1)^2 + [(mx_2 + b) - (mx_1 + b)]^2}$$
$$= \sqrt{(x_2 - x_1)^2 + m^2(x_2 - x_1)^2} = \sqrt{(x_2 - x_1)^2(1 + m^2)}$$
$$= (x_2 - x_1)\sqrt{1 + m^2} \quad \text{(since } x_2 > x_1)$$

Similarly,

$$\overline{P_3 P_2} = (x_2 - x_3)\sqrt{1 + m^2}$$
$$\overline{P_1 P_3} = (x_3 - x_1)\sqrt{1 + m^2}$$

Hence $\overline{P_1 P_3} + \overline{P_3 P_2} = \overline{P_1 P_2}$, and P_3 is on the line through P_1 and P_2. The other cases are similarly proved.

If we know that the graph of $Ax + By = C$ is a straight line, then its graph is easily found by plotting two points of the solution set (a third can be used if a checkpoint is desired) and then using a straightedge through these two points to plot other points of the solution set.

Example 5.
Graph of $x + 3y = 6$

Graph of $y = 4$, that is, $0x + y = 4$

Graph of $x = -3$, that is $x + 0y = -3$

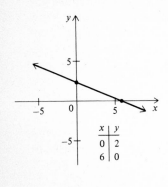

x	y
0	2
6	0

(a)

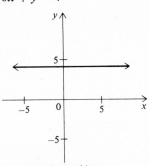

x can be anything as
long as y is 4

(b)

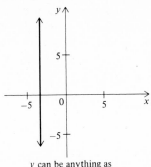

y can be anything as
long as x is −3

(c)

Problem 5. Graph (A) $2x - 3y = 6$, (B) $y = -3$, and (C) $x = 5$.

ANSWER

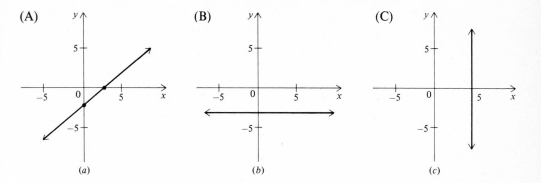

(a)   (b)   (c)

Slope-Intercept Form of the Equation of a Line

The equation $Ax + By = C$, $B \neq 0$, can always be written in the form

$$y = mx + b$$

where m and b are constants. This form has several interesting and useful properties. In particular, the constants m and b have special geometric significance. The significance of b is easily seen by assigning x the value 0 and observing that $y = b$. Since $(0, b)$ is the point where the graph crosses the y axis, b is called the y *intercept*.

To determine the geometric significance of m, let us choose two points (x_1, y_1) and (x_2, y_2) on the line $y = mx + b$ (Fig. 3). Since these points lie on the line, their coordinates must satisfy the equation $y = mx + b$.

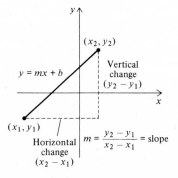

FIGURE 3

Since $y_1 - mx_1$ and $y_2 - mx_2$ are both equal to b, we set them equal to each other and solve for m. Thus

$$m = \frac{y_2 - y_1}{x_2 - x_1} = \frac{\text{vertical change}}{\text{horizontal change}}$$

Interpreting this last equation in terms of Fig. 3, it is seen that m is the ratio of the change in y to the corresponding change in x between any two distinct points on the line. The number m is called the *slope* of the line, and is a measure of the steepness of the line. Thus if an equation of a line is written in the form $y = mx + b$, the constant m is the slope of the line. If we are given the coordinates of two points (x_1, y_1) and (x_2, y_2) and want to find the slope of the line joining the two points, then we use the formula $m = (y_2 - y_1)/(x_2 - x_1)$.

Example 6. (A)   Find the slope and y intercept of the line $y = \frac{1}{3}x + 2$.

SOLUTION

Slope $= m = \frac{1}{3}$; y intercept $= b = 2$

(B)   Find the equation of a line with slope -2 and y intercept 3.

SOLUTION

$y = -2x + 3$

(C)   Find the slope of a line passing through $(1, 5)$ and $(6, -7)$.

SOLUTION

$$m = \frac{y_2 - y_1}{x_2 - x_1} = \frac{-7 - 5}{6 - 1} = -\frac{12}{5} \quad \text{or} \quad \frac{5 - (-7)}{1 - 6} = -\frac{12}{5}$$

NOTE: It does not matter which we call P_1 and P_2, as long as we stick to the choice once it is made.

Problem 6. (A)   Find the slope and y intercept of the line $y = -(x/2) - 7$.
(B)   Find the equation of a line with slope $-\frac{1}{3}$ and y intercept 6.
(C)   Find the slope of a line passing through $(-3, 5)$ and $(-1, -3)$.

ANSWER

(A) $m = -\frac{1}{2}$, $b = -7$; (B) $y = -(x/3) + 6$; (C) $m = -4$.

The slope of a line may be positive, negative, zero, or not defined. (What is the slope of a vertical line?) It should now be clear why $y = mx + b$ is called the *slope-intercept form* of the equation of a line.

Point-Slope Form of the Equation of a Line

In Example 6 we found the equation of a line given its slope and y intercept. Often it is necessary to find the equation of a line given its slope and the coordinates of a point through which it passes, or to find the equation of a line given the coordinates of two points through which it passes.

Let a line have slope m and pass through the fixed point (x_1, y_1). If (x, y) is to be a point on the line, the slope of the line passing through (x, y) and (x_1, y_1) must be m (see Fig. 4). Thus the equation

$$\frac{y - y_1}{x - x_1} = m$$

restricts a variable point (x, y), so that only those points in the plane lying on the line will have coordinates that satisfy the equation, and vice versa. This equation is usually written in the form

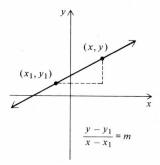

FIGURE 4

$$y - y_1 = m(x - x_1)$$

and is referred to as the *point-slope form* of the equation of a line. Using this equation in conjunction with the slope formula, we can also find the equation of a line knowing only the coordinates of two points through which it passes.

Example 7. (A) Find an equation of a line with slope $-\frac{1}{3}$ that passes through $(6, -3)$. Write the resulting equation in the form $y = mx + b$.

SOLUTION

$$y - y_1 = m(x - x_1)$$
$$y - (-3) = -\tfrac{1}{3}(x - 6)$$
$$y = -\tfrac{1}{3}x - 1$$

(B) Find an equation of a line that passes through the two points $(-2, -6)$ and $(2, 2)$.

SOLUTION

First find the slope of the line using the slope formula, then proceed as in the last example, using the coordinates of either point for (x_1, y_1).

$$m = \frac{y_2 - y_1}{x_2 - x_1} = \frac{2 - (-6)}{2 - (-2)} = 2$$
$$y - y_1 = m(x - x_1)$$
$$y - (-6) = 2[x - (-2)]$$
$$y = 2x - 2$$

Problem 7. (A) Find the equation of a line with slope $\frac{2}{3}$ that passes through $(-3, 4)$.

(B) Find the equation of a line that passes through the two points $(6, -1)$ and $(-2, 3)$.

ANSWER

(A) $y = \frac{2}{3}x + 6$; (B) $y = -(x/2) + 2$.

Vertical Lines

What do we do about vertical lines? If a line is vertical, its slope is not defined. Since points on a vertical line have constant abscissas and arbitrary ordinates, the equation of a vertical line is of the form

$$x + 0y = c$$

or simply

$$x = c$$

where c is the abscissa of each point on the line.

Example 8. The equation of a vertical line through $(-2, -4)$ is $x = -2$.

Problem 8. What is the equation of a vertical line through $(3, -8)$?

ANSWER

$x = 3$.

Parallel and Perpendicular Lines

The concept of slope has many uses. If you intend to take calculus, you will find the idea of slope generalized to apply to curves other than straight lines. Now, with relatively little effort, we can prove two theorems that enable us to tell whether lines are parallel or perpendicular merely by looking at their slopes.

Theorem 2. Two nonvertical lines are parallel if and only if they have the same slope.

PROOF

PART I: Show that if two nonvertical lines are parallel, then they have the same slope. Refer to the figure. Let B and E be the y intercepts of the parallel lines L_1 and L_2. Choose A and D on L_1 and L_2, respectively, both on the same side of the y axis. Now choose C and F on the y axis with the same ordinates as A and D, respectively. Thus $AC \| DF$ (why?).

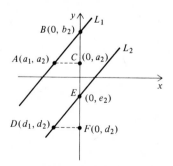

From plane geometry, we know that if two parallel li..es are cut by a transversal, then the corresponding angles are equal. Thus $\angle ABC = \angle DEF$, and $\angle ACB = \angle DFE$, and we can conclude that $\triangle ACB$ is similar to $\triangle DFE$. Corresponding sides of similar triangles are proportional, thus $\overline{CB}/\overline{AC} = \overline{FE}/\overline{DF}$, but $m_1 = \overline{CB}/\overline{AC}$ and $m_2 = \overline{FE}/\overline{DF}$, therefore, $m_1 = m_2$.

Part II, the converse of Part I, is similarly proved. Also, using essentially the same device, we can prove the next theorem on perpendicular lines.

Theorem 3. Two nonvertical lines with slopes m_1 and m_2 are perpendicular to each other if and only if $m_1 = -(1/m_2)$.

Example 9. Given the line $L: 3x - 2y = 5$ and the point $P(-3, 5)$, find an equation of a line through P which is (A) parallel to L, and (B) perpendicular to L.

SOLUTION

First find the slope of L by writing $3x - 2y = 5$ in the equivalent form $y = \frac{3}{2}x - \frac{5}{2}$. Thus the slope of L is $\frac{3}{2}$. The slope of a line parallel to L is the same, $\frac{3}{2}$, and that of a line perpendicular to L, $-\frac{2}{3}$. Now we can find equations for the indicated lines by using the point-slope formula.

(A) $y - 5 = \frac{3}{2}(x + 3)$
$\quad\quad y = \frac{3}{2}x + \frac{19}{2}$

(B) $y - 5 = -\frac{2}{3}(x + 3)$
$\quad\quad y = -\frac{2}{3}x + 3$

Problem 9. Given the line $L: 4x + 2y = 3$ and the point $P(2, -3)$, find an equation of a line through P which is (A) parallel to L, and (B) perpendicular to L.

ANSWER

(A) $y = -2x + 1$; (B) $y = (x/2) - 4$.

EXERCISE 26

A *Find the distance between each pair of points.*

1. $(-3, -2)$ and $(1, 1)$
2. $(2, 3)$ and $(5, 7)$
3. $(4, -2)$ and $(-1, 3)$
4. $(-2, 5)$ and $(-3, -4)$

Graph each of the following equations.

5. $3x + 4y = 12$
6. $2x + 3y = 6$
7. $2y - 3x = 15$
8. $2x - 3y = 15$
9. $y = 2x + 4$
10. $y = 4x - 3$
11. $y = 6 - 2x$
12. $y = 9 - 3x$
13. $y = -3$
14. $x = -4$
15. $x = 0$
16. $y = 0$
17. $A = 100 + 10t, 0 \le t \le 10$
18. $v = 10 + 32t, 0 \le t \le 5$

Find the slope and y intercept, and graph each equation.

19. $y = -\frac{1}{3}x + 2$

20. $y = \frac{1}{4}x - 1$

21. $3x + 4y = 12$

22. $2x + 3y = 6$

Write the equation of the line with slope and y intercept as indicated.

23. slope $= -1$
    y intercept $= -1$

24. slope $= \frac{1}{2}$
    y intercept $= -3$

25. slope $= \frac{2}{3}$
    y intercept $= \frac{3}{2}$

26. slope $= -\frac{3}{2}$
    y intercept $= 2$

27. (A) Graph $y = -2x + b$ for $b = -5$, $b = 0$, $b = 5$, all on the same co-ordinate system.

    (B) Graph $y = mx$ for $m = 6$, $m = 1$, $m = 0$, $m = -1$, $m = -6$, all on the same coordinate system.

28. (A) Graph $y = -\frac{1}{2}x + b$ for $b = -6$, $b = 0$, and $b = 6$, all on the same coordinate system.

    (B) Graph $y = mx - 2$ for $m = 2$, $m = \frac{1}{2}$, $m = 0$, $m = -\frac{1}{2}$, and $m = -2$, all on the same coordinate system.

B 29. Use the distance formula to determine if the triangle with vertices $(-4, 5)$, $(5, 1)$, and $(0, -2)$ is a right triangle. (*Note:* A triangle is a right triangle if and only if the square of its longest side is equal to the sum of the squares of its shorter sides.)

30. Repeat Prob. 29 with the vertices $(-5, 2)$, $(5, 3)$, and $(2, -2)$.

31. Use Definition 1 to determine if the three points $(-6, -2)$, $(-1, 1)$, and $(4, 4)$ lie on the same line.

32. Repeat Prob. 31 using the points $(-2, 2)$, $(3, -1)$, and $(6, -3)$.

33. Graph each equation that is linear (that is, a first-degree polynomial equation in two variables).

    (A) $y = x^2$

    (B) $y = 1/x$

    (C) $y = \frac{1}{3}x - 7$

    (D) $2x^2 - 3y = 6$

34. Graph each equation that is linear:

    (A) $xy = 9$

    (B) $2x = \frac{1}{3}y$

    (C) $x - (9/y) = 0$

    (D) $x^2 + y^2 = 25$

35. Graph $y = |x|$. (*Hint:* Graph $y = x$ for $x \geq 0$ and $y = -x$ for $x < 0$.)

36. Graph $y = |2x|$ and $y = |\frac{1}{2}x|$ on the same coordinate system.

Write the equation of the line that passes through the given point with the indicated slope.

37. $m = 1$, $(5, 5)$

38. $m = 2$, $(2, 0)$

39. $m = -\frac{1}{3}$, $(3, -3)$

40. $m = -\frac{2}{5}$, $(-5, 4)$

Find the slope of the line that passes through the given points.

41. $(2, 1)$ and $(10, 5)$

42. $(1, 2)$ and $(3, 4)$

43. $(-6, 4)$ and $(3, 7)$

44. $(-5, -2)$ and $(5, -4)$

Write the equations of the lines through the given pairs of points.

45. $(2, 1)$ and $(10, 5)$

46. $(1, 2)$ and $(3, 4)$

47. $(2, 5)$ and $(2, -1)$

48. $(-4, 2)$ and $(-4, -9)$

49. Given the line $L: 2y - 3x = 4$ and the point $P(-1, -2)$, find an equation of a line that passes through P which is (A) parallel to L, and (B) perpendicular to L.

50. Repeat Prob. 49 for $L: 8x + 3y = -6$ and $P(-6, 5)$.

51. Show that $L_1: 3x - 2y = 8$ and $L_2: -6x + 4y = -1$ are parallel, using the concept of slope.

52. Repeat Prob. 51 with $L: 3y = 9x + 7$ and $L_2: 6x = 2y - 4$.

53. Use the concept of slope to determine if the triangle with vertices $(-5, 2)$, $(5, 3)$, and $(2, -2)$ is a right triangle.

54. Repeat Prob. 53 with vertices $(-4, 5)$, $(5, 1)$, and $(0, -2)$.

55. The management of a company manufacturing ballpoint pens estimates costs for running the company to be $200 per day at zero output, and $700 per day at an output of 1,000 pens. (A) Assuming total cost per day c is linearly related to total output per day x, write an equation relating these two quantities. (B) Graph the equation for $0 \le x \le 2{,}000$.

56. A sporting goods store sells a pair of ski boots costing $20 for $33, and a pair of skis costing $60 for $93. (A) If the markup policy of the store for items costing over $10 is assumed to be linear and is reflected in the pricing of these two items, write an equation that relates retail price R to cost c. (B) Graph this equation for $10 \le C \le 300$. (C) Use the equation to find the cost of a surfboard retailing for $240.

C 57. Find x such that $(x, 8)$ is 13 units from $(2, -4)$.

58. Find y such that $(-2, y)$ is five units from $(-6, 6)$.

59. Find the equation of the perpendicular bisector of the line joining the two points $(-6, -2)$ and $(4, 4)$ by finding the equation of the set of all points equidistant from the two points.

60. Find the equation of the set of points five units from $(-2, 3)$.

61. Prove that if L_1 and L_2 are two nonvertical perpendicular lines, then $m_1 = -1/m_2$.

4.3 CONIC SECTIONS

In the last section we discussed the equation of a straight line

$$Ax + By = C$$

This is a first-degree equation in two variables. If we increase the degree of the equation by 1, what kind of graphs will we have? That is, what kind of graphs will the relation defined by

$$Ax^2 + Bxy + Cy^2 + Dx + Ey + F = 0 \qquad (1)$$

yield for different sets of values of the coefficients (not all A, B, and C zero at the same time)? The graphs of Eq. (1) for various choices of the coefficients are plane curves obtainable by intersecting a general cone with a plane—thus the name conic section (see Fig. 5). The principal conic sections are circles, parabolas, ellipses, and hyperbolas. A basic tool in studying Eq. (1) is the distance-between-two-points formula discussed in the last section.

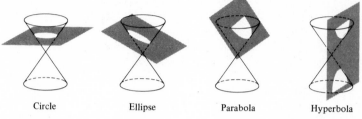

| Circle | Ellipse | Parabola | Hyperbola |

FIGURE 5

In this section we will consider only a few interesting (and useful) special cases of Eq. (1); the subject is treated more thoroughly in courses in analytic geometry.

Circle

How do we find an equation of a circle with radius r whose center is at the origin? We start with the definition of a circle, and then use the distance formula.

Definition 2. A *circle* is a set of points equidistant from a fixed point. The fixed distance is called the *radius*, and the fixed point is called the *center*.

The variable point $P(x, y)$ is a point on a circle with center at the origin (see Fig. 6), if and only if its distance to the origin is r. Stated in terms of an equation,

$$d = \sqrt{(x - 0)^2 + (y - 0)^2} = r$$

or

$$x^2 + y^2 = r^2 \qquad \text{(circle)}$$ (2)

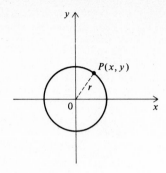

FIGURE 6

We conclude that Eq. (2) is an equation of a circle with center at the origin with radius r.

Example 10. (A) Graph $x^2 + y^2 = 16$.

(B) Find the equation of a circle with radius 3 and center at the origin.

SOLUTION

(A) Since $x^2 + y^2 = 16$ is an equation of a circle with radius 4 and center at the origin, we simply sketch the circle as described with a compass without point-by-point plotting.

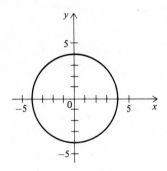

(B) We use Eq. (2) as a standard form, and write $x^2 + y^2 = 9$.

Problem 10. (A) Graph $x^2 + y^2 = 10$.

(B) Find the equation of a circle with radius $\sqrt{5}$ and center at the origin.

ANSWER

(A)

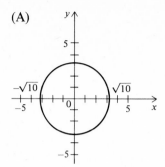

(B) $x^2 + y^2 = 5$.

Parabola

As above, we start with a definition of the curve in which we are interested.

Definition 3. A *parabola* is the set of all points equidistant from a fixed point and a fixed line. The fixed point is called the *focus*, and the fixed line the *directrix*.

We will begin by finding an equation of a parabola with focus $(a, 0)$, $a > 0$, and directrix $x = -a$ (see Fig. 7)

$$d_1 = d_2$$
$$|x + a| = \sqrt{(x - a)^2 + (y - 0)^2}$$
$$(x + a)^2 = (x - a)^2 + y^2$$
$$x^2 + 2ax + a^2 = x^2 - 2ax + a^2 + y^2$$
$$4ax = y^2$$

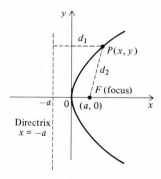

FIGURE 7

Thus,

$$y^2 = 4ax \qquad \text{(parabola)} \qquad (3)$$

We conclude that Eq. (3) is an equation of a parabola with focus $(a, 0)$ and directrix $x = -a$. Similarly, equations of parabolas opening in other directions are as indicated in Fig. 8.

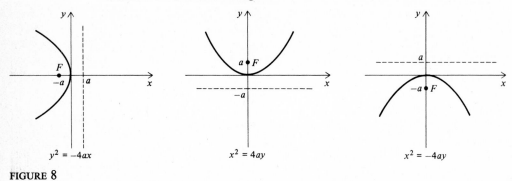

$$y^2 = -4ax \qquad\qquad x^2 = 4ay \qquad\qquad x^2 = -4ay$$

FIGURE 8

Example 11. Graph $x^2 = -16y$ and locate the focus and directrix.

SOLUTION

This is a parabola passing through the origin and opening downward. Plot at least three points and sketch in the curve. Since

$$-4a = -16$$
$$a = 4$$

the focus is at $(0, -4)$, and the directrix is $y = 4$.

Problem 11.   Graph $y^2 = -8x$, and locate the focus and directrix.

ANSWER

Focus $(-2, 0)$ and directrix $x = 2$.

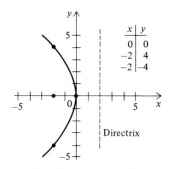

x	y
0	0
-2	4
-2	-4

Directrix

Parabolas are encountered frequently in the physical world. Suspension bridges, arch bridges, reflecting telescopes, radio telescopes, radar equipment, solar furnaces, and searchlights are a few examples of many that utilize parabolic forms in their design.

Ellipse

You are no doubt aware of many uses or occurrences of elliptical forms; orbits of satellites, orbits of planets and comets, gears and cams, and domes in buildings are but a few examples. Formally, we define an ellipse as follows.

Definition 4.   An *ellipse* is the set of all points such that the sum of the distances of each to two fixed points is constant. The fixed points are called *foci*, and each separately is a *focus*.

An ellipse is easy to draw. Place two pins in a piece of cardboard at the foci and tie a piece of loose string (representing the constant sum) to the pins; then move a pencil within the string, keeping it taut.

With regard to an equation of an ellipse, we will limit ourselves to the cases in which the foci are symmetrically located on either coordinate axis. Thus, if $(-c, 0)$ and $(c, 0)$, $c > 0$, are the foci, and $2a$ is the constant sum of the distances (note from Fig. 9 that $2a > 2c$, hence $a > c$), then

$$d_1 + d_2 = 2a$$
$$\sqrt{(x + c)^2 + y^2} + \sqrt{(x - c)^2 + y^2} = 2a$$

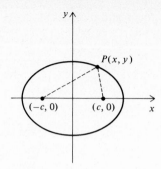

FIGURE 9

After eliminating radicals and simplifying—a good exercise for the reader—
we obtain

$$(a^2 - c^2)x^2 + a^2y^2 = a^2(a^2 - c^2)$$

or

$$\frac{x^2}{a^2} + \frac{y^2}{a^2 - c^2} = 1$$

Since $a > c$, then $a^2 - c^2 > 0$. To simplify the equation further, we choose
to let $b^2 = a^2 - c^2$. Thus,

$$\frac{x^2}{a^2} + \frac{y^2}{b^2} = 1 \qquad \text{(ellipse)} \qquad (4)$$

If $0 < b < a$, we can conclude that Eq. (4) is an equation of an ellipse with
foci $(-c, 0)$ and $(c, 0)$ and with constant sum $2a$. If $b > a > 0$, then one can
show that Eq. (4) is the equation of an ellipse with foci $(0, -c)$ and $(0, c)$
and with constant sum $2b$.

Example 12. Graph.

(A) $\dfrac{x^2}{16} + \dfrac{y^2}{9} = 1$

(B) $\dfrac{x^2}{9} + \dfrac{y^2}{16} = 1$

SOLUTION

The easiest way to draw graphs of these equations—since we know they are ellipses—is to find the x and y intercepts (the points where the graphs cross the coordinate axes), and then sketch in the curves.

(A)

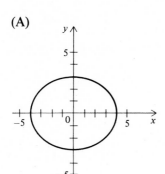

(B)

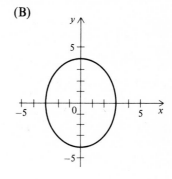

Problem 12. Graph.

(A) $\dfrac{x^2}{4} + \dfrac{y^2}{1} = 1$

(B) $\dfrac{x^2}{1} + \dfrac{y^2}{4} = 1$

ANSWER

(A)

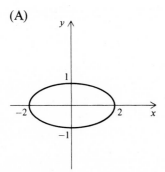

(B)

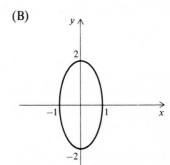

Hyperbola

Definition 5. A *hyperbola* is the set of all points such that the absolute value of the difference of the distances of each to two fixed points is constant. The two fixed points are called *foci*.

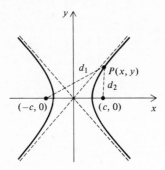

FIGURE 10

As with the ellipse, we will limit our investigation to cases in which the foci are symmetrically located on either coordinate axis. Thus if $(-c, 0)$ and $(c, 0)$ are the foci, and $2a$ is the constant difference (Fig. 10), then

$$|d_1 - d_2| = 2a$$

$$\left| \sqrt{(x + c)^2 + y^2} - \sqrt{(x - c)^2 + y^2} \right| = 2a$$

After eliminating radicals and absolute value signs (by appropriate use of squaring) and simplifying—another good exercise for the reader—we obtain

$$\frac{x^2}{a^2} + \frac{y^2}{a^2 - c^2} = 1$$

which looks exactly like the equation we obtained for the ellipse. However, from Fig. 10 we see that $2a < 2c$; hence $a^2 - c^2 < 0$. To simplify the equation further, we let $-b^2 = a^2 - c^2$. Thus

$$\frac{x^2}{a^2} - \frac{y^2}{b^2} = 1 \qquad \text{(hyperbola)} \tag{5}$$

is the equation of a hyperbola with foci $(-c, 0)$ and $(c, 0)$, and the absolute value of the difference of the distances the constant $2a$.

If we had started with the foci $(0, -c)$ and $(0, c)$ on the y axis and a constant difference $2b$ instead, we would have obtained

$$\frac{y^2}{b^2} - \frac{x^2}{a^2} = 1 \qquad \text{(hyperbola)} \tag{6}$$

As an aid to graphing Eqs. (5) and (6), we solve each equation for y in terms of x. From Eq. (5) we obtain

$$y = \pm \frac{bx}{a} \sqrt{1 - \frac{a^2}{x^2}}$$

and from Eq. (6) we obtain

$$y = \pm \frac{bx}{a} \sqrt{1 + \frac{a^2}{x^2}}$$

As x gets large, the radicals approach 1; hence the equations (for large x) behave very much as if

$$y = \pm \frac{b}{a} x \tag{7}$$

Sketches of hyperbolas can be made rather easily by locating the x or y intercepts and then using the graphs of Eq. (7) as guidelines. (These guidelines are formally referred to as *asymptotes*.) These asymptotes can be sketched directly from either Eq. (5) or (6) by first sketching in a rectangle with intercepts $\pm\sqrt{a}$ and $\pm\sqrt{b}$, as indicated in the next example.

Example 13. Graph.

(A) $\dfrac{x^2}{25} - \dfrac{y^2}{16} = 1$

(B) $\dfrac{y^2}{16} - \dfrac{x^2}{25} = 1$

SOLUTION

(A)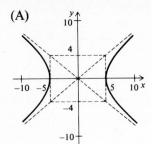

(B)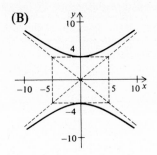

Problem 13. Graph.

(A) $\dfrac{x^2}{4} - \dfrac{y^2}{9} = 1$

(B) $\dfrac{y^2}{9} - \dfrac{x^2}{4} = 1$

ANSWER

(A)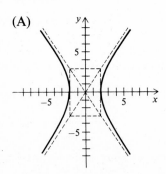

(B)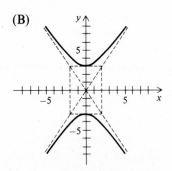

Hyperbolic forms are encountered in the study of comets, the loran system of navigation for ships and aircraft, some modern architectural structures, and optics, to name a few examples of many.

EXERCISE 27

A   *Graph each of the following circles.*

1. $x^2 + y^2 = 49$ 2. $x^2 + y^2 = 100$
3. $x^2 + y^2 = 12$ 4. $x^2 + y^2 = 8$

Graph each of the following parabolas.

5. $y^2 = 4x$ 6. $y^2 = x$ 7. $y^2 = -12x$
8. $y^2 = -16x$ 9. $x^2 = y$ 10. $x^2 = 12y$
11. $x^2 = -16y$ 12. $x^2 = -4y$

Graph each of the following ellipses.

13. $\dfrac{x^2}{25} + \dfrac{y^2}{4} = 1$

14. $\dfrac{x^2}{9} + \dfrac{y^2}{4} = 1$

15. $\dfrac{x^2}{4} + \dfrac{y^2}{25} = 1$

16. $\dfrac{x^2}{4} + \dfrac{y^2}{9} = 1$

Graph each of the following hyperbolas.

17. $\dfrac{x^2}{4} - \dfrac{y^2}{25} = 1$

18. $\dfrac{x^2}{4} - \dfrac{y^2}{9} = 1$

19. $\dfrac{y^2}{25} - \dfrac{x^2}{4} = 1$

20. $\dfrac{y^2}{9} - \dfrac{x^2}{4} = 1$

B *Graph each of the following equations.*

21. $4y^2 - 8x = 0$
22. $3x^2 + 9y = 0$
23. $4x^2 + 9y^2 = 36$
24. $4x^2 - 9y^2 = 36$
25. $y^2 = 5 - x^2$
26. $4x^2 + 25y^2 = 100$
27. $x^2 = 7 - y^2$
28. $25y^2 - 4x^2 = 100$
29. $x^2 + y^2 = -4$
30. $x^2 + y^2 = 0$

Find the equation of a circle given the following information.

31. Center (0, 0); radius $\sqrt{11}$ 32. Center (0, 0); radius $\sqrt{3}$
33. Center (0, 0); passes through (3, 4)
34. Center (0, 0); passes through (12, −5)
35. Find the coordinates of the focus and the equation of the directrix for the parabola in Prob. 5.
36. Find the coordinates of the focus and the equation of the directrix for the parabola in Prob. 7.
37. Find the coordinates of the foci for the ellipse in Prob. 15.
38. Find the coordinates of the foci for the ellipse in Prob. 14.
39. Find the coordinates of the foci for the hyperbola in Prob. 18.
40. Find the coordinates of the foci for the hyperbola in Prob. 19.
41. A parabolic concrete bridge is to span 100 ft. If the arch rises 25 ft above its ends, find the equation of the parabola, assuming that it passes through the origin and has its focus on the y axis. (*Hint:* $(50, -25)$ must satisfy $x^2 = 4ay$.)
42. A radar bowl, in the form of a rotated parabola, is 20 ft in diameter and 5 ft deep. Find the equation of the parabola, assuming it passes through the origin and has its focus on the positive y axis. (*Hint:* See Prob. 41.)

C 43. Use the distance formula to find the equation of a circle with center $(-4, 5)$ and radius $\sqrt{10}$.
44. Use the distance formula to find the equation of a circle with center (3, 5) and radius 2.
45. Use the distance formula to show that the general equation of a circle with center (h, k) and radius r is $(x - h)^2 + (y - k)^2 = r^2$.
46. Use the results of Prob. 45 to obtain the equation of a circle with center $(3, -2)$ and radius 7.

47. Use the definition of a parabola and the distance formula to find the equation of a parabola with directrix $y = 4$ and focus at (2, 2).

48. Use the definition of a parabola and the distance formula to find the equation of a parabola with directrix $x = 2$ and focus at (6, 4).

4.4 FUNCTIONS AND FUNCTION NOTATION

Function

Many situations in science and mathematics require us to restrict a relation so that each element in the domain is paired with one and only one element in the range, that is, so that no two distinct ordered pairs belonging to the relation can have the same first component. A relation so restricted is called a *function*. All functions are relations, but some relations are not functions.

Example 14. Graph each of the following relations, and indicate which are functions. State the domain and range of each function, and indicate if it is one-to-one.

(A) $f = \{(1, 3), (2, 5), (3, 5), (4, 3)\}$
(B) $g = \{(-1, 1), (0, 1), (-1, 3), (1, 2)\}$
(C) $F = \{(x, y)\,|\,y = |x|, x \in R\}$
(D) $G = \{(x, y)\,|\,|y| = x, x \geq 0\}$

SOLUTION

(A)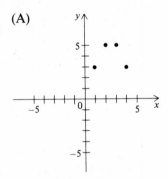

f is a function
$d_f = \{1, 2, 3, 4\}$
$r_f = \{3, 5\}$
not one-to-one

(B)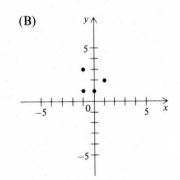

g is not a function

(C)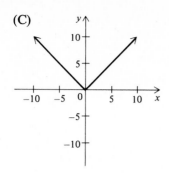

(D)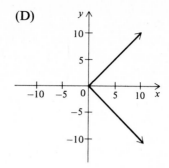

F is a function
$d_F = R$
$r_F = \{y \mid y \geq 0\}$
not one-to-one

G is not a function

Problem 14. Repeat Example 14 for

(A) $m = \{(3, 4), (2, 4), (3, 5), (4, 4)\}$
(B) $n = \{(1, 2), (2, 2), (3, 2), (4, 2)\}$
(C) $M = \{(x, y) \mid y = x^2, x \in R\}$
(D) $N = \{(x, y) \mid y^2 = x, x \geq 0\}$

ANSWER

(A)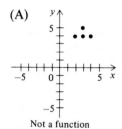

Not a function

(B)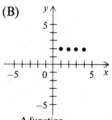

A function
$d_n = \{1, 2, 3, 4\}$
$r_n = \{2\}$
Not 1-to-1

(C)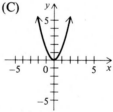

A function
$d_M = R$
$r_M = \{y \mid y \geq 0\}$
Not 1-to-1

(D)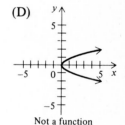

Not a function

It is very easy to determine whether a relation is a function if one has its graph. A relation is a function if each vertical line in the coordinate system contains at most one point of the graph.

Any variable used as a placeholder for elements from the domain of a function is called an *independent variable*; any variable used as a placeholder for elements from the range of a function is called a *dependent variable*. In Example 14, x is an independent variable, and y is a dependent variable.

Function Notation

We have just seen that a function involves two sets of elements, a domain and a range, and a rule that enables one to assign each element in the domain to exactly one element in the range. We use different letters to denote names for numbers; in essentially the same way, we will now use different letters to denote names for functions. For example, f and g may be used to name the two functions

$$f = \{(x, y) \mid y = 2x + 1\}$$
$$g = \{(x, y) \mid y = x^2\}$$

Unless otherwise stated, the functions we are considering are real functions; that is, functions whose domains and ranges are real numbers.*

If x represents an element in the domain of a function f, then we will often use the symbol $f(x)$ in place of y to designate the number in the range of f to which x is paired. Thus x is an independent variable, and $f(x)$ and y are dependent variables. It is important not to confuse this new symbol and think of it as the product of f and x. The symbol $f(x)$ is read "f of x," or "the value of f at x."

This new function symbol is extremely important, and you should master its correct use at once. For example, in place of the more formal representation of the functions f and g above, we can now write

$$f(x) = 2x + 1 \qquad \text{and} \qquad g(x) = x^2$$

Thus, $f(x)$ and $2x + 1$ name the same number in the range of f for each replacement of the variable x from the domain of f; $g(x)$ and x^2 name the same number in the range of g for each replacement of the variable x from the domain of g. In particular,

$$f(3) = 2(3) + 1 = 7 \qquad \text{and} \qquad g(5) = 5^2 = 25$$

That is, the function f assigns 7 to the number 3, and g assigns 25 to 5. The ordered pair $(3, 7)$ belongs to the function f, and $(5, 25)$ belongs to the function g.

Example 15. Let $F(x) = |x| - 1$, $G(x) = 1 - x^2$, and $I(x) = x$. Then

(A) $F(-2) = |-2| - 1 = 2 - 1 = 1$
(B) $G(-3) = 1 - (-3)^2 = 1 - 9 = -8$

---

* If a function is specified by an equation, and the domain and range are not specifically stated, then the domain and range of the function are assumed to include all those real-number replacements of the independent and dependent variables for which both members of the equation are defined and are equal.

(C) $3F(-1) + 2G(0) + I(5) = 3 \cdot 0 + 2 \cdot 1 + 5 = 7$

(D) $F(a) + G(a) = (|a| - 1) + (1 - a^2) = |a| - a^2$

(E) $\dfrac{F(a+h) - F(a)}{h} = \dfrac{(|a+h| - 1) - (|a| - 1)}{h} = \dfrac{|a+h| - |a|}{h}$

Problem 15.   For F, G, and I as defined in Example 15, find

(A) $F(-6)$ (B) $G(-1)$ (C) $2F(0) - G(-2) + 3I(2)$

(D) $G(b) - F(b)$ (E) $\dfrac{G(a+h) - G(a)}{h}$

ANSWER

(A) 5; (B) 0; (C) 7; (D) $2 - b^2 - |b|$; (E) $-2a - h$.

Functions as Mappings

Just as with relations—since a function is a relation—we can think of a function as a mapping. A function from a set X to a set Y is a rule that sends or maps each x in X into a unique y in Y. The element y is called the *image* of x under the mapping f and is denoted by $f(x)$. Thus

$f: x \rightarrow f(x)$

$f: X \rightarrow Y$

both denote the function f as a mapping from X to Y. For example, if f is defined by $f(x) = 2x - 1$, each x in the domain of f is mapped into $f(x)$ or $2x - 1$ in the range of f. Thus

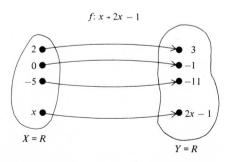

Example 16. Let $f: x \to 2x^2 - x$ and $g: m \to m^4$, then

(A) $f(-1) = 2(-1)^2 - (-1) = 3$

(B) $g(-2) = (-2)^4 = 16$

(C) $2f(a) + g(a) = 2(2a^2 - a) + a^4 = a^4 + 4a^2 - 2a$

(D) $\dfrac{f(a+h) - f(a)}{h} = \dfrac{[2(a+h)^2 - (a+h)] - (2a^2 - a)}{h} = 4a - 1 + 2h$

Problem 16. If $F: x \to x - x^2$ and $G: u \to u^3$, find

(A) $F(-2)$ (B) $G(-2)$ (C) $F(a) + 2G(a)$ (D) $\dfrac{F(a+h) - F(a)}{h}$

ANSWER

(A) -6; (B) -8; (C) $2a^3 - a^2 + a$; (D) $1 - 2a - h$.

Composite Functions

There are many ways of forming new functions from old ones. One of particular importance is the composite function. Given functions f and g, then $f \circ g$ is called their *composite*, and is defined by the formula

$$(f \circ g)(x) = f[g(x)]$$

for those values of the range of g which are in the domain of f (see Fig. 11).

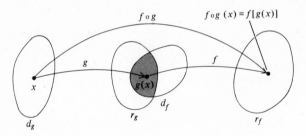

FIGURE 11

Example 17. Let $f(x) = |x|$ and $g(x) = 2x - 1$, then

(A) $(f \circ g)(x) = f[g(x)] = |g(x)| = |2x - 1|$

(B) $(g \circ f)(x) = g[f(x)] = 2f(x) - 1 = 2|x| - 1$

(C) $(f \circ g)(-1) = |2(-1) - 1| = 3$

(D) $(g \circ f)(-1) = 2|-1| - 1 = 1$

Problem 17. Let $f(x) = \sqrt{x}$ and $g(x) = 1 - 2x$. Find

(A) $(f \circ g)(x)$ (B) $(g \circ f)(x)$ (C) $(f \circ g)(-4)$ (D) $(g \circ f)(-4)$

ANSWER

(A) $\sqrt{1 - 2x}$; (B) $1 - 2\sqrt{x}$; (C) 3; (D) not real.

A Brief History of Function

In reviewing the history of function, we are once again made aware of an example of the tendency of mathematicians to extend and generalize a concept. The word *function* appears to have been first used by Leibnitz in 1694 to stand for any quantity associated with a curve. By 1718, Johann Bernoulli considered a function any expression made up of constants and a variable. Later in the same century, Euler came to regard a function as any equation made up of constants and variables. Euler made extensive use of the extremely important notation $f(x)$, although its origin is generally attributed to Clairaut (1734).

The form of the definition of function that has been used until well into this century (many texts still contain this definition) was formulated by Dirichlet (1805–1859). He stated that, if two variables x and y are so related that for each value of x there corresponds exactly one value of y, then y is said to be a (single-valued) function of x. He called x, the variable to which values are assigned at will, the independent variable, and y, the variable whose values depend on the values assigned to x, the dependent variable. He called the values assumed by x the domain of the function, and the corresponding values assumed by y the range of the function.

Now, since set concepts permeate almost all mathematics, we have the more general definitions of function presented in this section—the more static definition in terms of sets of ordered pairs of elements and the more dynamic mapping definition. The function concept is one of the most important concepts in mathematics, and as such it plays a central and natural role as a guide for the selection and development of material in many mathematics courses.

EXERCISE 28

A   *Graph each relation in Probs. 1 to 4, and indicate which are functions. State the domain and range of each function.*

1. $f = \{(-2, -1), (-1, -1), (0, 0), (1, 1), (2, 1)\}$
2. $F = \{(-3, 0), (0, 3), (3, 0)\}$
3. $g = \{(-4, 5), (-2, 0), (0, 4), (-2, 3), (-4, 0)\}$
4. $G = \{(1, 1), (1, 4), (1, -3), (0, 0), (2, 0)\}$

For $f(x) = 10x - 7$
  $g(t) = 6 - 2t$
  $F(u) = 3u^2$
  $G(v) = v - v^2$, *find:*

5. $f(1)$ 6. $f(0)$ 7. $g(2)$

8. $g(3)$ 9. $F(-1)$ 10. $F(1)$

11. $G(1)$ 12. $G(-1)$ 13. $f(-2)$

14. $g(-3)$ 15. $G(-2)$ 16. $G(-3)$

17. $f(3) + g(2)$ 18. $F(2) + G(3)$ 19. $2g(-1) - 3G(-1)$

20. $4G(-2) - g(-3)$

21. $f(2) \cdot g(-4)/G(-1)$

22. $F(-1) \cdot G(2)/g(-1)$

23. If $h(s) = s/(s - 2)$, find $h(3)$, $h(0)$, and $h(2)$.

24. If $A(w) = (w - 3)/(w + 5)$, find $A(5)$, $A(0)$, and $A(-5)$.

B   *Given the domain* $X = \{-2, -1, 0, 1, 2\}$, *find the image set* Y *under each of the following mappings.*

25. $f: x \to 3x - 2$ 26. $g: u \to 5 - 3u$

27. $h: v \to (v + 1)/(v - 4)$ 28. $H: x \to (2 + x)/(5 - x)$

29. $F: t \to 2t - t^2$ 30. $G: x \to 3 - x^2$

Graph each of the following relations, and indicate which are functions. State the domain and range of each function, and indicate if it is one-to-one.

31. $h = \{(x, y) \mid y = (x/2) - 4, \ 0 \le x \le 6\}$

32. $H = \{(x, y) \mid y = 6 - 2x, \ 0 \le x \le 6\}$

33. $m = \{(x, y) \mid x^2 + y^2 = 4\}$

34. $M = \{(x, y) \mid y^2 = 4x\}$

35. $n = \{(x, y) \mid x^2 + y^2 = 4, \ y \ge 0\}$

36. $N = \{(x, y) \mid y^2 = 4x, \ y \ge 0\}$

For $g(x) = 3 - 2x$
  $f(x) = 3x + 5$
  $Q: t \to t^2 - 2t + 1$
  $P: t \to 2t^2 + 3$, *find:*

37. $g[f(-1)]$ 38. $f[g(-1)]$

39. $(g \circ f)(x)$ and $(g \circ f)(-1)$ 40. $(f \circ g)(x)$ and $(f \circ g)(-1)$

41. $(Q \circ P)(t)$ and $(Q \circ P)(2)$ 42. $(P \circ Q)(t)$ and $(P \circ Q)(2)$

43. $\dfrac{g(1 + h) - g(1)}{h}$ 44. $\dfrac{f(2 + h) - f(2)}{h}$

45. $\dfrac{Q(1 + h) - Q(1)}{h}$ 46. $\dfrac{P(2 + h) - P(2)}{h}$

47. Let g be a function that describes the relationship between the distance in feet that an object falls in a vacuum and the time t in seconds that it falls $(d = 16t^2)$. (A) Write a formula for $g(t)$. (B) Find $g(0)$, $g(1)$, $g(2)$, and $g(3)$. (C) Find $[g(2 + h) - g(2)]/h$, and interpret the result physically.

48. Let f be a function that describes the relationship between the distance a car travels at 30 mph and time t. (A) Write a formula for $f(t)$. (B) Find $f(1)$, $f(10)$, and $[f(2 + h) - f(2)]/h$.

Each of the relationships in Probs. 49 and 50 can be described by a function. Write an equation that specifies the function.

49. The cost C of manufacturing x pairs of skis if fixed costs are \$300 per day and the variable costs are \$50 per pair of skis. (The cost per day depends on the number of pairs of skis manufactured per day.)
50. The cost per day C for renting a car at \$5 per day plus 5 cents a mile for x miles. (The rental cost per day depends on the mileage per day.)

C *Given functions f and g, we define the new functions $(f + g)$, $(f - g)$, (fg), and (f/g) as follows:*

$$(f + g)(x) = f(x) + g(x)$$
$$(f - g)(x) = f(x) - g(x)$$
$$(fg)(x) = f(x) \cdot g(x)$$
$$(f/g)(x) = f(x)/g(x) \qquad g(x) \neq 0$$

where the domain of the new function is $d_f \cap d_g$, division by zero excluded. If $f(x) = x^2$ and $g(x) = 2x - 1$, find each of the following.

51. $(f + g)(x)$ and $(f + g)(-1)$
52. $(f - g)(x)$ and $(f - g)(2)$
53. $(fg)(x)$ and $(fg)(-2)$
54. $(f/g)(x)$ and $(f/g)(-1)$
55. For $f: x \to \sqrt{x}$ and $g: x \to x + 2$, find the domain and range of $f \circ g$.
56. Repeat the preceding problem for $g \circ f$.
57. For $f(x) = 5x$: (A) Does $f(at) = af(t)$? (B) Does $f(a + b) = f(a) + f(b)$? (C) Does $f(ab) = f(a) \cdot f(b)$?
58. For $g(x) = x^2$: (A) Does $g(at) = ag(t)$? (B) Does $g(a + b) = g(a) + g(b)$? (C) Does $g(ab) = g(a) \cdot g(b)$?
59. From $f(x) = ax^2 + bx + c$, form $F(h) = [f(k + h) - f(k)]/h$. Simplify the right-hand member, and determine what $F(h)$ tends to as h tends to 0.
60. Repeat the preceding problem for $f(x) = x$.

Let $I(x) = x$ *(identity function)*
    $A(x) = |x|$ *(absolute-value function)*
    $G(x) = [x] = $ *largest integer* $\leq x, x \in R$ *(greatest integer function)*

61. Graph I, A, and G.
62. Graph $A \circ G$ and $G \circ A$.

4.5 INVERSE RELATIONS AND FUNCTIONS

In this section we are going to discuss another important method of obtaining new relations and functions from old relations and functions. We will use this method in Chap. 6 to obtain logarithmic functions from exponential functions, and again in Chap. 7 to obtain inverse trigonometric functions.

Given a relation R, if we interchange the order of the components in each ordered pair belonging to R, we obtain a new relation R^{-1}, called the *inverse of R*. Thus,

$$R^{-1} = \{(b, a) | (a, b) \in R\}$$

For example, if

$$R = \{(3, 5), (5, -1), (7, 0)\}$$

then

$$R^{-1} = \{(5, 3), (-1, 5), (0, 7)\}$$

It follows from the definition (and is evident from the example) that the domain of R is the *range of* R^{-1} and the range of R is the *domain of* R^{-1}.

If a relation R is specified by an equation, how do we obtain the inverse of R? For example, if

$$R = \{(x, y) | y = x^2\}$$

then how do we obtain R^{-1}? The procedure is easy. We simply interchange the variables in the equation $y = x^2$, so that $x = y^2$. Any ordered pair of numbers that satisfies the first equation will, after reversing the components, satisfy the second equation. For example, $(2, 4)$ satisfies the first equation, and $(4, 2)$ satisfies the second equation. By interchanging the variables in the equation specifying R, we change the order of the components of the ordered pairs of numbers belonging to R. Thus,

$$R^{-1} = \{(x, y) | x = y^2\}$$

The graphs of R and R^{-1} are given in Fig. 12. Note the relationship of the graphs to the line $y = x$. It appears that if we fold the paper along this line, R and R^{-1} will match; that is, if we draw R with ink and fold the paper along $y = x$ before the ink dries, it appears that we will obtain R^{-1}. This turns out to be the case. It can be shown that the graphs of a relation R and its inverse R^{-1} are symmetric with respect to the line $y = x$. To show this, we would have to show that the line $y = x$ is the perpendicular bisector of the line joining (a, b) and (b, a). This is left as an exercise.

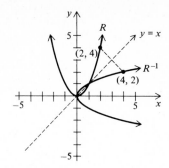

FIGURE 12

Knowing that the graphs of R and R^{-1} are symmetric relative to the line $y = x$ makes it easy to graph R^{-1} if R is known, and vice versa.

Example 18. If $f(x) = (x - 4)/2$, find

(A) $f^{-1}(x)$
(B) $(f \circ f^{-1})(5)$ and $(f \circ f^{-1})(x)$
(C) Graph f, f^{-1}, and $y = x$ on the same coordinate system, and indicate whether f or f^{-1} are functions.

SOLUTION

(A) First let $y = (x - 4)/2$ specify the relation f, and interchange the variables x and y to obtain

$$x = \frac{y - 4}{2}$$

which specifies f^{-1}. Solving the last equation for y in terms of x, we obtain

$$y = 2x + 4$$

or

$$f^{-1}(x) = 2x + 4$$

(B) $(f \circ f^{-1})(5) = f[f^{-1}(5)] = f(2 \cdot 5 + 4) = f(14) = \dfrac{14 - 4}{2} = 5$

$(f \circ f^{-1})(x) = f[f^{-1}(x)] = \dfrac{f^{-1}(x) - 4}{2} = \dfrac{(2x + 4) - 4}{2} = x$

(C)

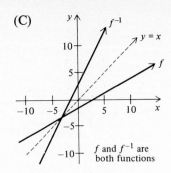

f and f^{-1} are both functions

Problem 18. If $g(x) = 2x - 3$, find

(A) $g^{-1}(x)$
(B) $(g \circ g^{-1})(2)$ and $(g \circ g^{-1})(x)$
(C) Graph g, g^{-1}, and $y = x$ on the same coordinate system, and indicate whether g or g^{-1} are functions.

ANSWER

(A) $g^{-1}(x) = (x + 3)/2$; (B) 2, x; (C)

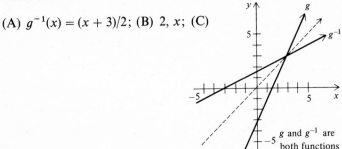

g and g^{-1} are both functions

Is the inverse of a function always a function? It should be clear from Fig. 12 that the inverse of a function may not be a function. We conclude this brief discussion of inverse relations with two important theorems. The proof of the first will be left as an exercise.

Theorem 4. If the function f is a one-to-one mapping, then f^{-1} is a function.

Theorem 5. If the function f is a one-to-one mapping, and $(m, n) \in f$, then

$$(f \circ f^{-1})(n) = n \qquad \text{and} \qquad (f^{-1} \circ f)(m) = m$$

PROOF

$(m, n) \in f, f$ a function $\Rightarrow f(m) = n \qquad n$ unique
$(m, n) \in f \Leftrightarrow (n, m) \in f^{-1}$
$(n, m) \in f^{-1}, f^{-1}$ a function $\Rightarrow f^{-1}(n) = m \qquad m$ unique

Thus

$$(f \circ f^{-1})(n) = f[f^{-1}(n)] = f(m) = n$$

and

$$(f^{-1} \circ f)(m) = f^{-1}[f(m)] = f^{-1}(n) = m$$

For special cases of Theorem 5, see part (B) of Example 18 and Prob. 18 above.

EXERCISE 29

A *Graph each relation, its inverse, and $y = x$, on the same coordinate system. Identify all functions in addition to $y = x$.*

1. $H = \{(-1, 3), (0, 2), (1, 3)\}$
2. $G = \{(-2, \frac{1}{4}), (0, 1), (1, 2), (2, 4)\}$
3. $M = \{(-3, 5), (1, 5), (5, 5), (9, 5)\}$
4. $f = \{(-5, 0), (0, 0), (0, 5)\}$
5. $g = \{(x, y) | y = \frac{1}{2}x - 2\}$
6. $F = \{(x, y) | y = x + 3\}$
7. $M = \{(x, y) | 3x + 4y = 12\}$
8. $L = \{(x, y) | 2x + y = 6\}$

Find the domain and range of each of the following relations.

9. H^{-1} in Prob. 1
10. G^{-1} in Prob. 2
11. M^{-1} in Prob. 3
12. f^{-1} in Prob. 4
13. Find $g(x)$ and $g^{-1}(x)$ for g in Prob. 5.
14. Find $F(x)$ and $F^{-1}(x)$ for F in Prob. 6.
15. Find $M(x)$ and $M^{-1}(x)$ for M in Prob. 7.
16. Find $L(x)$ and $L^{-1}(x)$ for L in Prob. 8.

B *Graph each relation, its inverse, and $y = x$, on the same coordinate axis. Identify all functions in addition to $y = x$.*

17. $P = \{(x, y) | x^2 = 4y, x \geq 0\}$
18. $F = \{(x, y) | y^2 = 8x, y \geq 0\}$
19. $E = \{(x, y) | y = 2^x, -3 \leq x \leq 3, x \in I\}$
20. $F = \{(x, y) | y = 10^x, -1 \leq x \leq 1, x \in I\}$
21. Find the domain and range of E^{-1} in Prob. 19.
22. Find the domain and range of F^{-1} in Prob. 20.
23. Find $P(x)$ and $P^{-1}(x)$ for P in Prob. 17.
24. Find $F(x)$ and $F^{-1}(x)$ for F in Prob. 18.
25. For $f(x) = 3x - 5$, find $(f \circ f^{-1})(3)$ and $(f \circ f^{-1})(x)$.
26. Find $(f^{-1} \circ f)(3)$ and $(f^{-1} \circ f)(x)$ for f in Prob. 25.
27. For $g(x) = x^2$, $x \geq 0$, find $(g \circ g^{-1})(2)$ and $(g \circ g^{-1})(x)$.
28. Find $(g^{-1} \circ g)(2)$ and $(g^{-1} \circ g)(x)$ for g in Prob. 27.

C 29. Prove Theorem 4.
30. Use Theorem 4 to determine which of the following functions have inverses that are functions.
   (A) $y = 2x + 3$
   (B) $y = x^2$, $x \geq 0$
   (C) $y = x^2$
   (D) $y = x^3$

31. Given two functions F and G with common domain X, then $F = G$ if and only if $F(x) = G(x)$ for all x in X. Using this definition, show that $f \circ f^{-1} = I$, where I is the identity function having the same domain as $f \circ f^{-1}$. This suggests why the notation f^{-1} is used for the inverse.

4.6 LINEAR AND QUADRATIC FUNCTIONS

We have studied linear and quadratic equations in some detail in this course. These equations (with certain restrictions) define linear and quadratic functions. In this section we will review some of the important properties of these equations within the framework of the function concept.

Linear Functions

Any function defined by an equation of the form

$$f(x) = ax + b$$

where a and b are constants and x is a variable, is called a *linear function*. The graph, of course, is a nonvertical straight line with slope a and y intercept b.

Example 19. Graph the linear function defined by $f(x) = (x/3) + 1$, and indicate its slope and y intercept.

SOLUTION

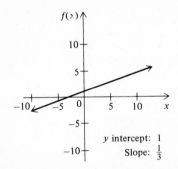

y intercept: 1

Slope: $\frac{1}{3}$

Problem 19. Graph the linear function defined by $f(x) = -(x/2) + 3$, and indicate its slope and y intercept.

ANSWER

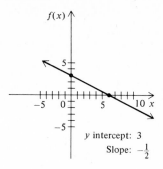

y intercept: 3

Slope: $-\frac{1}{2}$

Quadratic Functions

Any function defined by an equation of the form

$$f(x) = ax^2 + bx + c \qquad a \neq 0 \tag{8}$$

where a, b, and c are constants and x is a variable, is called a *quadratic function*. In earlier sections you graphed some of these functions and found that they are not linear. In fact, you found the graphs of $f(x) = ax^2$ to be parabolas—opening upward if a is positive and downward if a is negative. In more advanced courses, it is shown that the graph of Eq. (8) is a parabola which has its axis (its line of symmetry) parallel to the y axis, and which opens upward if $a > 0$ and downward if $a < 0$.

To graph a quadratic function, plot enough points so that when they are joined by a smooth curve the resulting figure will look like a parabola (or part of a parabola if the domain of the function is restricted).

Example 20. Graph $f(x) = x^2 - 2x - 3$, $x \geq 0$.

SOLUTION

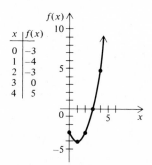

x	$f(x)$
0	−3
1	−4
2	−3
3	0
4	5

Problem 20.   Graph $g(t) = 12t - 2t^2$, $0 \leq t \leq 6$.

ANSWER

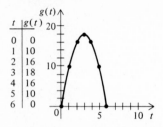

t	$g(t)$
0	0
1	10
2	16
3	18
4	16
5	10
6	0

Quadratic Functions and Quadratic Equations

In Chap. 3 we discussed the quadratic equation $ax^2 + bx + c = 0$ in detail. We found, among other things, that this equation has two real, one real, or no real roots, depending on whether $b^2 - 4ac$ is positive, zero, or negative. Now that we have discussed quadratic functions and their graphs, we have another way of looking at real solutions of quadratic equations. This method will be useful to us in Chap. 5, when we discuss higher-degree equations.

For a given function f, if r is a number such that $f(r) = 0$, then r is called a *zero of f*. Thus if r is a zero of a quadratic function $f(x) = ax^2 + bx + c$, then r is a solution of the corresponding quadratic equation $ax^2 + bx + c = 0$, and vice versa.

To solve a quadratic equation for real solutions by graphing, one forms the related quadratic function, graphs the function, and estimates the x intercepts if they exist.

Example 21.   Solve $x^2 - 4x + 3 = 0$, $x^2 - 6x + 9 = 0$, and $x^2 - 4x + 5 = 0$ by graphing.

SOLUTION

Graph the related functions $f(x) = x^2 - 4x + 3$, $f(x) = x^2 - 6x + 9$, and $f(x) = x^2 - 4x + 5$, and estimate the x intercepts.

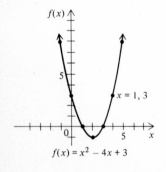

$f(x) = x^2 - 4x + 3$

$x = 1, 3$

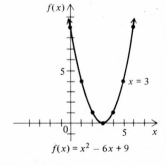

$f(x) = x^2 - 6x + 9$

$x = 3$

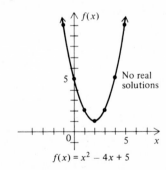

$f(x) = x^2 - 4x + 5$

No real solutions

Problem 21. Solve $x^2 + x - 2 = 0$, $x^2 + 4x + 4 = 0$, and $x^2 + 4 = 0$ by graphing.

ANSWER

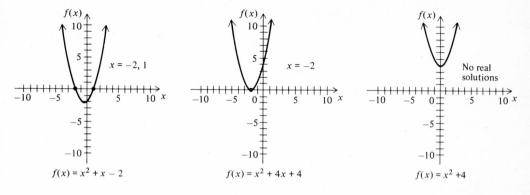

$f(x) = x^2 + x - 2$ $f(x) = x^2 + 4x + 4$ $f(x) = x^2 + 4$

$x = -2, 1$ $x = -2$ No real solutions

EXERCISE 30

A Graph each of the following functions. Indicate whether they are linear, quadratic, or neither.

1. $f(u) = 2u - 4$
2. $g(u) = 4 - 2u$
3. $g(t) = t^2$
4. $g(x) = -x^2$
5. $f(t) = t$
6. $f(x) = -x$
7. $P(x) = x^3, \ -3 \le x \le 3$
8. $Q(x) = -x^3, \ -3 \le x \le 3$

Find all real solutions of the quadratic equations in the following problems by graphing associated quadratic functions.

9. $x^2 - 4 = 0$
10. $x^2 - 16 = 0$
11. $x^2 + 1 = 0$
12. $x^2 + 9 = 0$

B Graph each of the following functions. Indicate whether they are linear, quadratic, or neither.

13. $f(x) = -4, \ -6 \le x \le 6$
14. $g(x) = -3, \ -1 \le x \le 5$
15. $G(x) = 16x - 2x^2, \ 0 \le x \le 8$
16. $g(t) = 96t - 16t^2, \ 0 \le t \le 6$
17. $f(x) = |x|/x, \ -3 \le x \le 3$
18. $g(x) = 2 - (|x|/x), \ -3 \le x \le 3$

Find all real zeros of the quadratic functions by graphing in Probs. 19 to 22.

19. $h(t) = t^2 - 2t - 3, \ -1 \le t \le 5$
20. $f(x) = 3 + 2x - x^2, \ -1 \le x \le 5$
21. $f = \{(x, y) \mid y = 4 - x^2, \ -4 \le x \le 4\}$
22. $g = \{(x, y) \mid y = x^2 - 4, \ -4 \le x \le 4\}$

Find all real solutions of the quadratic equations in the following problems by graphing associated quadratic functions.

23. $x^2 - 10x + 25 = 0$
24. $x^2 + 8x + 16 = 0$
25. $4 + 3x - x^2 = 0$
26. $6x - x^2 = 0$
27. $x^2 + x + 1 = 0$
28. $x^2 - 2x + 4 = 0$

29. If an object is projected vertically from the ground at 96 fps, then (neglecting air resistance) its velocity $v(t)$ at time t is given by the equation $v(t) = 96 - 32t$. (A) Graph the function v for $0 \leq t \leq 6$. (B) Find the zero(s) of the function from the graph and interpret the result physically.

30. If an object is projected vertically from the ground at 96 fps, then (neglecting air resistance) its distance above the ground $d(t)$ at time t is given by the equation $d(t) = 96t - 16t^2$. (A) Graph the function d for a suitable set of values of t. (B) Determine from the graph the zero(s) of the function (interpret the result physically), the domain of the function, and the maximum height of the object.

31. A rectangular dog pen is to be made with 100 ft of fence wire. (A) If x represents the length of the pen, express its area $A(x)$ in terms of x. (B) What is the domain of the resulting function? (C) Graph the function for this domain. (D) From the graph estimate the dimensions of the rectangle that will make the area maximum.

32. Work Prob. 31 with the added assumption that an existing property fence will be used for one side of the pen. (Let x equal the width of the pen.)

C 33. Estimate the cube root of 7 to the nearest tenth of a unit by solving $x^3 - 7 = 0$ graphically.

34. Estimate the positive square root of 5 to the nearest tenth of a unit by solving $x^2 - 5 = 0$ graphically for its positive root.

35. Find all real roots of $x^3 - x^2 + 2x - 2 = 0$ graphically.

36. Find all real roots of $x^4 - 13x^2 + 36 = 0$ graphically.

4.7 DIRECT AND INVERSE VARIATION

In reading scientific material, one is likely to come across statements such as "The pressure of an enclosed gas varies directly as the absolute temperature," or, "The frequency of vibration of air in an organ pipe varies inversely as the length of the pipe," or even more complicated statements such as "The force of attraction between two bodies varies jointly as their masses and inversely as the square of the distance between the two bodies." These statements have precise mathematical meaning in that they represent particular types of functions. The purpose of this section is to investigate these special functions.

The statement "y varies directly as x" means

$$y = kx \qquad k \neq 0$$

where k is a constant called the *constant of variation*. Similarly, the statement "y varies directly as the square of x" means

$$y = kx^2 \qquad k \neq 0$$

and so on. The first equation defines a linear function, and the second a quadratic function.

Direct variation is illustrated by the familiar formulas

$$C = \pi D \quad \text{and} \quad A = \pi r^2$$

where the first asserts that the circumference of a circle varies directly as the diameter, and the second that the area of a circle varies directly as the square of the radius. In both cases, π is the constant of variation.

The statement "y varies inversely as x" means

$$y = \frac{k}{x} \qquad k \neq 0$$

where k is a constant (the constant of variation). As in the case of direct variation, we also discuss y varying inversely as the square of x, and so on.

An illustration of inverse variation is given in the distance-rate-time formula. In driving a fixed distance, time varies inversely as the rate. Thus,

$$t = \frac{d}{r}$$

where d is the constant of variation—as the rate increases, the time decreases, and vice versa.

Example 22. Translate each of the following statements into appropriate equations, and find the constants of variation if $y = 16$ when $x = 4$: (A) y varies directly as the cube of x; (B) y varies inversely as the positive square root of x.

SOLUTION

(A) $y = kx^3$; $16 = k4^3$. Thus $k = \frac{1}{4}$ and $y = \frac{1}{4}x^3$. (B) $y = k/\sqrt{x}$; $16 = k/\sqrt{4}$. Thus $k = 32$ and $y = 32/\sqrt{x}$.

Problem 22. If $y = 4$ when $x = 8$, find the equation of variation for each of the following statements: (A) y varies directly as the cube root of x; (B) y varies inversely as the square of x.

ANSWER

(A) $y = 2\sqrt[3]{x}$; (B) $y = 256/x^2$.

The statement "w varies jointly as x and y" means

$$w = kxy \qquad k \neq 0$$

---

where k is a constant (the constant of variation). Similarly, if

$$w = kxyz^2 \qquad k \neq 0$$

we would say that "w varies jointly as x, y, and the square of z," and so on. For example, the area of a rectangle varies jointly as its length and width (recall $A = lw$), and the volume of a right circular cylinder varies jointly as the square of its radius and its height (recall $V = \pi r^2 h$). What is the constant of variation in each case?

The above types of variation are often combined. For example, the statement "w varies jointly as x and y, and inversely as the square of z" means

$$w = k\frac{xy}{z^2} \qquad k \neq 0$$

Thus the statement, "The force of attraction F between two bodies varies jointly as their masses m_1 and m_2, and inversely as the square of the distance d between the two bodies," means

$$F = k\frac{m_1 m_2}{d^2} \qquad k \neq 0$$

If (assuming k is positive) either of the two masses is increased, the force of attraction increases; on the other hand, if the distance is increased, the force of attraction decreases.

Example 23.   The pressure P of enclosed gas varies directly as the absolute temperature T, and inversely as the volume V. If 500 ft^3 of gas yields a pressure of 10 lb per sq ft at a temperature of 300 K (absolute temperature), what will be the pressure of the same gas if the volume is decreased to 300 ft^3 and the temperature increased to 360 K?

SOLUTION

METHOD 1:   Write the equation of variation $P = k(T/V)$, and find k using the first set of values:

$$10 = k\tfrac{300}{500}$$

$$k = \tfrac{50}{3}$$

Hence, the equation of variation for this particular gas is $P = \frac{50}{3}(T/V)$. Now find the new pressure P, using the second set of values:

$$P = \frac{50}{3} \frac{360}{300} = 20 \text{ lb per ft}^2$$

METHOD 2 (generally faster than Method 1): Write the equation of variation $P = k(T/V)$; then convert to the equivalent form:

$$\frac{PV}{T} = k$$

If P_1, V_1, and T_1 are one set of values for the gas, and P_2, V_2, and T_2 are another set, then

$$\frac{P_1 V_1}{T_1} = k \quad \text{and} \quad \frac{P_2 V_2}{T_2} = k$$

Hence

$$\frac{P_1 V_1}{T_1} = \frac{P_2 V_2}{T_2}$$

Since all values are known except P_2, substitute and solve. Thus

$$\frac{(10)(500)}{300} = \frac{P_2(300)}{360}$$

$$P_2 = 20 \text{ lb per ft}^2$$

Problem 23. The length L of skid marks of a car's tires (when brakes are applied) varies directly as the square of the speed v of the car. If skid marks of 20 ft are produced at 30 mph, how fast would the same car be going if it produced skid marks of 80 ft? Solve two ways (see Example 23).

Answer

60 mph.

EXERCISE 31

A *Translate each problem into an equation using k as the constant of variation.*

1. F varies directly as the square of v.
2. u varies directly as v.
3. The pitch or frequency f of a guitar string of a given length varies directly as the square root of the tension T of the string.
4. Geologists have found in studies of earth erosion that the erosive force (sediment-carrying power) P of a swiftly flowing stream varies directly as the sixth power of the velocity v of the water.

5. y varies inversely as the square root of x.

6. I varies inversely as t.

7. The biologist Reaumur suggested in 1735 that the length of time t that it takes fruit to ripen during the growing season varies inversely as the sum of the average daily temperatures T during the growing season.

8. In a study on urban concentration, F. Auerbach discovered an interesting law. After arranging all the cities of a given country according to their population size, starting with the largest, he found that the population P of a city varied inversely as the number n indicating its position in the ordering.

9. R varies jointly as S, T, and V.

10. g varies jointly as x and the square of y.

11. The volume of a cone V varies jointly as its height h and the square of the radius r of its base.

12. The amount of heat put out by an electrical appliance (in calories) varies jointly as time t, resistance R in the circuit, and the square of the current I.

Solve using either of the two methods illustrated in Example 23.

13. u varies directly as the square root of v. If $u = 2$ when $v = 2$, find u when $v = 8$.

14. y varies directly as the square of x. If $y = 20$ when $x = 2$, find y when $x = 5$.

15. L varies inversely as the square root of m. If $L = 9$ when $M = 9$, find L when $M = 3$.

16. I varies inversely as the cube of t. If $I = 4$ when $t = 2$, find I when $t = 4$.

B *Translate each problem into an equation using k as the constant of variation.*

17. U varies jointly as a and b, and inversely as the cube of c.

18. w varies directly as the square of x, and inversely as the square root of y.

19. The maximum safe load L for a horizontal beam varies jointly as its width w and the square of its height h, and inversely as its length l.

20. Joseph Cavanaugh, a sociologist, found that the number of long-distance phone calls n between two cities in a given time period varied (approximately) jointly as the populations P_1 and P_2 of the two cities, and inversely as the distance d between the two cities.

Solve using either of the two methods illustrated in Example 23.

21. Q varies jointly as m and the square of n, and inversely as P. If $Q = -4$ when $m = 6$, $n = 2$, and $P = 12$, find Q when $m = 4$, $n = 3$, and $P = 6$.

22. w varies jointly as x, y, and z, and inversely as the square of t. If $w = 2$ when $x = 2$, $y = 3$, $z = 6$, and $t = 3$, find w when $x = 3$, $y = 4$, $z = 2$, and $t = 2$.

23. The weight w of an object on or above the surface of the earth varies inversely as the square of the distance d between the object and the center of the earth. If a girl weighs 100 lb on the surface of the earth, how much would she weigh (to the nearest pound) 400 mi above the earth's surface? (Assume the radius of the earth is 4,000 mi.)

24. A child was struck by a car in a crosswalk. The driver of the car had slammed on his brakes and left skid marks 160 ft long. He told the police he had been

driving at 30 mph. The police know that the length of skid marks L (when brakes are applied) varies directly as the square of the speed of the car v, and that at 30 mph (under ideal conditions) skid marks would be 40 feet long. How fast was the driver actually going before he applied his brakes?

25. Ohm's law states that the current I in a wire varies directly as the electromotive force E, and inversely as the resistance R. If $I = 22$ amperes when $E = 110$ volts and $R = 5$ ohms, find I if $E = 220$ volts and $R = 11$ ohms.

26. Anthropologists, in their study of race and human genetic groupings, often use an index called the cephalic index. The cephalic index C varies directly as the width w of the head, and inversely as the length l of the head (both when viewed from the top). If an Indian in Baja, California (Mexico), has measurements of $C = 75$, $w = 6$ in., and $l = 8$ in., what is C for an Indian in northern California with $w = 8.1$ in. and $l = 9$ in.?

C 27. If the horsepower P required to drive a speedboat through water varies directly as the cube of the speed v of the boat, what change in horsepower is required to double the speed of the boat?

28. The intensity of illumination E on a surface varies inversely as the square of its distance d from a light source. What is the effect on the total illumination on a book if the distance between the light source and the book is doubled?

29. The frequency of vibration f of a musical string varies directly as the square root of the tension T, and inversely as the length L of the string. If the tension of the string is increased by a factor of 4 and the length of the string is doubled, what is the effect on the frequency?

30. In an automobile accident the destructive force F of a car varies (approximately) jointly as the weight w of the car and the square of the speed v of the car. (This is why accidents at high speed are generally so serious.) What would be the effect on the destructive force of a car if its weight were doubled and its speed were doubled?

Additional Applications

The next exercise includes significant applications from social sciences, life sciences, police science, physics and engineering, music, photography, chemistry, business, and geometry.

EXERCISE 32

Astronomy

1. The square of the time t required for a planet to make one orbit around the sun varies directly as the cube of its mean (average) distance d from the sun. Write the equation of variation, using k as the constant of variation.

2. The centripetal force F of a body moving in a circular path at constant speed varies inversely as the radius r of the path. What happens to F if r is doubled?

3. The length of time t a satellite takes to complete a circular orbit of the earth varies directly as the radius r of the orbit, and inversely as the orbital velocity v of the satellite. If $t = 1.42$ hr when $r = 4,050$ mi and $v = 18,000$ mph (Sputnik I), find t for $r = 4,300$ mi and $v = 18,500$ mph.

Life Science

4. The number N of gene mutations resulting from x-ray exposure varies directly as the size of the x-ray dose r. What is the effect on N if r is quadrupled?
5. In biology there is an approximate rule, called the bioclimatic rule for temperate climates, which states that the difference d in time for fruit to ripen (or insects to appear) varies directly as the change in altitude h. If $d = 4$ days when $h = 500$ ft, find d when $h = 2,500$ ft.

Physics—Engineering

6. Over a fixed distance d, speed r varies inversely as time t. Police use this relationship to set up speed traps. (The graph of the resulting function is a hyperbola.) If in a given speed trap $r = 30$ mph when $t = 6$ sec, what would be the speed of a car if $t = 4$ sec?
7. The length L of skid marks of a car's tires (when the brakes are applied) varies directly as the square of the speed v of the car. How is the length of skid marks affected by doubling the speed?
8. The time t required for an elevator to lift a weight varies jointly as the weight w and the distance d through which it is lifted, and inversely as the power P of the motor. Write the equation of variation, using k as the constant of variation.
9. The total pressure P of the wind on a wall varies jointly as the area of the wall A and the square of the velocity of the wind v. If $P = 120$ lb when $A = 100$ sq ft and $v = 20$ mph, find P if $A = 200$ sq ft and $v = 30$ mph.
10. The thrust T of a given type of propeller varies jointly as the fourth power of its diameter d and the square of the number of revolutions per minute n it is turning. What happens to the thrust if the diameter is doubled and the number of revolutions per minute is cut in half?

Psychology

11. In early psychological studies on sensory perception (hearing, seeing, feeling, and so on), the question was asked, Given a certain level of stimulation S, what is the minimum amount of added stimulation ΔS that can be detected? A German physiologist E. H. Weber (1795–1878) formulated, after many experiments, the famous law that now bears his name, "The amount of

change ΔS that will be just noticed varies directly as the magnitude S of the stimulus."

(A) Write the law as an equation of variation.

(B) If a person lifting weights can just notice a difference of 1 oz at the 50-oz level, what will be the least difference he will be able to notice at the 500-oz level?

(C) Determine the just noticeable difference in illumination a person is able to perceive at 480 candlepower if he is just able to perceive a difference of 1 candlepower at the 60-candlepower level.

12. Psychologists in their study of intelligence often use an index called IQ. IQ varies directly as mental age MA, and inversely as chronological age CA (up to the age of 15). If a 12-year-old boy with a mental age of 14.4 has an IQ of 120, what will be the IQ of an 11-year-old girl with a mental age of 15.4?

Music

13. The frequency of vibration of air in an open organ pipe varies inversely as the length of the pipe. If the air column in an open 32-ft pipe vibrates 16 times per sec (low C), then how fast would the air vibrate in a 16-ft pipe?

14. The frequency of pitch f of a musical string varies directly as the square root of the tension T, and inversely as the length l and the diameter d. Write the equation of variation, using k as the constant of variation. (It is interesting to note that if pitch depended only on length, then pianos would have to have strings varying from 3 in. to 38 ft.)

Photography

15. The f-stop numbers N on a camera, known as focal ratios, vary directly as the focal length F of the lens, and inversely as the diameter d of the diaphragm opening (effective lens opening). Write the equation of variation, using k as the constant of variation.

16. In taking pictures using flashbulbs, the lens opening (f-stop number) N varies inversely as the distance d from the object being photographed. What adjustment should you make on the f-stop number if the distance between the camera and object is doubled?

Chemistry

17. Atoms and molecules that make up the air constantly fly about like microscopic missiles. The velocity v of a particular particle at a fixed temperature varies directly as the square root of its molecular weight w. If an oxygen molecule in air at room temperature has an average velocity of 0.3 mi per sec, what will be the average velocity of a hydrogen molecule, given that the hydrogen molecule is one-sixteenth as heavy as the oxygen molecule?

18. The Maxwell-Boltzmann equation says that the average velocity v of a molecule varies directly as the square root of the absolute temperature T, and inversely as the square root of its molecular weight w. Write the equation of variation, using k as the constant of variation.

Business

19. The amount of work A completed varies jointly as the number of men M used and the time t they spend. If 10 men can finish a job in 8 days, how long will it take 4 men to do the same job?

20. The simple interest I earned in a given time varies jointly as the principal p and the interest rate r. If \$100 at 4% interest earns \$8, how much will \$150 at 3% interest earn in the same time period?

Geometry

21. The volume of a sphere varies directly as the cube of its radius r. What happens to the volume if the radius is doubled?

22. The surface area S of a sphere varies directly as the square of its radius r. What happens to the area if the radius is cut in half?

EXERCISE 33 CHAPTER REVIEW EXERCISES

A
1. If $A = \{-3, -2\}$ and $B = \{4, 6, 8\}$, find the Cartesian product $A \times B$.
2. Given the relation $M = \{(2, 3), (3, 3), (4, 4), (5, 4)\}$: (A) State its domain and range. (B) Graph M. (C) Is M a function? (D) Represent M as a mapping. (E) Is M single-valued, multivalued, or one-to-one?
3. Find the slope and y intercept, and graph $2y - 3x = 12$.
4. Find the distance between $(3, 4)$ and $(-5, 1)$.
5. What is the slope of the line $x = 3$? Of the line $y = -2$?
6. Graph $x^2 + y^2 = 16$.
7. Graph $(x^2/16) + (y^2/25) = 1$.
8. Graph $(x^2/16) - (y^2/9) = 1$.
9. Graph $y = x^2$.
10. Is every relation a function? Explain.
11. If $f(x) = 6 - x$, find $f(6)$, $f(0)$, $f(-3)$, and $f(m)$.
12. If $G(z) = z - 2z^2$, find $G(2)$, $G(0)$, $G(-1)$, and $G(c)$.
13. Given the domain $X = \{-2, 0, 2\}$, find the image set Y under the mapping $f: x \rightarrow 2x^3 - 1$.
14. Graph $f = \{(u, v) \mid u = -v, -5 \leq v \leq 1\}$. Is this function linear, quadratic, or neither?
15. Graph the relation $M = \{(0, 5), (2, 7), (2, 3)\}$, its inverse M^{-1}, and $y = x$, all on the same coordinate system. Indicate whether M or M^{-1} is a function.
16. What is the domain and range of M^{-1} in Prob. 15?

17. If y varies directly as x, and inversely as z: (A) Write the equation of variation. (B) If $y = 4$ when $x = 6$ and $z = 2$, find y when $x = 4$ and $z = 4$.

B 18. Describe $N \times R$ using set-builder notation. ($N = $ set of natural numbers and $R = $ set of real numbers.)

19. Graph the relation $F = \{(x, y) \in I \times I \mid 0 < x < y,\ 0 \le y \le 3\}$, and state its domain and range. ($I = $ set of integers.)

20. Given the relation $H = \{(x, y) \mid y = 3x - 2,\ x \in \{-2, 0, 2\}\}$: (A) State its domain and range. (B) Graph H. (C) Is H a function? (D) Represent H as a mapping. (E) Is H single-valued, multivalued, or one-to-one?

21. Find the equation of the line that passes through $(3, -9)$ with slope $-\frac{2}{3}$.

22. Find the equation of a line that passes through the two points $(-2, 4)$ and $(4, -5)$.

23. Is the triangle with vertices $(-3, 0)$, $(3, 0)$, and $(0, 5)$ an equilateral (all sides equal) triangle?

24. Find the equation of a circle with center at the origin that passes through $(12, -5)$.

25. Graph $9x^2 + 16y^2 - 144 = 0$.

26. Graph $4x^2 - 25y^2 - 100 = 0$.

27. Graph $y^2 = -12x$.

28. If $f: t \to 4 - t^2$ and $g: t \to t - 3$, find (A) $f(0) - g(0)$, (B) $g(6)/f(-1)$, (C) $g(x) - f(x)$, (D) $f[g(2)]$, (E) $(f \circ g)(2)$, (F) $(f \circ g)(t)$.

29. If $g(t) = 1 - t^2$, find $g(1 + h)$ and $[g(1 + h) - g(1)]/h$.

30. The cost $C(x)$ for renting a business copying machine is \$200 per month, plus 5 cents a copy for x copies. Express this functional relationship in terms of an equation, and graph it for $0 \le x \le 3{,}000$.

31. Graph $g(t) = 8t - t^2,\ 0 \le t \le 10$. Is this function linear, quadratic, or neither?

32. Solve the quadratic equation $x^2 + 6x + 5 = 0$ graphically.

33. Graph the relation $M = \{(x, y) \mid y = |x| + 2\}$, its inverse M^{-1}, and $y = x$, all on the same coordinate system. Indicate whether M or M^{-1} is a function.

34. Let $M(x) = (x + 3)/2$. (A) Find $M^{-1}(x)$. (B) Are both M and M^{-1} functions? (C) Find $M^{-1}[M(3)]$. (D) Find $(M^{-1} \circ M)(a)$.

35. The time t required for an elevator to lift a weight varies jointly as the weight w and the distance d through which it is lifted, and inversely as the power P of the motor. Write the equation of variation, using k as the constant of variation.

36. The intensity of illumination E at a given point varies inversely as the square of the distance d that the point is from a light source. If the illumination is 50 foot-candles at a point 2 ft from a light, what will be the illumination at a point 5 ft from the same light? At what distance will the illumination be 100 foot-candles?

C 37. Is the relation "has the same birthday as" an equivalence relation? Explain.

38. Find the equation of the set of points equidistant from $(3, 3)$ and $(6, 0)$.

39. Find the equation of a circle with radius $\sqrt{2}$ and center $(3, -2)$.

40. Find an equation of a parabola with directrix $y = -8$ and focus $(2, 2)$.

41. If $f: x \to x - x^2$ and $g: x \to 5$, find (A) $(f + g)(3)$, (B) $(fg)(x)$, (C) $(f \circ g)(x)$.

42. If $g(x) = 7x$, (A) Does $g(at) = ag(t)$? (B) Does $g(a + b) = g(a) + g(b)$?

43. Graph $h(x) = 2^x$, $x \in \{-2, -1, 0, 1, 2\}$. Is this function linear, quadratic, or neither?

44. Which of the following functions have inverses that are functions?
    (A) $f: x \to x^3$ (B) $g: x \to x^2$
    (C) $h: x \to 2x - 3$ (D) $F(x) = x^2$, $x \geq 0$.

45. The total force F of a wind on a wall varies jointly as the area of the wall A and the square of the velocity of the wind. How is the total force on the wall affected if the area is cut in half and the velocity is doubled?

Chapter

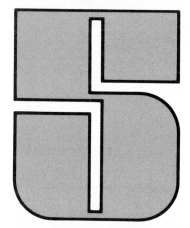

Polynomial Functions and Theory of Equations

A function defined by the equation

$$P(x) = a_n x^n + a_{n-1} x^{n-1} + \cdots + a_1 x + a_0 \qquad a_n \neq 0$$

where n is a nonnegative integer and the coefficients are constants, is called a *polynomial function of degree n*. A number r is said to be a *zero of a polynomial function P*, a zero of a polynomial $P(x)$, or a *root* of the equation $P(x) = 0$, if

$$P(r) = 0$$

We already know how to find zeros of first- and second-degree polynomials. For example, if

185 | $P(x) = ax + b \qquad a \neq 0$

then

$$r = -\frac{b}{a}$$

If

$$P(x) = ax^2 + bx + c = 0 \qquad a \neq 0$$

then

$$r = \frac{-b \pm \sqrt{b^2 - 4ac}}{2a}$$

What happens if $P(x)$ is third degree or higher? It turns out that there are direct methods (though complicated) for finding all zeros of any third- or fourth-degree polynomial; however, we can prove that there is no general method for finding all zeros of polynomials of fifth degree or higher. This does not mean that we give up looking for zeros for higher-degree polynomials. In this chapter we will see that, if we restrict a polynomial to integral coefficients, we will be able to find all rational zeros, if they exist, and we will be able to approximate any irrational zero to any decimal accuracy desired (which is different from finding the zero exactly).

Evariste Galois (1811–1832), a Frenchman, proved at the age of 20 that a polynomial equation of degree greater than four has no general solution. Galois' contribution, using the new concept of "group," was of the highest mathematical significance and originality. However, his contemporaries hardly read his papers, dismissing them as "almost unintelligible." At the age of 21, involved in political agitation, Galois met an untimely death in a duel. A short but fascinating account of Galois tragic life can be found in E. T. Bell's *Men of Mathematics* (Simon and Schuster, New York, 1937, pp. 362–377).

5.1 SYNTHETIC DIVISION

Being able to divide a polynomial $P(x)$ by a linear polynomial of the form $x - r$ quickly and accurately will be of great aid to us (as strange as it may seem now) in the search for zeros of higher-degree polynomial functions. This kind of division can be carried out efficiently by a method called *synthetic division*. The method is most easily understood through an example. Let us start by dividing $P(x) = 2x^4 + 3x^3 - x - 5$ by $x + 2$, using ordinary long division. The critical parts of the process are indicated in boldface.

$$\begin{array}{r}
\mathbf{2x^3 - 1x^2 + 2x - 5}\ \text{(quotient)} \\
(divisor)\ x + 2\overline{)2x^4 + 3x^3 + 0x^2 - 1x - 5}\ \text{(dividend)} \\
\mathbf{2x^4 + 4x^3} \\
\hline
\mathbf{-1x^3} + 0x^2 \\
\mathbf{-1x^3 - 2x^2} \\
\hline
\mathbf{2x^2} - 1x \\
\mathbf{2x^2 + 4x} \\
\hline
\mathbf{-5x} - 5 \\
-5x - \mathbf{10} \\
\hline
\mathbf{5}\ \text{(remainder)}
\end{array}$$

The numerals printed in boldface, which represent the essential part of the division process, are arranged more conveniently as:

Dividend coefficients

$$\begin{array}{rrrrr}
2 & 3 & 0 & -1 & -5 \\
& 4 & -2 & 4 & -10 \\
\hline
2\ |\ 2 & -1 & 2 & -5 & 5
\end{array}$$

Quotient coefficients   Remainder

Mechanically, we see that the second and third rows of numerals are generated as follows. The first coefficient 2 of the dividend is brought down and multiplied by 2 from the divisor, and the product 4 is placed under the second dividend coefficient 3 and subtracted. The difference -1 is again multiplied by the 2 from the divisor, and the product is placed under the third coefficient from the dividend and subtracted. This process is repeated until the remainder is reached. The process can be made a little faster, and less prone to sign errors, by changing $+2$ from the divisor to -2 and adding instead of subtracting. Thus,

Dividend coefficients

$$\begin{array}{rrrrr}
2 & 3 & 0 & -1 & -5 \\
& -4 & 2 & -4 & 10 \\
\hline
-2\ |\ 2 & -1 & 2 & -5 & 5
\end{array}$$

Quotient coefficients   Remainder

The Key
Steps in the
Synthetic
Division
Process

1. Arrange the coefficients of $P(x)$ in order of descending powers of x (write zero as the coefficient for each missing power).
2. After writing the divisor in the form $x - r$, use r to generate the second and third rows of numbers as follows. Bring down the first coefficient of the dividend and multiply it by r; then add the product to the second coefficient of the dividend. Multiply this sum by r, and add the product to the third coefficient of the dividend. Repeat the process until a product is added to the constant term of $P(x)$.
3. The last number in the third row of numbers is the remainder; the other numbers in the third row are the coefficients of the quotient, which is of degree 1 less than $P(x)$.

Example 1. Use synthetic division to find the quotient and remainder resulting from dividing $P(x) = 4x^5 - 30x^3 - 50x - 2$ by $x + 3$. Write the answer in the form $Q(x) + R/(x - r)$, where R is a constant.

SOLUTION

$x + 3 = x - (-3)$, therefore, $r = -3$.

$$
\begin{array}{r|rrrrrr}
 & 4 & 0 & -30 & 0 & -50 & -2 \\
 & & -12 & 36 & -18 & 54 & -12 \\
\hline
-3 & 4 & -12 & 6 & -18 & 4 & -14 \\
\end{array}
$$

The quotient is $4x^4 - 12x^3 + 6x^2 - 18x + 4$ with a remainder of -14. Thus,

$$\frac{P(x)}{x + 3} = 4x^4 - 12x^3 + 6x^2 - 18x + 4 + \frac{-14}{x + 3}$$

Problem 1. Repeat Example 1 with $P(x) = 3x^4 - 11x^3 - 18x + 8$ and divisor $x - 4$.

ANSWER

$[P(x)]/(x - 4) = 3x^3 + x^2 + 4x - 2 + [0/(x - 4)] = 3x^3 + x^2 + 4x - 2.$

EXERCISE 34

A *Use synthetic division to write the quotient $P(x)/(x - r)$ in the form $Q(x) + R/(x - r)$, where R is a constant.*

1. $(x^2 + 3x - 3)/(x - 3)$
2. $(x^2 + 3x - 7)/(x - 2)$
3. $(2x^2 + 7x - 5)/(x + 4)$
4. $(4x^2 + 10x - 9)/(x + 3)$

5. $(2x^3 - 3x + 1)/(x - 2)$ 6. $(x^3 + 2x^2 - 3x - 4)/(x + 2)$
7. $(3x^4 - x - 4)/(x + 1)$ 8. $(5x^4 - 2x^2 - 3)/(x - 1)$
9. $(2x^3 + 4x^2 - 9x - 11)/(x + 3)$
10. $(x^4 - 3x^3 - 5x^2 + 6x - 3)/(x - 4)$
B 11. $(2x^4 - 13x^3 + 14x + 15)/(x - 5)$
12. $(x^5 + 10x^2 + 5x + 2)/(x + 2)$
13. $(3x^6 - 2x^4 + x^3 - 3x - 3)/(x + 1)$
14. $(x^5 - 26x^2 - 1)/(x - 3)$
15. $(x^5 + 1)/(x + 1)$
16. $(x^4 - 16)/(x - 2)$
17. $(4x^4 + 2x^3 - 6x^2 - 5x + 1)/(x + \frac{1}{2})$
18. $(2x^3 - 5x^2 + 6x + 3)/(x - \frac{1}{2})$
19. $(3x^3 - x^2 + x + 2)/(x + \frac{2}{3})$
20. $(4x^3 + 4x^2 - 7x - 6)/(x + \frac{3}{2})$
21. $(2x^3 + 3x^2 - 2x + 1)/(x - 0.2)$
22. $(x^3 - 2x^2 + 3x - 1)/(x - 0.3)$

Write the first polynomial as a product of two polynomials, given that the second polynomial is a factor of the first.

23. $(4x^3 - 15x + 2), (x + 2)$ 24. $(2x^4 - 7x^3 + 10x - 3), (x - 3)$
25. $(x^5 + 32), (x + 2)$ 26. $(x^6 - 64), (x - 2)$
C 27. $(x^5 + a^5), (x + a)$ 28. $(x^4 - a^4), (x - a)$
29. $(x^3 - 3x^2 + x - 3), (x - i)$ 30. $(x^3 - 2x^2 + x - 2), (x + i)$
31. (A) Divide $P(x) = a_2 x^2 + a_1 x + a_0$ by $x - r$, using synthetic division and the long-division process, and compare the coefficients of the quotient and the remainder.
    (B) Expand the expression representing the remainder. What do you observe?
32. Repeat Prob. 31 for $P(x) = a_3 x^3 + a_2 x^2 + a_1 x + a_0$.

5.2 REMAINDER AND FACTOR THEOREMS

If we divide $P(x) = 2x^4 - 5x^3 - 4x^2 + 13$ by $x - 3$, then we obtain

$$\frac{2x^4 - 5x^3 - 4x^2 + 13}{x - 3} = (2x^3 + x^2 - x - 3) + \frac{4}{x - 3} \qquad x \neq 3$$

If we multiply both members by $x - 3$, then

$$2x^4 - 5x^3 - 4x^2 + 13 = (x - 3)(2x^3 + x^2 - x - 3) + 4$$

This suggests the following important theorem, which we state without proof.

Theorem 1.   For each polynomial $P(x)$ and each number r, there exists a unique polynomial $Q(x)$ of degree 1 less than $P(x)$ and a number R (which may be zero) such that

$$P(x) = (x - r)Q(x) + R$$

The polynomial $Q(x)$ is the quotient, and R is the remainder.

The equation in Theorem 1 is an identity, that is, it is true for all replacements of x by real or complex numbers. In particular, if we let $x = r$, then we observe a very interesting and extremely useful relationship:

$$
\begin{aligned}
P(r) &= (r - r)Q(r) + R \\
&= 0 \cdot Q(r) + R \\
&= 0 + R \\
&= R
\end{aligned}
$$

In words, the value of a polynomial $P(x)$ at $x = r$ is the same as the remainder R one obtains by dividing $P(x)$ by $x - r$. We have proved the well-known remainder theorem.

Theorem 2.
The Remain-
der Theorem

If R is the remainder after dividing the polynomial $P(x)$ by $x - r$, then

$$P(r) = R$$

Example 2.   If $P(x) = 4x^4 + 10x^3 + 19x + 5$, find $P(-3)$ by (A) using the remainder theorem and synthetic division, and (B) evaluating $P(-3)$ directly.

Solution

(A)
$$
\begin{array}{r|rrrrr}
 & 4 & 10 & 0 & 19 & 5 \\
 & & -12 & 6 & -18 & -3 \\
\hline
-3 & 4 & -2 & 6 & 1 & 2 = R = P(-3)
\end{array}
$$

(B) $P(-3) = 4(-3)^4 + 10(-3)^3 + 19(-3) + 5$
$\qquad\quad = 2$

Problem 2.   Repeat Example 2 for $P(x) = 3x^4 - 16x^2 - 3x + 7$ and $x = -2$.

Answer

$P(-2) = -3$ for both (A) and (B), as it should.

The equation in Theorem 1 may, because of the remainder theorem, be written in the form

$$P(x) = (x - r)Q(x) + P(r)$$

where it is easy to see that $x - r$ is a factor of $P(x)$ if and only if $P(r) = 0$, that is, if and only if r is a zero of the polynomial $P(x)$ [or a root of the polynomial equation $P(x) = 0$]. This result is known as the factor theorem.

Theorem 3.
The Factor
Theorem

If r is a zero of the polynomial $P(x)$, then $x - r$ is a factor of $P(x)$; conversely, if $x - r$ is a factor of $P(x)$, then r is a zero of $P(x)$.

Thus, if we can find a zero of a polynomial, then we can find one of its factors. On the other hand, if we can find a linear factor of a polynomial, we can find a zero of the polynomial.

Example 3.

(A) Use the factor theorem to show that $x + 1$ is a factor of $P(x) = x^{25} + 1$.

(B) What are the zeros of the polynomial $P(x) = 3(x - 5)(x + 2)(x - 3)$?

SOLUTION

(A) By direct substitution we see that -1 is a zero of $P(x)$:

$$P(-1) = (-1)^{25} + 1 = 0$$

Since -1 is a zero of $P(x) = x^{25} + 1$, the linear polynomial

$$x - (-1) = x + 1$$

is, by the factor theorem, a factor of $x^{25} + 1$.

(B) $5, -2, 3$, since $x - 5$, $x + 2$, and $x - 3$ are each factors of $P(x)$.

Problem 3.

(A) Use the factor theorem to show that $x - 1$ is a factor of $P(x) = x^{54} - 1$.

(B) What are the zeros of the polynomial

$$P(x) = 2(x + 3)(x + 7)(x - 8)(x + 1)?$$

ANSWER

(A) $r = 1$ and $P(1) = 1^{54} - 1 = 0$, therefore, $x - r = x - 1$ is a factor of $P(x)$. (B) $-3, -7, 8, -1$.

EXERCISE 35

A *Use synthetic division and the remainder theorem in each of the following problems.*

1. Find $P(-2)$, given $P(x) = 3x^2 - x - 10$.
2. Find $P(-3)$, given $P(x) = 4x^2 + 10x - 8$.
3. Find $P(2)$, given $P(x) = 2x^3 - 5x^2 + 7x - 7$.

4. Find $P(5)$, given $P(x) = 2x^3 - 12x^2 - x + 30$.
5. Find $P(-4)$, given $P(x) = x^4 - 10x^2 + 25x - 2$.
6. Find $P(-7)$, given $P(x) = x^4 + 5x^3 - 13x^2 - 30$.

Find the zeros for the following polynomials.

7. $P(x) = (x - 3)(x + 5)$
8. $P(x) = (x + 2)(x - 7)$
9. $P(x) = 2(x + \frac{1}{2})(x - 8)(x + 2)$
10. $P(x) = 3(x - \frac{2}{3})(x - 5)(x + 7)$

Determine whether the second polynomial is a factor of the first polynomial without dividing or using synthetic division. (Hint: Evaluate directly and use the factor theorem.)

11. $x^{18} - 1$; $x - 1$
12. $x^{18} - 1$; $x + 1$
13. $x^9 + 2^9$; $x - 2$
14. $x^9 - 2^9$; $x + 2$
15. $3x^3 - 7x^2 - 8x + 2$; $x + 1$
16. $3x^4 - 2x^3 + 5x - 6$; $x - 1$

B *Use synthetic division and the remainder theorem in each of the following problems.*

17. Find $P(3)$, given $P(x) = x^5 - 10x^3 + 7x + 6$.
18. Find $P(-6)$, given $P(x) = x^4 + 4x^3 - 9x^2 + 19x + 16$.
19. Find $P(\frac{1}{2})$, given $P(x) = 4x^3 - 8x^2 + 5x - 4$.
20. Find $P(\frac{1}{3})$, given $P(x) = 6x^3 + 4x^2 - 5x - 4$.
21. Find $P(0.3)$ for $P(x) = x^3 - 2x + 1$.
22. Find $P(0.7)$ for $P(x) = 2x^3 + 3x^2 - 5x + 2$.

Find three solutions for each equation.

23. $(x + 4)(x + 8)(x - 1) = 0$
24. $(x - 2)(x + 5)(x - 3) = 0$
25. $7(x - \frac{1}{8})(x + \frac{3}{8})(x + 4) = 0$
26. $4(x + \frac{3}{4})(x - 5)(x - \frac{2}{3}) = 0$

Use the quadratic formula and the factor theorem to factor each polynomial.

27. $P(x) = x^2 - 3x + 1$
28. $P(x) = x^2 - 4x - 2$
29. $P(x) = x^2 - 6x + 10$
30. $P(x) = x^2 - 4x + 5$

Determine whether the second polynomial is a factor of the first polynomial, without dividing or using synthetic division.

31. $x^n - a^n$; $x - a$
32. $x^n - a^n$, n even; $x + a$
33. $2x^5 - 5x^2 - x + 4$; $x + 1$
34. $4x^7 - 2x^6 + x^2 + 2x + 5$; $x - 1$
35. $5x^8 - 2x^5 + 3x^3 + 6x + 2$; $x + 1$
36. $5x^6 - 7x^3 - 6x + 8$; $x - 1$

C *Find the lowest-degree polynomial, with the highest-degree term having a coefficient of 1, that has zeros as given. (Leave the answer in factored form.)*

37. $3, -2$
38. $1, -4$
39. $-8, -7, 1$
40. $2, -3, 4$
41. $\frac{3}{8}, -\frac{1}{4}, 9$
42. $\frac{1}{4}, 5, -\frac{2}{3}$
43. In some computer work polynomials are evaluated by using a factoring scheme. For example, to evaluate $P(x) = x^4 - 6x^3 - 19x^2 - 26x + 18$ for

$x = 2$, we first write $P(x) = \{[(x - 6)x - 19]x - 26\}x + 18$. Find $P(2)$, using this "factored" form, and by synthetic division using the remainder theorem. How do the two methods compare step for step.

44. Repeat Prob. 43 for $P(x) = 3x^4 - 10x^2 + 5x - 2$ and $x = -2$.

45. (A) Write $P(x) = a_2 x^2 + a_1 x + a_0$ in the form $P(x) = (a_2 x + a_1)x + a_0$, and find $P(r)$ using the latter.

    (B) Find $P(r)$, using synthetic division and the remainder theorem, and compare with part (A).

46. Repeat Prob. 45 for $P(x) = a_3 x^3 + a_2 x^2 + a_1 x + a_0$.

5.3 COMPLEX ZEROS OF POLYNOMIALS WITH REAL COEFFICIENTS

Recall from Chap. 1 that if $z = x + yi$ is a complex number, then the *conjugate* of z, denoted by $\bar{z}$, is defined as $\bar{z} = x - yi$. Thus, $2 - 3i$ is the conjugate of $2 + 3i$, $-5i$ is the conjugate of $5i$, and 2 is the conjugate of 2. In the last two cases recall that $5i = 0 + 5i$ and $2 = 2 + 0i$.

Conjugates of complex numbers have several useful properties, which are stated in the following theorem.

Theorem 4. If $z_1 = x_1 + y_1 i$ and $z_2 = x_2 + y_2 i$ are complex numbers, and if a is a real number, then

---

(A) $\overline{z_1 + z_2} = \bar{z}_1 + \bar{z}_2$

(B) $\overline{z_1 z_2} = \bar{z}_1 \bar{z}_2$

(C) $\bar{a} = a$

PROOF

(A) $\overline{z_1 + z_2} = \overline{(x_1 + y_1 i) + (x_2 + y_2 i)}$
$= \overline{(x_1 + x_2) + (y_1 + y_2)i}$
$= (x_1 + x_2) - (y_1 + y_2)i$
$= (x_1 - y_1 i) + (x_2 - y_2 i)$
$= \bar{z}_1 + \bar{z}_2$

(B) The proof is left as an exercise.

(C) $\bar{a} = \overline{a + 0i} = a - 0i = a$

The above theorem states in words that the conjugate of a sum of two complex numbers is the sum of their conjugates, the conjugate of a product of two complex numbers is the product of their conjugates, and the conjugate of a real number is that number.

Let us use the quadratic formula to find the zeros of the polynomial

$$P(x) = x^2 - 6x + 10$$

Thus,

$$x = \frac{6 \pm \sqrt{36 - 40}}{2}$$

$$= 3 \pm i$$

We see that $3 + i$ and $3 - i$, a conjugate pair, are zeros of $P(x)$. The fact that these zeros form a conjugate pair is not a coincidence, as is seen in Theorem 5.

Theorem 5. If $P(x) = a_n x^n + a_{n-1} x^{n-1} + \cdots + a_1 x + a_0$ is a polynomial with real coefficients, and if $P(r) = 0$, where r is a complex number, then $P(\bar{r}) = 0$ (that is, complex zeros of polynomials with real coefficients, if they exist, occur in conjugate pairs).

PROOF

If r is a complex zero of $P(x)$, then

$$P(r) = a_n r^n + a_{n-1} r^{n-1} + \cdots + a_1 r + a_0 = 0$$

Taking the conjugate of both members, we have

$$\overline{a_n r^n + a_{n-1} r^{n-1} + \cdots + a_1 r + a_0} = \bar{0}$$

Since the conjugate of the sum of two or more terms is the sum of the conjugates of the individual terms (repeated application of Theorem 4), and since the conjugate of 0 is 0, then

$$\overline{a_n r^n} + \overline{a_{n-1} r^{n-1}} + \cdots + \overline{a_1 r} + \overline{a_0} = 0$$

Also, by repeated application of Theorem 4, the conjugate of the product of two or more factors is the product of the conjugate of the individual factors. Hence,

$$\bar{a}_n \bar{r}^n + \bar{a}_{n-1} \bar{r}^{n-1} + \cdots + \bar{a}_1 \bar{r} + \bar{a}_0 = 0$$

Since the conjugate of a real number is that number, we can write [since the coefficients of $P(x)$ are real numbers]

$$a_n \bar{r}^n + a_{n-1} \bar{r}^{n-1} + \cdots + a_1 \bar{r} + a_0 = 0$$

or

$$P(\bar{r}) = 0$$

Thus $\bar{r}$ is a zero of $P(x)$.

Example 4. If $2 + i$ is a zero of $P(x) = x^3 - 7x^2 + 17x - 15$, find two other zeros of $P(x)$ and then factor $P(x)$ as a product of linear factors.

SOLUTION

Since $P(x)$ is a polynomial with real coefficients, the conjugate of $2 + i$ must also be a zero of $P(x)$. Thus two linear factors of $P(x)$ are

$$[x - (2 + i)] \quad \text{and} \quad [x - (2 - i)]$$

Dividing $P(x)$ by the product of these factors, $x^2 - 4x + 5$, we easily obtain $x - 3$, a third linear factor of $P(x)$ and a third zero 3. We can now write

$$P(x) = [x - (2 + i)][x - (2 - i)](x - 3)$$

Problem 4. If $3 - i$ is a zero of $P(x) = x^3 - 4x^2 - 2x + 20$, find two other zeros of $P(x)$ and then factor $P(x)$ as a product of linear factors.

ANSWER

$3 + i, -2; P(x) = [x - (3 - i)][x - (3 + i)](x + 2)$.

EXERCISE 36

A *In Probs. 1 to 12 perform the indicated operations, using $a = 5 - 2i$, $b = -3 + 5i$, $c = 4i$, and $d = 8$.*

1. $\bar{b} = ?$	2. $\bar{a} = ?$	3. $\bar{c} = ?$
4. $\bar{d} = ?$	5. $b + \bar{b}$	6. $a + \bar{a}$
7. $b \cdot \bar{b}$	8. $a \cdot \bar{a}$	9. $\bar{a} + \bar{b}$
10. $\overline{a + b}$	11. $\overline{a \cdot b}$	12. $\bar{a} \cdot \bar{b}$

13. Multiply $[x - (3 + i)][x - (3 - i)]$.
14. Multiply $[x - (4 - i)][x - (4 + i)]$.
15. Multiply $[x - (4 - 5i)][x - (4 + 5i)]$.
16. Multiply $[x - (2 - 3i)][x - (2 + 3i)]$.

Find one other zero of $P(x)$, given the indicated zero.

17. $P(x) = x^2 - 2x + 2$; $1 - i$ is one zero.
18. $P(x) = x^2 - 8x + 17$; $4 + i$ is one zero.
19. $P(x) = 2x^2 + 8$; $2i$ is one zero.
20. $P(x) = x^2 + 9$; $3i$ is one zero.

Write each polynomial in Probs. 21 to 24 as a product of linear factors.

21. The polynomial in Prob. 17
22. The polynomial in Prob. 18
23. The polynomial in Prob. 19
24. The polynomial in Prob. 20

B 25. If $z = x + yi$, find $z\bar{z}$.
26. If $z = x + yi$, find $z + \bar{z}$.

Find two other zeros of $P(x)$, given the indicated zeros.

27. $P(x) = x^4 - 3x^3 + 14x^2 - 4x + 13$; i and $2 - 3i$ are zeros.
28. $P(x) = x^4 - 10x^3 + 3x^2 - 50x + 34$; $1 + i$ and $4 - i$ are two zeros.
29. $P(x) = x^3 - 3x^2 + 25x - 75$; $-5i$ is one zero.
30. $P(x) = x^3 + 2x^2 + 16x + 32$; $4i$ is one zero.
31. $P(x) = x^3 - 5x^2 + 4x + 10$; $3 - i$ is one zero.
32. $P(x) = x^3 + x^2 - 4x + 6$; $x + i$ is one zero.

Write each polynomial in Probs. 33 to 36 as a product of linear factors.

33. The polynomial in Prob. 29
34. The polynomial in Prob. 30
35. The polynomial in Prob. 31
36. The polynomial in Prob. 32

c 37. Given $P(x) = x^2 + 2ix - 5$ with $2 - i$ a zero, show that $2 + i$ is not a zero of $P(x)$. Does this contradict Theorem 5? Explain.

38. If $z_1 = x_1 + y_1 i$ and $z_2 = x_2 + y_2 i$, show that $\overline{z_1 z_2} = \bar{z}_1 \bar{z}_2$.
39. Multiply $[x - (a + bi)][x - (a - bi)]$.
40. Prove Theorem 5 for the case $n = 2$.

5.4 FUNDAMENTAL THEOREM OF ALGEBRA

In our search for zeros of polynomial functions it would be useful to know at the outset how many zeros to expect for a given function. The following two theorems tell us exactly how many zeros exist for a polynomial function of a given degree. Even though the theorems do not tell us how to find the zeros, it is still very helpful to know that what we are looking for exists. These theorems were first proved in 1797 by Carl Friedrich Gauss, probably the greatest mathematician of all time, at the age of 20. The proof of the first theorem requires techniques beyond this course, so we state it without proof.

Theorem 6. Every polynomial $P(x)$ of degree $n \geq 1$, with real or complex coefficients, has at least one real or complex zero.

If $P(x) = a_n x^n + a_{n-1} x^{n-1} + \cdots + a_1 x + a_0$ is a polynomial of degree $n \geq 1$ then, according to this theorem, it has at least one zero, say r_1. According to the factor theorem, $x - r_1$ is a factor of $P(x)$. Thus,

$$P(x) = (x - r_1) Q_1(x)$$

where $Q_1(x)$ is a polynomial of degree $n - 1$. If $n - 1 = 0$, then $Q_1(x) = a_n$. If $n - 1 \geq 1$ then, by the fundamental theorem, $Q_1(x)$ has at least one zero, say r_2. And

$$Q_1(x) = (x - r_2) Q_2(x)$$

where $Q_2(x)$ is a polynomial of degree $n - 2$. Thus,

$$P(x) = (x - r_1)(x - r_2)Q_2(x)$$

If $n - 2 = 0$, then $Q_2(x) = a_n$. If $n - 2 \geq 1$, then $Q_2(x)$ has at least one zero, say r_3. And

$$Q_2(x) = (x - r_3)Q_3(x)$$

where $Q_3(x)$ is a polynomial of degree $n - 3$.

We continue in this way until $Q_k(x)$ is of degree 0, that is, until $k = n$. At this point, $Q_n(x) = a_n$ and we have

$$P(x) = (x - r_1)(x - r_2) \cdots (x - r_n)a_n$$

Thus, $r_1, r_2, \ldots, r_n$ are n zeros (not necessarily distinct) of $P(x)$. Is it possible for $P(x)$ to have more than these n zeros? Let us assume that r is a number different from the zeros above; then

$$P(r) = a_n(r - r_1)(r - r_2) \cdots (r - r_n) \neq 0$$

since r is not equal to any of the zeros. Thus r cannot be a zero of $P(x)$, and we conclude that $r_1, r_2, \ldots, r_n$ are the only zeros of $P(x)$. We have just finished sketching a proof of the following important theorem.

Theorem 7. Every polynomial $P(x)$ of degree $n \geq 1$, with real or complex coefficients, can be expressed as the product of n linear factors (hence has exactly n zeros—not necessarily distinct).

If $P(x)$ is represented as the product of linear factors and $x - r$ occurs m times, then r is called a *zero of multiplicity m*. For example, if

$$P(x) = 4(x - 5)^3(x + 1)^2(x - i)(x + i)$$

then this seventh-degree polynomial has seven zeros, not all distinct. Five is a zero of multiplicity 3 (or a triple zero); -1 is a zero of multiplicity 2 (or a double zero). Thus, this seventh-degree polynomial has exactly seven zeros if we count 5 and -1 with their respective multiplicities.

Example 5. If -2 is a double zero of $P(x) = x^4 - 7x^2 + 4x + 20$, write $P(x)$ as a product of first-degree factors.

SOLUTION

Since -2 is a double zero of $P(x)$, we can write

$$\begin{aligned} P(x) &= (x + 2)^2 Q(x) \\ &= (x^2 + 4x + 4)Q(x) \end{aligned}$$

and find $Q(x)$ by dividing $P(x)$ by $x^2 + 4x + 4$. Carrying out the division, we obtain

$$Q(x) = x^2 - 4x + 5$$

The zeros of $Q(x)$ are found, using the quadratic formula, to be $2 - i$ and $2 + i$. Thus $P(x)$ written as a product of linear factors is

$$P(x) = (x + 2)^2[x - (2 - i)][x - (2 + i)]$$

Problem 5. If 3 is a double zero of $P(x) = x^4 - 12x^3 + 55x^2 - 114x + 90$, write $P(x)$ as a product of first-degree factors.

ANSWER

$$P(x) = (x - 3)^2[x - (3 - i)][x - (3 + i)].$$

Remarks

The fundamental theorem of algebra tells us that in the field of complex numbers not only $x^2 + 1 = 0$ has a solution, but every polynomial equation with real or complex coefficients has a solution. This is the reason for saying that the field of complex numbers is algebraically closed.

This important and useful result does not come free. In extending the real numbers to a number system that provides solutions for all polynomial equations we have to give up something, namely, an ordering of the number system. The complex numbers cannot be ordered.

EXERCISE 37

A *Write down the zeros of the following polynomials, and indicate the multiplicity of each if over one. What is the degree of the polynomial?*

1. $P(x) = (x - 5)(x + 7)^2$ 2. $P(x) = (x + 8)^3(x - 6)^2$
3. $P(x) = (x - 2)^3(x + 3)^2(x - 1)$ 4. $P(x) = (x + 4)^3(x - 3)^2(x + 1)$

Find a polynomial $P(x)$ of lowest degree, with leading coefficient 1, that has the indicated set of zeros. (Leave the answer in factored form.) Indicate the degree of the polynomial.

5. -2 (multiplicity 3) and 1 (multiplicity 2)
6. 3 (multiplicity 2) and -4
7. -7 (multiplicity 3), $\frac{2}{3}$, and -5
8. $\frac{1}{4}$ (multiplicity 2), 5, and -1

B 9. $i\sqrt{3}$ (multiplicity 2), $-i\sqrt{3}$ (multiplicity 2), and 4 (multiplicity 3)
10. $(2 - 3i)$, $(2 + 3i)$, -4 (multiplicity 2)

Write P(x) as a product of linear factors.

11. $P(x) = x^3 - 4x^2 - 3x + 18$; 3 is a double zero.
12. $P(x) = x^3 + 9x^2 + 24x + 16$; -1 is a zero.
13. $P(x) = x^4 - 1$; 1 and -1 are zeros.
14. $P(x) = x^4 + 2x^2 + 1$; i is a double zero.
15. $P(x) = x^5 - 2x^4 + 5x^3 - 10x^2 - 36x + 72$; 2 is a double zero and -2 is a zero.
16. $P(x) = x^5 - 9x^4 + 30x^3 - 46x^2 + 33x - 9$; 1 is a triple zero.

In Probs. 17 to 22 write down all the zeros of the indicated polynomials. If a zero appears more than once, indicate its multiplicity.

17. The polynomial in Prob. 11   18. The polynomial in Prob. 12
19. The polynomial in Prob. 13   20. The polynomial in Prob. 14
21. The polynomial in Prob. 15   22. The polynomial in Prob. 16

c 23. If P is a polynomial function of degree n, n even, then what is the maximum number of times the graph of $y = P(x)$ can cross the x axis? What is the minimum number of times?
24. Answer the question in Prob. 23 for n odd.
25. How do we know that any polynomial with real coefficients, and of odd degree, must have at least one real zero?
26. If $P(x)$ and $G(x)$ are two polynomials of degree n, and if $P(x) = G(x)$ for more than n values of x, then how are $P(x)$ and $G(x)$ related?

**5.5 ISOLATING REAL ZEROS
OF POLYNOMIALS WITH
REAL COEFFICIENTS**

For the rest of this chapter we will focus on the problem of finding real zeros of polynomials with real coefficients. There are three theorems that will help us greatly in this regard. The first theorem gives us useful information as to the possible number of real zeros of a given polynomial; the second theorem tells us how to determine a finite interval that contains all the real zeros, if they exist; and the third theorem will help us isolate particular zeros further within this interval.

Descartes' Rule of Signs

When the terms of a polynomial with real coefficients are arranged in order of descending powers, we say that a *variation in sign* occurs if two successive terms have opposite signs. Missing terms are ignored. For example, $P(x) = 3x^4 - 2x^3 + 3x - 5$ has three variations in sign, and $P(-x) = 3x^4 + 2x^3 - 3x - 5$ has one variation in sign. How many variations in sign are in $P(x)$ and $P(-x)$ if $P(x) = 2x^5 - x^4 - x^3 + x + 5$? [*Answer:* Two in $P(x)$ and three in $P(-x)$.]

In 1637, Rene Descartes, a French philosopher-mathematician, gave the first proof of a simplified version of the theorem that now bears his name. We state a modern version of the theorem without proof, since a proof is beyond the scope of this book.

Theorem 8.
Descartes'
Rule of Signs

If $P(x)$ is a polynomial with real coefficients, then the number of positive real zeros of $P(x)$ is never greater than the number of variations in sign in $P(x)$ and, if less, then always by an even number. The number of negative real zeros of $P(x)$ is never greater than the number of variations in sign in $P(-x)$ and, if less, then always by an even number.

Example 6. What can you say about the number of positive and negative real zeros of

(A) $P(x) = 3x^4 - 2x^3 + 3x - 5$
(B) $Q(x) = 2x^6 + x^4 - x + 3$

SOLUTION

(A) $P(x)$ has three variations in sign, hence has either three or one positive real zeros. $P(-x) = 3x^4 + 2x^3 - 3x - 5$ has one variation in sign, hence $P(x)$ *has* one negative real zero.

(B) $Q(x)$ has two variations in sign, hence has either two or no positive real zeros. $Q(-x) = 2x^6 + x^4 + x + 3$ has no variations in sign, hence $Q(x)$ *has* no negative real zeros.

Problem 6. What can you say about the number of positive and negative real zeros of

(A) $P(x) = 4x^5 + 2x^4 - x^3 + x - 5$
(B) $Q(x) = x^3 + 3x^2 + 5$

ANSWER

(A) Positive real zeros: three or one; negative real zeros: two or none;
(B) positive real zeros: none; negative real zeros: one.

Bounding Real Zeros

Any number that is greater than or equal to the largest zero of a polynomial is called an *upper bound of the zeros* of the polynomial; any number that is less than or equal to the smallest zero of a polynomial is called a *lower bound of the zeros* of the polynomial. The next theorem enables us to determine upper and lower bounds of all real zeros of a polynomial with real coefficients.

Theorem 9.
Upper and
Lower Bounds
of Real
Zeros

If $P(x) = a_n x^n + a_{n-1}x^{n-1} + \cdots + a_0$, $a_n > 0$, is a polynomial with real coefficients, and if $P(x)$ is divided by $x - r$ using synthetic division, then

(A) If $r > 0$ and all the numbers in the third row of the synthetic division are nonnegative, then there are no zeros of $P(x)$ greater than r, that is, r is an upper bound of the zeros of $P(x)$.

(B) If $r < 0$ and all the numbers in the third row of the synthetic division alternate in sign (zeros in the third row can be denoted by $+0$ or -0 as desired), then there are no zeros of $P(x)$ less than r. Thus r is a lower bound of the zeros of $P(x)$.

PROOF

(A) If all the numbers in the third row of the synthetic division are nonnegative, then

$$P(x) = (x - r)Q(x) + R$$

where the coefficients of $Q(x)$ are nonnegative and R is nonnegative. If $x > r > 0$, then $x - r > 0$ and $Q(x) > 0$ (recall that $a_n > 0$ by hypothesis); hence, $P(x) = (x - r)Q(x) + R > 0$ for $x > r$. Thus $P(x)$ cannot be zero for any x greater than r, and r is an upper bound for the real zeros of $P(x)$.

(B) The proof of the second part of the theorem is similar to the proof of the first part, only longer. Two cases must be considered—the case in which the degree of $Q(x)$ is even, and the case in which the degree of $Q(x)$ is odd. The details of the proof are left as an exercise.

It is easy to see that 6 is an upper bound and -4 is a lower bound for the real zeros of $P(x) = x^3 - 3x^2 - 18x + 4$. In the first case we simply divide $P(x)$ by $x - 6$, using synthetic division, and observe that all the numbers in the third row are nonnegative:

$$
\begin{array}{r|rrrr}
 & 1 & -3 & -18 & 4 \\
 &   & 6 & 18 & 0 \\
\hline
6 & 1 & 3 & 0 & 4 \\
\end{array}
$$

Similarly, to check that -4 is a lower bound, we divide $P(x)$ by $x + 4$, using synthetic division, and observe that the numbers in the third row alternate in sign:

$$
\begin{array}{r|rrrr}
 & 1 & -3 & -18 & 4 \\
 &   & -4 & 28 & -40 \\
\hline
-4 & 1 & -7 & 10 & -36 \\
\end{array}
$$

Show that 7 is also an upper bound and -5 is also a lower bound.

Example 7. Find the smallest positive integer and the largest negative integer that, by Theorem 9, are upper and lower bounds, respectively, for the real zeros of $P(x) = x^3 - 3x^2 - 2x + 6$.

SOLUTION

An easy way to locate these numbers, particularly if the coefficients of $P(x)$ are not too large, is to test 1, 2, 3, and so on, until an upper bound is reached, and then $-1, -2, -3$, and so on, until a lower bound is found. The process is speeded by mentally (or on scratch paper) computing the second row in the synthetic division and writing only the third row each time in table form. Thus,

	1	-3	-2	6	
1	1	-2	-4	2	
2	1	-1	-4	-2	
3	1	0	-2	0	
4	1	1	2	14	(4 is an upper bound)
-1	1	-4	2	4	
-2	1	-5	8	-10	(-2 is a lower bound)

We conclude that all the real zeros lie between the two integers -2 and 4.

Problem 7. Repeat Example 7 for $P(x) = x^3 - 4x^2 - 5x + 8$.

ANSWER

Lower bound: -2; upper bound: 5.

Isolating Real Zeros Further by Observing Sign Changes in $P(x)$

The graph of $P(x) = x^3 - 2x^2 - 5x + 5$ is illustrated in Fig. 1. The x intercepts of the curve are the real zeros of $P(x)$. We note two things relative to this graph: (1) the curve is continuous in that it contains no holes or breaks; (2) $P(x)$ changes sign as x moves across a zero. In general, we can prove that any polynomial has a continuous graph. Though the proof is difficult and beyond this course, it is the basis for the following useful theorem, which we state without proof.

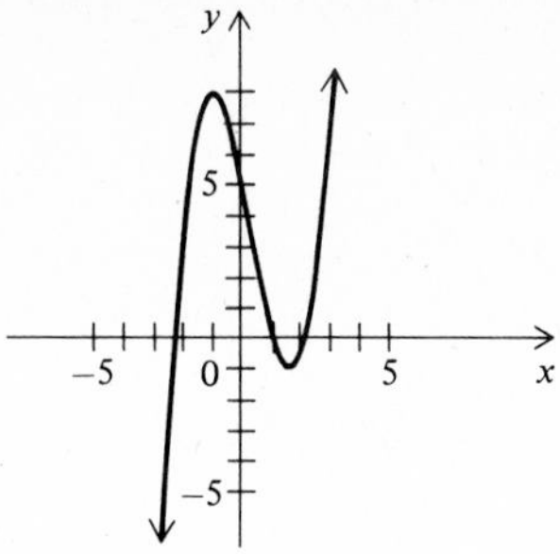

FIGURE 1

Theorem 10.   If $P(x)$ is a polynomial with real coefficients, and if $P(a)$ and $P(b)$ are of opposite sign, then there is an odd number of real zeros between a and b.

It follows that if there is an odd number of real zeros between a and b, then there is at least one real zero between a and b. The converse of the theorem is false, as can be seen by considering $P(x) = (x - 1)^2$. This polynomial has a real zero at $x = 1$, but $P(x)$ does not change sign as x crosses 1.

Example 8.   Show that there is at least one real zero of $P(x) = x^4 - 2x^3 - 6x^2 + 6x + 9$ between 1 and 2.

SOLUTION

Show that $P(1)$ and $P(2)$ are of opposite sign:

$$
\begin{array}{r|rrrrl}
 & 1 & -2 & -6 & 6 & 9 \\
\hline
1 & 1 & -1 & -7 & -1 & 8 = P(1) \\
2 & 1 & 0 & -6 & -6 & -3 = P(2)
\end{array}
$$

Since $P(1)$ and $P(2)$ are of opposite sign, there is at least one real zero between 1 and 2.

Problem 8.   Show that there is at least one real zero of $P(x) = 2x^4 - 3x^3 - 3x - 4$ between 2 and 3.

ANSWER

$P(2) = -2$ and $P(3) = 68$, and the conclusion follows from Theorem 10.

EXERCISE 38

A *Using Descartes' rule of signs, what can you say about the number of positive and negative zeros of each of the following polynomials?*

1. $P(x) = 2x^2 + x - 4$
2. $Q(x) = 3x^2 - x - 5$
3. $M(x) = 7x^2 + 2x + 4$
4. $N(x) = -3x^2 - 2x - 1$
5. $Q(x) = 2x^3 - 4x^2 + x - 3$
6. $P(x) = x^3 + 7x^2 - x + 2$

Find the smallest positive integer and the largest negative integer that, by Theorem 9, are upper and lower bounds, respectively, for the real zeros of each of the following polynomials.

7. $P(x) = x^2 - 2x + 3$
8. $Q(x) = x^2 - 3x - 2$
9. $M(x) = x^3 - 3x + 5$
10. $R(x) = x^3 - 2x^2 + 3$
11. $M(x) = x^4 - x^2 + 3x + 2$
12. $N(x) = x^4 - 2x^3 + 4x - 3$

Show, using Theorem 10, that for each polynomial there is at least one real zero between the given values of a and b.

13. $P(x) = x^2 - 3x - 2,\ a = 3,\ b = 4$
14. $Q(x) = x^2 - 3x - 2,\ a = -1,\ b = 0$
15. $P(x) = x^3 - 3x + 5,\ a = -3,\ b = -2$
16. $P(x) = x^3 - 2x^2 - 4,\ a = 2,\ b = 3$
17. $Q(x) = x^3 - 3x^2 - 3x + 9,\ a = 1,\ b = 2$
18. $G(x) = x^3 - 3x^2 - 3x + 9,\ a = -2,\ b = -1$

B *For each polynomial $P(x)$*

(A) *Discuss the possible number of real zeros using Descartes' rule of signs.*
(B) *Find the smallest and largest integers that are, respectively, upper and lower bounds of the zeros of $P(x)$ according to Theorem 9.*
(C) *Discuss the location of real zeros within the lower and upper bound interval by applying Theorem 10 to integral values of x within this interval.*

19. $P(x) = x^3 - x^2 - 6x + 6$
20. $P(x) = x^3 - 3x^2 - 2x + 6$
21. $P(x) = x^3 - 2x - 6$
22. $P(x) = x^3 - 3x^2 - 5$
23. $P(x) = x^4 + 4x^3 - 2x^2 - 12x - 3$
24. $P(x) = x^4 - 4x^3 + 8x - 4$
25. $P(x) = x^5 - 3x^3 + 2x - 5$
26. $P(x) = 2x^5 - 5x^4 - 2x + 5$

C 27. Prove that $P(x) = x^4 + 3x^2 - x - 5$ has two complex and two real zeros, without finding the zeros.

28. Prove that $P(x) = x^3 + 3x^2 + 5$ has one negative real zero and two complex zeros, without finding the zeros.

29. Prove that the graph of $P(x) = x^5 + 3x^3 + x$ crosses the x axis only once.

30. Prove that the graph of $P(x) = x^4 + 3x^2 + 7$ does not cross the x axis at all.

5.6 RATIONAL ZEROS OF POLYNOMIALS WITH INTEGERS AS COEFFICIENTS

If all the coefficients of a polynomial $P(x)$ are integers, then by means of the next theorem, we will be able to find all rational zeros of $P(x)$, if they exist.

Theorem 11. If the rational number b/c, in lowest terms, is a zero of the polynomial $P(x) = a_n x^n + a_{n-1} x^{n-1} + \cdots + a_0$ with integers as coefficients, then b is a factor of a_0 and c is a factor of a_n.

PROOF

Since b/c is a zero of $P(x)$

$$a_n \left(\frac{b}{c}\right)^n + a_{n-1} \left(\frac{b}{c}\right)^{n-1} + \cdots + a_1 \left(\frac{b}{c}\right) + a_0 = 0 \tag{1}$$

If we multiply both members of Eq. (1) by c^n, we obtain

$$a_n b^n + a_{n-1} b^{n-1} c + \cdots + a_1 b c^{n-1} + a_0 c^n = 0 \tag{2}$$

which can be written in the form

$$a_n b^n = c(-a_{n-1} b^{n-1} - \cdots - a_0 c^{n-1}) \tag{3}$$

Thus c is a factor of $a_n b^n$, since the expression in parentheses is an integer (why?). And since b and c are relatively prime (that is, have no common factors other than ± 1), b^n and c must be relatively prime, hence c must be a factor of a_n (why?).

Now, if we write Eq. (2) in the form

$$a_0 c^n = b(-a_n b^{n-1} - \cdots - a_1 c^{n-1})$$

we see that b is a factor of $a_0 c^n$, hence a factor of a_0, since b and c are relatively prime.

Again we emphasize that this theorem does not say that a polynomial with integers as coefficients has rational zeros; it simply states that if it does, then they must meet the conditions stated in the theorem. In short, it enables us to list a set of rational numbers that must include all rational zeros if they exist.

Example 9. Find all rational zeros of $P(x) = 2x^3 - 5x^2 - 8x + 6$.

SOLUTION

If b/c is a rational zero of $P(x)$, then b must be a factor of 6 and c a factor of 2. The possible values of b (factors of 6) are

$$\pm 1, \ \pm 2, \ \pm 3, \ \pm 6$$

and the possible values of c (factors of 2) are

$$\pm 1, \ \pm 2$$

Thus the rational zeros of $P(x)$, if they exist must be among the following rational numbers:

$$\pm1, \ \pm2, \ \pm3, \ \pm6, \ \pm\tfrac{1}{2}, \ \pm\tfrac{3}{2}$$

We could test each one of these numbers using synthetic division; however, it is more efficient, since the number of possibilities is fairly large, to use the theorems in the last section to first narrow down the choice.

Descartes' rule of signs tells us there are

0 or 2 positive real zeros

and

1 negative real zero

We next make up a synthetic division table to locate upper and lower bounds of the real zeros and to locate smaller intervals over which $P(x)$ changes sign to isolate zeros further.

		2	−5	−8	6	
Real zero	0	2	−5	−8	6	
	1	2	−3	−11	−5	
	2	2	−1	−10	−14	
Real zero	3	2	1	−5	−9	
	4	2	3	4	22	(4 is an upper bound)
Real zero	−1	2	−7	−1	7	
	−2	2	−9	10	−14	(−2 is a lower bound)

From this table and from the theorems in the last section, we can eliminate all possible zeros listed except $\tfrac{1}{2}$ and $-\tfrac{3}{2}$. (The reader should carefully check this statement.) We now test $\tfrac{1}{2}$ and $-\tfrac{3}{2}$ separately:

	2	−5	−8	6
$\tfrac{1}{2}$	2	−4	−10	1
$-\tfrac{3}{2}$	2	−8	4	0

Thus, $-\tfrac{3}{2}$ is the only rational zero of $P(x)$.

It is easy to find all other zeros of $P(x)$, should we be interested. Since $-\tfrac{3}{2}$ is a zero of $P(x)$, $x + \tfrac{3}{2}$ is a factor of $P(x)$. Hence,

$$P(x) = (x + \tfrac{3}{2})(2x^2 - 8x + 4)$$

$Q(x) = 2x^2 - 8x + 4$ is called the *depressed polynomial* relative to $P(x)$. The zeros of $Q(x)$ are easily found, using the quadratic formula, to be the irrational numbers $2 + \sqrt{2}$ and $2 - \sqrt{2}$.

Problem 9.   Find all rational zeros of $P(x) = 3x^3 - 8x^2 - 2x + 4$.

ANSWER

$\frac{2}{3}$.

Example 10.   Find all rational zeros of $P(x) = x^3 - 5x^2 + 5x + 3$.

SOLUTION

Since the leading coefficient is 1, the only possible rational zeros are integers, namely, ± 1 and ± 3. Since there are only a few choices, we test each directly:

$$
\begin{array}{r|rrrr}
 & 1 & -5 & 5 & 3 \\
\hline
1 & 1 & -4 & 1 & 4 \\
-1 & 1 & -6 & 11 & -8 \quad (-1 \text{ is a lower bound}) \\
3 & 1 & -2 & -1 & 0 \\
\end{array}
$$

Omit the test for -3, since -1 is a lower bound. Thus 3 is the only rational zero. [The zeros of the depressed polynomial $Q(x) = x^2 - 2x - 1$ are the irrational numbers $1 + \sqrt{2}$ and $1 - \sqrt{2}$.]

Problem 10.   Find all rational zeros of $P(x) = x^3 - 15x + 4$.

ANSWER

-4.

EXERCISE 39

A   *For each polynomial list all possible rational zeros according to Theorem 11.*

1. $P(x) = x^3 + 3x^2 - 6x - 8$
2. $P(x) = x^3 - 2x^2 - 5x + 6$
3. $P(x) = x^3 - 3x^2 + 6$
4. $P(x) = x^3 - 3x + 1$
5. $P(x) = 2x^3 + x^2 - 4x - 3$
6. $P(x) = 3x^3 - 11x^2 + 8x + 4$
7. $P(x) = 2x^3 - 5x^2 - 2x + 15$
8. $P(x) = 2x^3 - 9x^2 + 14x - 5$

Find all rational zeros for each polynomial $P(x)$.

9. $P(x) = x^3 + 3x^2 - 6x - 8$
10. $P(x) = x^3 - 2x^2 - 5x + 6$
11. $P(x) = x^3 - 3x^2 + 6$
12. $P(x) = x^3 - 3x + 1$
13. $P(x) = 2x^3 + x^2 - 4x - 3$
14. $P(x) = 3x^3 - 11x^2 + 8x + 4$
15. $P(x) = 2x^3 - 5x^2 - 2x + 15$
16. $P(x) = 2x^3 - 9x^2 + 14x - 5$

B
17. $P(x) = x^4 - 2x^3 - 2x^2 + 8x - 8$
18. $P(x) = x^4 - 16x^2 - 225$
19. $P(x) = 12x^3 - 16x^2 - 5x + 3$
20. $P(x) = 18x^3 - 21x^2 - 10x + 8$

Find all roots (rational, irrational, and complex) for each polynomial equation.

21. $2x^3 - 10x^2 + 12x - 4 = 0$ 22. $2x^3 - 5x^2 + 1 = 0$
23. $x^4 + 4x^3 - x^2 - 20x - 20 = 0$ 24. $x^4 - 4x^2 - 4x - 1 = 0$
25. $2x^5 - 3x^4 - 2x + 3 = 0$ 26. $x^4 - 2x^2 + 16x - 15 = 0$

C *Write each polynomial as a product of linear factors.*

27. $P(x) = 2x^3 - 10x^2 + 12x - 4$ 28. $P(x) = 2x^3 - 5x^2 + 1$
29. $P(x) = 2x^5 - 3x^4 - 2x + 3$ 30. $P(x) = x^4 - 2x^2 + 16x - 5$

Show that each of the following real numbers is not rational by suitable use of Theorem 11.

31. $\sqrt{6}$ 32. $\sqrt{12}$ 33. $\sqrt[3]{5}$
34. $\sqrt[3]{9}$ 35. $\sqrt[5]{8}$ 36. $\sqrt[7]{4}$

Graph each polynomial function, making use of material in this chapter as aids to graphing.

37. $P(x) = x^3 + 3x^2 - 6x - 8$ 38. $P(x) = x^3 - 2x^2 - 5x + 6$
39. $P(x) = x^4 - 2x^3 - 2x^2 + 8x - 8$ 40. $P(x) = x^4 - 2x^2 + 16x - 15$
41. $P(x) = x^4 + 4x^3 - x^2 - 20x - 20$
42. $P(x) = x^4 - 4x^2 - 4x - 1$

5.7 IRRATIONAL ZEROS BY SUCCESSIVE APPROXIMATIONS

If a polynomial $P(x)$ is of degree greater than 2 and has no rational zeros but has irrational zeros, then the rational-zero theorem will be of little use to us. However, we can make considerable use of some of the earlier theorems. In particular, we can find upper and lower bounds of real zeros, and then locate intervals over which $P(x)$ changes sign. Sketching graphs of $y = P(x)$ over certain intervals can also be of help. When we finally locate an interval in which an irrational zero exists, we can then use the *method of successive approximations* to approximate it to any decimal accuracy desired. The process is best understood through an example.

Example 11. Find all real zeros for $P(x) = 2x^4 + x^3 + 4x^2 - 6x - 4$, approximating irrational zeros to two decimal places.

SOLUTION

First, locate rational zeros (if any). Using methods of the last section, we find $-\frac{1}{2}$ to be the only rational zero. Thus, using the factor theorem,

$$P(x) = (x + \tfrac{1}{2})(2x^3 + 4x - 8)$$
$$= 2(x + \tfrac{1}{2})(x^3 + 2x + 4)$$

We now seek the irrational zeros of the depressed polynomial

$$Q(x) = x^3 + 2x - 4$$

Second, locate irrational zeros (if any). Since $Q(x)$ is of degree 3, we know that it has either one real zero or three (why?). By Descartes' rule of signs we can narrow this down to exactly one positive real zero and no negative real zeros. To limit our search, we locate upper and lower bounds for real zeros, and intervals over which $Q(x)$ changes sign. We know at the start that 0 is a lower bound (why?), so we start there and work up.

$$
\begin{array}{r|rrrr}
 & 1 & 0 & 2 & -4 \\
\hline
0 & 1 & 0 & 2 & -4 \\
1 & 1 & 1 & 3 & -1 \\
2 & 1 & 2 & 6 & 8 \\
\end{array}
$$

Real zero $\begin{cases} 1 \\ 2 \end{cases}$ (2 is an upper bound)

From the table, we see that the positive real (irrational) zero is between 1 and 2. To obtain a clearer picture of where the zero lies in this interval, we sketch a graph of $y = Q(x)$ over the interval (Fig. 2). We proceed now, by the method of successive approximation, to find this zero to two decimal places.

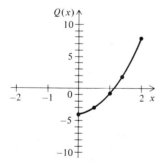

FIGURE 2

[The *method of successive approximation* is not difficult to understand. The first step is to divide the unit interval containing the zero into tenths. To determine the first decimal of the zero, we locate the interval in this subdivision within which $P(x)$ changes sign. We repeat this process, dividing this subinterval into 10 parts, to locate the second decimal place, and so on. The process can be repeated as long as desired (barring fatigue) to produce a decimal approximation of an irrational zero to any accuracy desired. To obtain an accuracy of two decimal places, we go to the third and round back to the second. In general, we go to one more place than the accuracy desired, and then round back one place.]

Now to proceed with our example. The irrational zero of $Q(x)$ is between 1 and 2. We divide the interval from 1 to 2 into tenths, locate $(1, P(1))$ and $(2, P(2))$, and join these two points with a straight line to determine approximately where the zero of $Q(x)$ lies (Fig. 3). From the figure it appears that

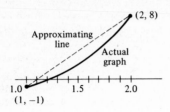

FIGURE 3

the zero is closer to 1 than to 2, so we start from that end. Using synthetic division, we find $P(1.0)$, $P(1.1)$, $P(1.2)$, and so on, until a sign change occurs:

	1	0	2	-4
1.0	1	1	3	-1
Zero⎰1.1	1	1.1	3.21	-0.47
⎱1.2	1	1.2	3.44	0.13

The zero is between 1.1 and 1.2. We now divide the interval from 1.1 to 1.2 into tenths to find the next decimal place (Fig. 4):

	1	0	2	-4
1.16	1	1.16	3.346	-0.119
Zero⎰1.17	1	1.17	3.369	-0.058
⎱1.18	1	1.18	3.392	0.003

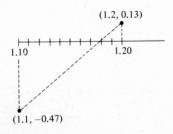

FIGURE 4

We now have the zero between 1.17 and 1.18. Continuing, we divide this interval into tenths, and proceed as above (Fig. 5).

$$
\begin{array}{r|cccc}
 & 1 & 0 & 2 & -4 \\
\hline
1.178 & 1 & 1.178 & 3.3876 & -0.0095 \\
\text{Zero}\begin{cases}1.179 \\ 1.180\end{cases} \begin{matrix} \\ \end{matrix} & \begin{matrix}1 \\ 1\end{matrix} & \begin{matrix}1.179 \\ 1.180\end{matrix} & \begin{matrix}3.3900 \\ 3.3924\end{matrix} & \begin{matrix}-0.0032 \\ 0.0030\end{matrix}
\end{array}
$$

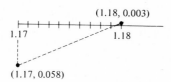

(1.18, 0.003)

1.17   1.18

(1.17, 0.058)

FIGURE 5

It is now clear that our zero to two decimal places is 1.18. And it is also clear that the process is practical without the aid of a calculator only to one or two decimal places. It is also useful to point out that the process is not limited to polynomial functions.

Problem 11. Given $P(x) = x^3 + 2x - 7$:

(A) What is the possible number of real zeros?
(B) Does $P(x)$ have rational zeros?
(C) Find the irrational zeros to one decimal place.

ANSWER

(A) One positive zero and no negative zeros; (B) no; (C) 1.6.

EXERCISE 40

A *Find the zeros accurate to one decimal place in the indicated interval.*

1. $P(x) = x^3 - 5x + 3$; (0, 1)
2. $P(x) = x^3 - 5x^2 + 3$; (4, 5)
3. $P(x) = x^3 - x^2 - x - 1$; (1, 2)
4. $P(x) = x^3 + x - 1$; (0, 1)

B *Find all real zeros of each polynomial. Find rational zeros first, and then irrational zeros to one-decimal-place accuracy.*

5. $P(x) = x^4 - x^3 + 10x^2 - 28x + 18$
6. $P(x) = x^4 - 6x - 7$
7. $P(x) = 2x^4 + 3x^3 + 6x^2 - x - 15$
8. $P(x) = 2x^5 - 5x^4 - 7x^3 + 4x^2 + 21x + 9$

Find real roots of each equation, in the indicated intervals, accurate to two decimal places.

9. $x^3 - 2x - 7 = 0$; (2, 3)   10. $x^3 - 5x^2 + 3 = 0$; (0, 1)
11. $x^3 + x^2 - 6x - 2 = 0$; (2, 3)   12. $x^3 - 3x^2 + 4x - 5 = 0$; (2, 3)
13. A rectangular box has dimensions of $1 \times 1 \times 2$ ft. If each dimension is increased by the same amount, how much should this amount be to triple the volume of the box? Approximate the answer to one decimal place.
14. An open metal container is to be made from a rectangular piece of sheet metal, 11×9 in., by cutting out squares of the same size from each corner and bending up the sides. If the volume of the container is to be 72 in.^{3}, how large a square should be cut from each corner?

c 15. In physics it can be shown that a solid buoy in the form of a sphere, with radius r and specific gravity s, $0 < s < 1$, will sink in water to a depth of x as given by the equation

$$x^3 - 3rx^2 + 4r^3 s = 0$$

How far will a plastic buoy of radius 1 ft and specific gravity $s = 0.1$ sink? Give the answer accurate to one decimal place.
16. Show that even though $P(2)$ and $P(3)$ have the same sign $P(x) = x^4 - 4x^3 + x^2 + 6x + 2$ has two real zeros between 2 and 3. Find the largest zero to one-decimal-place accuracy.

5.8 PARTIAL FRACTION DECOMPOSITION

You have now had some experience in combining two or more algebraic fractions into single fractions by addition or subtraction. For example, problems such as

$$\frac{2}{x + 5} + \frac{3}{x - 4} = \frac{5x + 7}{x^2 + x - 20}$$

should be routine. There are several places in more advanced courses, particularly in calculus and differential equations, where it is a great advantage to be able to reverse the process; that is, to be able to express the quotient of two polynomials as the sum of two or more simpler quotients called *partial fractions*. This process of decomposing a quotient into partial fractions, like many reverse processes, is more difficult than the original.

We confine our attention to quotients of the form $P(x)/D(x)$, where $P(x)$ and $D(x)$ are real polynomials. In addition, we will assume that the degree of $P(x)$ is less than the degree of $D(x)$. If the degree of $P(x)$ is greater than or equal to that of $D(x)$, we have only to divide $P(x)$ by $D(x)$ to obtain

$$\frac{P(x)}{D(x)} = Q(x) + \frac{R(x)}{D(x)}$$

where the degree of $R(x)$ is less than that of $D(x)$. For example,

$$\frac{x^4 - 3x^3 + 2x^2 - 5x + 1}{x^2 - 2x + 1} = x^2 - x - 1 + \frac{-6x + 2}{x^2 - 2x + 1}$$

If the degree of $P(x)$ is less than that of $D(x)$, then $P(x)/D(x)$ is called a *proper fraction*. Our task now is to figure out a systematic way to decompose proper fractions into the sum of two or more partial fractions. The following three theorems take care of the problem completely. The first and third are stated without proof.

Theorem 12. Two polynomials are equal to each other if and only if the coefficients of like-degree terms are equal.

Theorem 13. A polynomial with real coefficients can always be represented as a product of irreducible (in the real numbers) linear or quadratic polynomials with real coefficients.

PROOF

By Theorems 3, 6, and 7, an nth-degree polynomial has n zeros in the field of complex numbers, and can be factored into n linear factors. If the coefficients of $P(x)$ are real, complex zeros occur in conjugate pairs. Thus, if we multiply the factors corresponding to each pair of conjugate complex zeros, we will obtain quadratic factors with real coefficients, as can readily be seen in the following multiplication, where $a, b \in R$:

$$[x - (a + bi)][x - (a - bi)] = x^2 - 2ax + (a^2 + b^2)$$

Theorem 14.
Partial Fraction Decomposition

Any reduced proper fraction $P(x)/D(x)$ can be decomposed into the sum of partial fractions as follows:

(A) If $D(x)$ has a nonrepeating linear factor of the form $ax + b$, then the partial fraction decomposition of $P(x)/D(x)$ contains a term of the form $A/(ax + b)$, A a constant.

(B) If $D(x)$ has a k-repeating linear factor of the form $(ax + b)^k$, then the partial fraction decomposition of $P(x)/D(x)$ contains terms of the form

$$\frac{A_1}{ax + b} + \frac{A_2}{(ax + b)^2} + \cdots + \frac{A_k}{(ax + b)^k}$$

$A_1, A_2, \ldots, A_k$ are constants

(C)   If $D(x)$ has a nonrepeating quadratic factor of the form $ax^2 + bx + c$, the partial fraction decomposition of $P(x)/D(x)$ contains a term of the form

$$\frac{Ax + B}{ax^2 + bx + c} \qquad A \text{ and } B \text{ constants}$$

(D)   If $D(x)$ has a k-repeating quadratic factor of the form $(ax^2 + bx + c)^k$, then the partial fraction decomposition of $P(x)/D(x)$ contains terms of the form

$$\frac{A_1 x + B_1}{ax^2 + bx + c} + \frac{A_2 x + B_2}{(ax^2 + bx + c)^2} + \cdots + \frac{A_k x + B_k}{(ax^2 + bx + c)^k}$$

$A_1, \ldots, A_k, B_1, \ldots, B_k$ are constants

Example 12.   Decompose $\dfrac{5x + 7}{x^2 + 2x - 3}$ into partial fractions.

SOLUTION

We first try to factor the denominator. If it is irreducible in the real numbers, then we will not be able to go further. In this example the denominator factors, so we apply the first part of Theorem 14 and write

$$\frac{5x + 7}{(x - 1)(x + 3)} = \frac{A}{x - 1} + \frac{B}{x + 3} \tag{1}$$

To find the constants A and B we combine the right member of Eq. (1) into a single fraction

$$\frac{A(x + 3) + B(x - 1)}{(x - 1)(x + 3)}$$

and equate the numerator to $5x + 7$. Thus

$$5x + 7 = A(x + 3) + B(x - 1) \tag{2}$$

We could multiply the right member and find A and B by using Theorem 12, but in this case it is easier to take advantage of the fact that Eq. (2) is an identity; that is, it must hold for all values of x. In particular, we note that if we let $x = 1$, then the second term of the right member drops out and we can solve for A.

$$5 \cdot 1 + 7 = A(1 + 3) + B(1 - 1)$$
$$12 = 4A$$
$$A = 3$$

Similarly, if we let $x = -3$, the first term will drop out and we find

$$-8 = -4B$$
$$B = 2$$

Hence,

$$\frac{5x + 7}{x^2 + 2x - 3} = \frac{3}{x - 1} + \frac{2}{x + 3}$$

Problem 12. Decompose $\dfrac{7x + 6}{x^2 + x - 6}$ into partial fractions.

ANSWER

$$\frac{4}{x - 2} + \frac{3}{x + 3}.$$

Example 13. Decompose $\dfrac{6x^2 - 14x - 27}{(x + 2)(x - 3)^2}$ into partial fractions.

SOLUTION

Using Theorem 14, we write

$$\frac{6x^2 - 14x - 27}{(x + 2)(x - 3)^2} = \frac{A}{x + 2} + \frac{B}{x - 3} + \frac{C}{(x - 3)^2}$$

$$= \frac{A(x - 3)^2 + B(x + 2)(x - 3) + C(x + 2)}{(x + 2)(x - 3)^2}$$

Thus for all x

$$6x^2 - 14x - 27 = A(x - 3)^2 + B(x + 2)(x - 3) + C(x + 2)$$

If $x = 3$, then

$$-15 = 5C$$
$$C = -3$$

If $x = -2$, then

$$25 = 25A$$
$$A = 1$$

If $x = 0$, then

$$-27 = 9 - 6B - 6$$
$$B = 5$$

Thus

$$\frac{6x^2 - 14x - 27}{(x + 2)(x - 3)^2} = \frac{1}{x + 2} + \frac{5}{x - 3} - \frac{3}{(x - 3)^2}$$

Problem 13. Decompose $\dfrac{x^2 + 11x + 15}{(x - 1)(x + 2)^2}$ into partial fractions.

ANSWER

$$\frac{3}{x - 1} - \frac{2}{x + 2} + \frac{1}{(x + 2)^2}.$$

Example 14. Decompose $\dfrac{5x^2 - 8x + 5}{(x - 2)(x^2 - x + 1)}$ into partial fractions.

SOLUTION

First we see that the quadratic in the denominator is irreducible in the real numbers, and then use Theorem 14 to write

$$\frac{5x^2 - 8x + 5}{(x - 2)(x^2 - x + 1)} = \frac{A}{x - 2} + \frac{Bx + C}{x^2 - x + 1}$$

$$= \frac{A(x^2 - x + 1) + (Bx + C)(x - 2)}{(x - 2)(x^2 - x + 1)}$$

Thus, for all x

$$5x^2 - 8x + 5 = A(x^2 - x + 1) + (Bx + C)(x - 2)$$

If $x = 2$, then

$$9 = 3A$$
$$A = 3$$

If $x = 0$, then

$$5 = 3 - 2C$$
$$C = -1$$

If $x = 1$, then

$$2 = 3 + (B - 1)(-1)$$
$$B = 2$$

Hence,

$$\frac{5x^2 - 8x + 5}{(x - 2)(x^2 - x + 1)} = \frac{3}{x - 2} + \frac{2x - 1}{x^2 - x + 1}$$

Problem 14. Decompose $\dfrac{7x^2 - 11x + 6}{(x - 1)(2x^2 - 3x + 2)}$ into partial fractions.

ANSWER

$$\frac{2}{x - 1} + \frac{3x - 2}{2x^2 - 3x + 2}.$$

Example 15. Decompose $\dfrac{x^3 - 4x^2 + 9x - 5}{(x^2 - 2x + 3)^2}$ into partial fractions.

SOLUTION

Since $x^2 - 2x + 3$ is irreducible in the real numbers, we proceed to use Theorem 14 to write

$$\frac{x^3 - 4x^2 + 9x - 5}{(x^2 - 2x + 3)^2} = \frac{Ax + B}{x^2 - 2x + 3} + \frac{Cx + D}{(x^2 - 2x + 3)^2}$$

$$= \frac{(Ax + B)(x^2 - 2x + 3) + Cx + D}{(x^2 - 2x + 3)^2}$$

Thus for all x

$$x^3 - 4x^2 + 9x - 5 = (Ax + B)(x^2 - 2x + 3) + Cx + D$$

Multiplying out and rearranging the right member, we obtain

$$x^3 - 4x^2 + 9x - 5 = Ax^3 + (B - 2A)x^2 + (3A - 2B + C)x + (3B + D)$$

Now we use Theorem 12 to equate coefficients of like-powered terms.

$$A = 1$$
$$B - 2A = -4$$
$$3A - 2B + C = 9$$
$$3B + D = -5$$

From these equations we easily find that $A = 1$, $B = -2$, $C = 2$, and $D = 1$. And now we can write

$$\frac{x^3 - 4x^2 + 9x - 5}{(x^2 - 2x + 3)^2} = \frac{x - 2}{x^2 - 2x + 3} + \frac{2x + 1}{(x^2 - 2x + 3)^2}$$

Problem 15. Decompose $\dfrac{3x^3 - 6x^2 + 7x - 2}{(x^2 - 2x + 2)^2}$ into partial fractions.

Answer

$$\frac{3x}{x^2 - 2x + 2} + \frac{x - 2}{(x^2 - 2x + 2)^2} .$$

It should be clear that one of the key problems in decomposing quotients of polynomials into partial fractions is factoring the denominator into linear and quadratic factors with real coefficients. The material in the earlier parts of this chapter can be put to effective use in this regard.

EXERCISE 41

A   *Find constant A, B, C, and D so that the right member is equal to the left.*

1. $\dfrac{7x - 14}{(x - 4)(x + 3)} = \dfrac{A}{x - 4} + \dfrac{B}{x + 3}$

2. $\dfrac{9x + 21}{(x + 5)(x - 3)} = \dfrac{A}{x + 5} + \dfrac{B}{x - 3}$

3. $\dfrac{17x - 1}{(2x - 3)(3x - 1)} = \dfrac{A}{2x - 3} + \dfrac{B}{3x - 1}$

4. $\dfrac{x - 11}{(3x + 2)(2x - 1)} = \dfrac{A}{3x + 2} + \dfrac{B}{2x - 1}$

5. $\dfrac{3x^2 + 7x + 1}{x(x + 1)^2} = \dfrac{A}{x} + \dfrac{B}{x + 1} + \dfrac{C}{(x + 1)^2}$

6. $\dfrac{x^2 - 6x + 10}{(x + 1)(x - 2)^2} = \dfrac{A}{x + 1} + \dfrac{B}{x - 2} + \dfrac{C}{(x - 2)^2}$

7. $\dfrac{3x^2 + x}{(x - 2)(x^2 + 3)} = \dfrac{A}{x - 2} + \dfrac{Bx + C}{x^2 + 3}$

8. $\dfrac{5x^2 - 9x + 19}{(x - 4)(x^2 + 5)} = \dfrac{A}{x - 4} + \dfrac{Bx + C}{x^2 + 5}$

9. $\dfrac{2x^2 + 4x - 1}{(x^2 + x + 1)^2} = \dfrac{Ax + B}{x^2 + x + 1} + \dfrac{Cx + D}{(x^2 + x + 1)^2}$

10. $\dfrac{3x^3 - 3x^2 + 10x - 4}{(x^2 - x + 3)^2} = \dfrac{Ax + B}{x^2 - x + 3} + \dfrac{Cx + D}{(x^2 - x + 3)^2}$

B   *Decompose into partial fractions.*

11. $\dfrac{-x + 22}{x^2 - 2x - 8}$

12. $\dfrac{-x - 21}{x^2 + 2x - 15}$

13. $\dfrac{3x - 13}{6x^2 - x - 12}$

14. $\dfrac{11x - 11}{6x^2 + 7x - 3}$

15. $\dfrac{x^2 - 12x + 18}{x^3 - 6x^2 + 9x}$

16. $\dfrac{5x^2 - 36x + 48}{x(x - 4)^2}$

17. $\dfrac{5x^2 + 3x + 6}{x^3 + 2x^2 + 3x}$

18. $\dfrac{6x^2 - 15x + 16}{x^3 - 3x^2 + 4x}$

19. $\dfrac{2x^3 + 7x + 5}{x^4 + 4x^2 + 4}$

20. $\dfrac{-5x^2 + 7x - 18}{x^4 + 6x^2 + 9}$

21. $\dfrac{x^3 - 7x^2 + 17x - 17}{x^2 - 5x + 6}$

22. $\dfrac{x^3 + x^2 - 13x + 11}{x^2 + 2x - 15}$

C   23. $\dfrac{4x^2 + 5x - 9}{x^3 - 6x - 9}$

24. $\dfrac{4x^2 - 8x + 1}{x^3 - x + 6}$

25. $\dfrac{x^2 + 16x + 18}{x^3 + 2x^2 - 15x - 36}$

26. $\dfrac{5x^2 - 18x + 1}{x^3 - x^2 - 8x + 12}$

27. $\dfrac{-x^2 + 5x - 7}{x^4 - 5x^3 + 9x^2 - 8x + 4}$

28. $\dfrac{-2x^3 + 12x^2 - 20x - 10}{x^4 - 7x^3 + 17x^2 - 21x + 18}$

29. $\dfrac{4x^5 + 12x^4 - x^3 + 7x^2 - 4x + 2}{4x^4 + 4x^3 - 5x^2 + 5x - 2}$

30. $\dfrac{6x^5 - 11x^4 + x^3 - 10x^2 - 2x - 2}{6x^4 - 7x^3 + x^2 - x - 1}$

EXERCISE 42   CHAPTER REVIEW EXERCISES

A   1.   Use synthetic division to divide $P(x) = 2x^3 + 3x^2 - 1$ by $D(x) = x + 2$, and write the answer in the form $P(x) = D(x)Q(x) + R$.

2.   If $P(x) = x^5 - 4x^4 + 9x^2 - 8$, find $P(3)$ using the remainder theorem and synthetic division.

3.   What are the zeros of $P(x) = 3(x - 2)(x + 4)(x + 1)$?

4.   If $P(x) = x^2 - 2x + 2$ and $P(1 + i) = 0$, find another zero of $P(x)$.

5. Using Descartes' rule of signs, what can you say about the number of positive and negative zeros of:
   (A) $P(x) = x^3 - x^2 - x + 3$
   (B) $P(x) = x^5 + x^3 + 4$

6. According to the upper-and-lower-bound theorem in this chapter, which of the following are upper and lower bounds of zeros of $P(x) = x^3 - 4x^2 + 2$; $-2, -1, 3, 4$?

7. How do you know that $P(x) = 2x^3 - 3x^2 + x - 5$ has at least one real zero between 1 and 2?

8. Write down the possible rational zeros for $P(x) = x^3 - 4x^2 + x + 6$.

9. Find all rational zeros for $P(x) = x^3 - 4x^2 + x + 6$.

10. Decompose $(7x - 11)/(x - 3)(x + 2)$ into partial fractions.

B 11. Use synthetic division to divide $P(x) = 3x^3 + 4x^2 - 7x - 3$ by $x - \frac{2}{3}$, and write the answer in the form $P(x) = D(x)Q(x) + R$.

12. If $P(x) = 4x^3 - 8x^2 - 3x - 3$, find $P(-\frac{1}{2})$ using the remainder theorem and synthetic division.

13. Use the quadratic formula and the factor theorem to factor $P(x) = x^2 - 2x - 1$.

14. Is $x + 1$ a factor of $P(x) = x^{25} + 1$? Explain without dividing or using synthetic division.

15. For $P(x) = 2x^4 - 3x^3 - 14x^2 + 2x + 4$
    (A) Using Descartes' rule of signs, discuss the possible number of real zeros.
    (B) Find the smallest and largest integers that are, respectively, upper and lower bounds of zeros of $P(x)$ according to Theorem 9.
    (C) Discuss location of real zeros within the lower- and upper-bound interval.

16. Determine all rational zeros of $P(x) = 2x^3 - 3x^2 - 18x - 8$.

17. Factor the polynomial in Prob. 16 into linear factors.

18. Find all rational zeros of $P(x) = x^3 - 3x^2 + 5$.

19. Find all zeros (rational, irrational, and complex) for $P(x) = 2x^3 - 3x^2 + 3x - 1$.

20. Factor the polynomial in Prob. 19 into linear factors.

21. Find the real zero of $P(x) = x^4 - x^2 - 2$ between 1 and 2 to one-decimal-place accuracy.

22. Decompose $(-x^2 + 3x + 4)/x(x - 2)^2$ into partial fractions.

23. Decompose $(8x^2 - 10x + 9)/(2x^3 - 3x^2 + 3x)$ into partial fractions.

C 24. Use synthetic division to divide $P(x) = x^3 + 3x + 2$ by $[x - (1 + i)]$, and write the answer in the form $P(x) = D(x)Q(x) + R$.

25. Find a polynomial of lowest degree with leading coefficient 1 that has zeros $\frac{1}{2}$ (multiplicity 2), -3, and 1 (multiplicity 3). (Leave the answer in factored form.) What is the degree of the polynomial?

26. Repeat Prob. 25 for a polynomial $P(x)$ with zeros $-5, 2 - 3i$, and $2 + 3i$.

27. Find all real roots of $2x^4 - x^3 - 12x^2 - 14x + 10 = 0$. (Irrational roots to one-decimal-place accuracy.)

28. Decompose $(5x^2 + 2x + 9)/(x^4 - 3x^3 + x^2 - 3x)$ into partial fractions.

Chapter

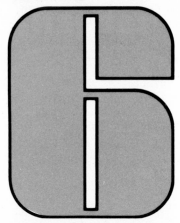

Exponential and Logarithmic Functions

Most of the functions we have considered have been algebraic functions, that is, functions defined by means of the basic algebraic operations on variables and constants. In this chapter we will define and investigate the properties of two new and important classes of functions, exponential and logarithmic functions.

6.1 EXPONENTIAL FUNCTIONS

What kind of function does

$$g(x) = 2^x \tag{1}$$

define? Since a variable cannot appear as an exponent in an algebraic function, g must be a new kind of function. The function g is a particular example of a general class of functions called exponential functions. An *exponential function* is a function defined by the equation

$$f(x) = b^x \qquad b > 0, \, b \neq 1$$

where b is a constant, called the base, and the exponent is variable. The replacement set for the exponent, the domain of g, is the set of real numbers R.

Most students, if asked to graph an exponential function such as that in Eq. (1), would not hesitate at all. They would likely make up a table by assigning integers to x, plot the resulting set of ordered pairs of numbers, and then join these points with a smooth curve (see Fig. 1). The only catch

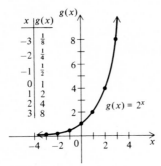

x	$g(x)$
-3	$\frac{1}{8}$
-2	$\frac{1}{4}$
-1	$\frac{1}{2}$
0	1
1	2
2	4
3	8

$g(x) = 2^x$

FIGURE 1

is that 2^x has not been defined for all real numbers. We know what 2^5, 2^{-3}, $2^{2/3}$, $2^{-3/5}$, $2^{1.4}$, and $2^{-3.15}$ all mean (that is, 2^p, where p is a rational number—see Chap. 2), but what does

$$2^{\sqrt{2}}$$

mean? The question is not easy to answer at this time. In fact, a precise definition of $2^{\sqrt{2}}$ must wait for more advanced courses, where we can show that

$$b^x$$

names a real number for b a positive real number and x any real number, and that the graph of $g(x) = 2^x$ is as indicated in Fig. 1. We can also show that, for x irrational, b^x can be approximated as closely as we like by using rational-number approximations for x. For example, each of the terms in the sequence

$$2^{1.4}, \, 2^{1.41}, \, 2^{1.414}, \, \ldots$$

approximates $2^{\sqrt{2}}$, and as we move to the right the approximation improves. Finally, we can show that the laws of exponents continue to hold for irrational exponents.

All these statements about irrational exponents (which can be justified in a course on calculus) will be assumed true for the rest of this book.

It is useful to compare the graphs of $y = 2^x$ and $y = (\frac{1}{2})^x = 2^{-x}$ by plotting them on the same coordinate system (Fig. 2). The graph of

$$f(x) = b^x \qquad b > 1$$

will look very much like $y = 2^x$, and the graph of

$$f(x) = b^x \qquad 0 < b < 1$$

will look very much like $y = (\frac{1}{2})^x$.

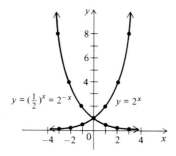

FIGURE 2

Exponential functions are often referred to as growth functions, because of their widespread use in describing different kinds of growth phenomena. These functions are used to describe population growth of people, animals, and bacteria; radioactive decay (negative growth); growth of a new chemical substance in a chemical reaction; increase or decline in the temperature of a substance being heated or cooled; growth of money at compound interest; light absorption (negative growth) as it passes through air, water, or glass; decline of atmospheric pressure as altitude is increased; and growth of learning a skill such as swimming or typing relative to practice.

For introductory purposes, the bases 2 and $\frac{1}{2}$ were convenient choices; however, a certain irrational number, denoted by e, is by far the most frequently used exponential base for both theoretical and practical purposes. In fact,

$$f(x) = e^x$$

is often referred to as *the* exponential function because of its very widespread use. The reasons for the preference for e as a base are made clear in more advanced courses. And at that time, we will show that e is approximated by $(1 + 1/n)^n$ to any decimal accuracy desired by taking n (an integer) sufficiently large. The irrational number e to five decimal places is

$$e = 2.71828$$

Similarly, e^x can be approximated to any decimal-place accuracy desired by using $[1 + (1/n)]^{nx}$ for sufficiently large n. Because of the importance of e^x, tables for its evaluation are readily available in almost any mathematical handbook. A short table for e^x and e^{-x} is included in the Appendix for convenient reference.

Finally, we state without proof that for $b > 0$, $b \neq 1$

$$b^{x_1} = b^{x_2} \Leftrightarrow x_1 = x_2$$

EXERCISE 43

A *Graph each exponential function for $-3 \leq x \leq 3$. Plot points using integers for x, and then join the points with a smooth curve.*

1. $y = 3^x$
2. $y = 2^x$
3. $y = (\frac{1}{3})^x = 3^{-x}$
4. $y = (\frac{1}{2})^x = 2^{-x}$
5. $y = 4(3)^x$
6. $y = 5(2)^x$
7. $y = 3(\frac{1}{3})^x = 3(3^{-x})$
8. $y = 4(\frac{1}{2})^x = 4(2^{-x})$

B *Graph for $-3 \leq x \leq 3$. Use Table 2 in the Appendix if the base is e.*

9. $y = 7(\frac{1}{2})^{2x} = 7(2^{-2x})$
10. $y = 11(2)^{-2x}$
11. $y = e^x$
12. $y = e^{-x}$
13. $y = 10e^{-0.12x}$
14. $y = 100e^{0.25x}$
15. $y = y_0 2^x$, y_0 constant
16. $y = y_0 3^{-x}$, y_0 constant
17. $y = y_0 e^{0.33x}$, y_0 constant
18. $y = y_0 e^{-0.22x}$, y_0 constant
19. For $f = \{(x, y) | y = 2^x\}$, graph f and f^{-1} using the same coordinate axes.
20. For $f = \{(x, y) | y = 10^x\}$, graph f and f^{-1} using the same coordinate axes.
21. If we start with 2 cents and double the amount each day, at the end of n days we will have 2^n cents. Graph $f(n) = 2^n$ for $1 \leq n \leq 10$. (Pick the scale on the vertical axis so that the graph will not go off the paper.)
22. If bacteria in a certain culture doubles every hour, write a formula that gives the number of bacteria N in the culture after n hours, assuming the culture has N_0 bacteria to start with.
23. Radioactive strontium 90 has a half-life of 28 years; that is, in 28 years one-half of any amount of strontium 90 will change to another substance because of radioactive decay. If we place a bar containing 100 mg of strontium 90 in a nuclear reactor, the amount of strontium 90 that will be left after t years is given by $A = 100(\frac{1}{2})^{t/28}$. Graph this exponential function for $t = 0, 28, 2(28), 3(28), 4(28), 5(28)$, and $6(28)$, and join these points with a smooth curve.

24. Radioactive argon 39 has a half-life of 4 min (that is, in 4 min one-half of any amount of argon 39 will change to another substance because of radioactive decay). If we start with A_0 milligrams of argon 39, the amount left after t minutes is given by $A = A_0(\frac{1}{2})^{t/4}$. Graph this exponential function for $A_0 = 100$ and $t = 0, 4, 8, 12, 16$, and 20, and join these points with a smooth curve.

C 25. Graph $y = e^{-x^2}$ for $x = -15, -1.0, -0.5, 0, 0.5, 1.0, 1.5$, and join these points with a smooth curve. (Use Table 2 in the Appendix.)

26. Sociologists Stephan and Mischler found that, when the members of a discussion group of 10 were ranked according to the number of times each participated, the number of times $N(i)$ the ith-ranked person participated was given approximately by the exponential function

$$N(i) = N_1 e^{-0.11(i-1)} \qquad 1 \leq i \leq 10$$

where N_1 is the number of times the top-ranked person participated in the discussion. Graph the exponential function, using N_1 as the basic unit on the vertical scale and Table 2 in the Appendix.

27. Daniel Lowenthal, a sociologist at Columbia University, made a study of the sale of popular records relative to their positions in the top 20. He found, over a 5-year period, that the average number of sales $N(i)$ of the ith-ranking record is given approximately by the exponential function

$$N(i) = N_1 e^{-0.09(i-1)} \qquad 1 \leq i \leq 20$$

where N_1 is the number of sales of the top-ranking record on the list. Graph the function using Table 2 in the Appendix.

Graph each function for $-2 \leq x \leq 2$, using Table 2. (Note: The first function is called the hyperbolic sine function, and the second the hyperbolic cosine function.)

28. $y = \sinh x = \frac{1}{2}(e^x - e^{-x})$.
29. $y = \cosh x = \frac{1}{2}(e^x + e^{-x})$.

6.2 LOGARITHMIC FUNCTIONS

If we start with the exponential function

$$f = \{(x, y) | y = 2^x\}$$

and interchange the variables x and y in $y = 2^x$, we obtain the inverse of f:

$$f^{-1} = \{(x, y) | x = 2^y\}$$

Graphing f and f^{-1} on the same coordinate system (Fig. 3), we see that f^{-1} is also a function. This new function is given the name *logarithmic function with base 2*, and we write

$$y = \log_2 x \Leftrightarrow x = 2^y$$

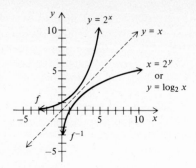

FIGURE 3

In general, we define the logarithmic function with base b to be the inverse of the exponential function with base b ($b > 0$, $b \neq 1$). Symbolically,

$$y = \log_b x \Leftrightarrow x = b^y \tag{2}$$

In words, Eq. (2) states that the log to the base b of x is the power y to which b must be raised to equal x. It is very important to remember that $y = \log_b x$ and $x = b^y$ define the same function, and as such can be used interchangeably.

Example 1.
Logarithmic
Form to
Exponential
Form

(A) $\log_2 8 = 3$ is equivalent to $8 = 2^3$
(B) $\log_{25} 5 = \frac{1}{2}$ is equivalent to $5 = 25^{1/2}$
(C) $\log_2 \frac{1}{4} = -2$ is equivalent to $\frac{1}{4} = 2^{-2}$

Problem 1.

Change to equivalent exponential form.

(A) $\log_3 27 = 3$ (B) $\log_{36} 6 = \frac{1}{2}$ (C) $\log_3 \frac{1}{9} = -2$

ANSWER

(A) $27 = 3^3$; (B) $6 = 36^{1/2}$; (C) $\frac{1}{9} = 3^{-2}$.

Example 2.
Exponential
Form to
Logarithmic
Form

(A) $49 = 7^2$ is equivalent to $\log_7 49 = 2$
(B) $3 = \sqrt{9}$ is equivalent to $\log_9 3 = \frac{1}{2}$
(C) $\frac{1}{5} = 5^{-1}$ is equivalent to $\log_5 \frac{1}{5} = -1$

Problem 2.   Change to equivalent logarithmic form.

(A) $64 = 4^3$ (B) $2 = \sqrt[3]{8}$ (C) $\frac{1}{16} = 4^{-2}$

ANSWER

(A) $\log_4 64 = 3$; (B) $\log_8 2 = \frac{1}{3}$; (C) $\log_4 \frac{1}{16} = -2$.

Example 3.   Find x, b, or y as indicated.

(A) $y = \log_4 8$ (B) $\log_3 x = -2$ (C) $\log_b 1,000 = 3$

SOLUTION

(A) $y = \log_4 8 \Rightarrow 8 = 4^y \Rightarrow 2^3 = 2^{2y} \Rightarrow y = \frac{3}{2}$
(B) $\log_3 x = -2 \Rightarrow x = 3^{-2} \Rightarrow x = \frac{1}{9}$
(C) $\log_b 1,000 = 3 \Rightarrow 1,000 = b^3 \Rightarrow 10^3 = b^3 \Rightarrow b = 10$

Problem 3.   Find x, b, or y as indicated.

(A) $y = \log_9 27$ (B) $\log_2 x = -3$ (C) $\log_b 100 = 2$

ANSWER

(A) $y = \frac{3}{2}$; (B) $x = \frac{1}{8}$; (C) $b = 10$.

Logarithmic-Exponential Identities

Recall from Sec. 4.5 that if f^{-1} is the inverse of the function f, and if f^{-1} is also a function, then

$$f[f^{-1}(x)] = x$$

and

$$f^{-1}[f(x)] = x$$

Since $f(x) = \log_b x$ and $g(x) = b^x$ are inverses of each other, then it must follow, since both are functions, that

$$g[f(x)] = x$$

and

$$f[g(x)] = x$$

that is,

$$\log_b b^x = x \tag{3}$$

and

$$b^{\log_b x} = x \tag{4}$$

Both of these identities are very useful, and are encountered in many mathematics courses.

Example 4. (A) $\log_{10} 10^5 = 5$
(B) $\log_2 8 = \log_2 2^3 = 3$
(C) $10^{\log_{10} 7} = 7$
(D) $2^{\log_2(1/4)} = \frac{1}{4}$

Problem 4. Evaluate each of the following.

(A) $\log_{10} 10^8$ (B) $\log_5 25$ (C) $10^{\log_{10} 3}$ (D) $3^{\log_3 (2/7)}$

ANSWER

(A) 8; (B) 2; (C) 3; (D) $\frac{2}{7}$.

EXERCISE 44

A *Rewrite in exponential form.*

1. $\log_3 9 = 2$
2. $\log_2 4 = 2$
3. $\log_3 81 = 4$
4. $\log_5 125 = 3$
5. $\log_{10} 1,000 = 3$
6. $\log_{10} 100 = 2$
7. $\log_e 1 = 0$
8. $\log_8 1 = 0$

Rewrite in logarithmic form.

9. $64 = 8^2$
10. $25 = 5^2$
11. $10,000 = 10^4$
12. $1,000 = 10^3$
13. $u = v^x$
14. $a = b^c$
15. $9 = 27^{2/3}$
16. $8 = 4^{3/2}$

Find each of the following.

17. $\log_{10} 10^5$
18. $\log_5 5^3$
19. $\log_2 2^{-4}$
20. $\log_{10} 10^{-7}$
21. $\log_6 36$
22. $\log_3 9$
23. $\log_{10} 1,000$
24. $\log_{10} 0.001$

Find x, y, or b as indicated.

25. $\log_2 x = 2$
26. $\log_3 x = 2$
27. $\log_4 16 = y$
28. $\log_8 64 = y$
29. $\log_b 16 = 2$
30. $\log_b 10^{-3} = -3$

B   *Rewrite in exponential form.*

31. $\log_{10} 0.001 = -3$
32. $\log_{10} 0.01 = -2$
33. $\log_{81} 3 = \frac{1}{4}$
34. $\log_4 2 = \frac{1}{2}$
35. $\log_{1/2} 16 = -4$
36. $\log_{1/3} 27 = -3$
37. $\log_a N = e$
38. $\log_k u = v$

Rewrite in logarithmic form.

39. $0.01 = 10^{-2}$
40. $0.001 = 10^{-3}$
41. $1 = e^0$
42. $1 = (\frac{1}{2})^0$
43. $\frac{1}{8} = 2^{-3}$
44. $\frac{1}{8} = (\frac{1}{2})^3$
45. $\frac{1}{3} = 81^{-1/4}$
46. $\frac{1}{2} = 32^{-1/5}$
47. $7 = \sqrt{49}$
48. $11 = \sqrt{132}$

Find each of the following.

49. $\log_b b^u$
50. $\log_b b^{uv}$
51. $\log_e e^{1/2}$
52. $\log_e e^{-3}$
53. $\log_2 \sqrt{8}$
54. $\log_5 \sqrt[3]{5}$
55. $\log_{23} 1$
56. $\log_{17} 1$
57. $\log_4 8$
58. $\log_4 \frac{1}{4}$

Find x, y, or b as indicated.

59. $\log_4 x = \frac{1}{2}$
60. $\log_{25} x = \frac{1}{2}$
61. $\log_{1/3} 9 = y$
62. $\log_{49} \frac{1}{7} = y$
63. $\log_b 1,000 = \frac{3}{2}$
64. $\log_b 4 = \frac{2}{3}$

C 65. $\log_b 1 = 0$
66. $\log_b b = 1$
67. For $f = \{(x, y) | y = 1^x\}$ discuss the domain and range for f and f^{-1}. Are both relations functions?
68. Why is 1 not a suitable logarithmic base? (*Hint:* Try to find $\log_1 5$.)
69. (A) For $f = \{(x, y) | y = 10^x\}$, graph f and f^{-1} using the same coordinate axes.
     (B) Discuss the domain and range of f and f^{-1}.
     (C) What other name could you use for the inverse of f?
70. Prove that $\log_b (1/x) = -\log_b x$.
71. If $\log_b x = 3$, find $\log_b (1/x)$.

6.3 PROPERTIES OF LOGARITHMIC FUNCTIONS

Logarithmic functions have several very useful properties that follow directly from the fact that they are inverses of exponential functions. These properties will enable us to convert multiplication problems into addition problems, division problems into subtraction problems, and power and root problems into multiplication problems. In addition, we will be able to solve exponential equations such as $2 = 10^x$.

Theorem 1.
Properties of
Logarithmic
Functions

If b, M, and N, are positive real numbers, $b \neq 1$, and if p is a real number, then

(A) $\log_b MN = \log_b M + \log_b N$

(B) $\log_b \dfrac{M}{N} = \log_b M - \log_b N$

(C) $\log_b M^p = p \log_b M$

The proof of the first property (as well as the proof of the other two) is based on the laws of exponents. To bring exponents into the proof, we let

$$u = \log_b M \qquad \text{and} \qquad v = \log_b N$$

and convert these to the equivalent exponential forms

$$M = b^u \qquad \text{and} \qquad N = b^v$$

Now, see if you can provide the reasons for each of the following steps:

$$\log_b MN = \log_b b^u b^v = \log_b b^{u+v} = u + v = \log_b M + \log_b N$$

The proofs of the other two properties are left as exercises.

Example 5. (A) $\log_b(mn/pq) = \log_b mn - \log_b pq$
$$= \log_b m + \log_b n - (\log_b p + \log_b q)$$
$$= \log_b m + \log_b n - \log_b p - \log_b q$$

(B) $\log_b (mn)^{2/3} = \frac{2}{3} \log_b mn = \frac{2}{3}(\log_b m + \log_b n)$

(C) $\log_b (x^8/y^{1/5}) = \log_b x^8 - \log_b y^{1/5} = 8 \log_b x - \frac{1}{5} \log_b y$

Problem 5. Write in terms of simpler logarithmic forms, as in Example 5.

(A) $\log_b(r/uv)$ (B) $\log_b(m/n)^{3/5}$ (C) $\log_b(u^{1/3}/v^5)$

ANSWER

(A) $\log_b r - \log_b u - \log_b v$; (B) $\frac{3}{5}(\log_b m - \log_b n)$; (C) $\frac{1}{3} \log_b u - 5 \log_b v$.

Example 6. If $\log_b 3 = 1.10$ and $\log_b 7 = 1.85$, find (A) $\log_b \frac{7}{3}$, and (B) $\log_b \sqrt[3]{21}$.

SOLUTION

(A) $\log_b \frac{7}{3} = \log_b 7 - \log_b 3 = 1.85 - 1.10 = 0.75$

(B) $\log_b \sqrt[3]{21} = \log_b (21)^{1/3} = \frac{1}{3} \log_b (3 \cdot 7) = \frac{1}{3}(\log_b 3 + \log_b 7)$
$= \frac{1}{3}(1.10 + 1.85) = 0.98$

Problem 6.   If $\log_b 5 = 0.699$ and $\log_b 8 = 0.903$, find (A) $\log_b (5^{10}/8)$ and (B) $\log_b \sqrt[4]{8/5}$.

ANSWER

(A) 6.087; (B) 0.051.

Finally, we state without proof that for n and m any positive real numbers,

---

$$\log_b m = \log_b n \Leftrightarrow m = n$$

Example 7.   Find x so that $\log_b x = \frac{2}{3} \log_b 27 + 2 \log_b 2 - \log_b 3$.

SOLUTION

$$\begin{aligned}
\log_b x &= \tfrac{2}{3} \log_b 27 + 2 \log_b 2 - \log_b 3 \\
&= \log_b 27^{2/3} + \log_b 2^2 - \log_b 3 \\
&= \log_b 9 + \log_b 4 - \log_b 3 \\
&= \log_b \frac{9 \cdot 4}{3} = \log_b 12
\end{aligned}$$

Thus

$$\log_b x = \log_b 12$$

hence

$$x = 12$$

Problem 7.   Find x so that $\log_b x = \frac{2}{3} \log_b 8 + \frac{1}{2} \log_b 9 - \log_b 6$.

ANSWER

$x = 2.$

EXERCISE 45

A *Write in terms of simpler logarithmic forms (going as far as you can with logarithmic properties—see Example 5).*

1. $\log_b uv$
2. $\log_b rt$
3. $\log_b (A/B)$
4. $\log_b (p/q)$
5. $\log_b u^5$
6. $\log_b w^{25}$
7. $\log_b N^{3/5}$
8. $\log_b u^{-2/3}$
9. $\log_b \sqrt{Q}$
10. $\log_b \sqrt[5]{M}$
11. $\log_b uvw$
12. $\log_b (u/vw)$

Write each expression in terms of a single logarithm with a coefficient of 1.
Example: $\log_b u^2 - \log_b v = \log_b (u^2/v)$.

13. $\log_b A + \log_b B$
14. $\log_b P + \log_b Q + \log_b R$
15. $\log_b X - \log_b Y$
16. $\log_b x^2 - \log_b y^3$
17. $\log_b w + \log_b x - \log_b y$
18. $\log_b w - \log_b x - \log_b y$

If $\log_b 2 = 0.69$, $\log_b 3 = 1.10$, *and* $\log_b 5 = 1.61$, *find the logarithm to the base b of each of the following numbers.*

19. $\log_b 30$
20. $\log_b 6$
21. $\log_b \frac{2}{5}$
22. $\log_b \frac{5}{3}$
23. $\log_b 27$
24. $\log_b 16$

B *Write in terms of simpler logarithmic forms (going as far as you can with logarithmic properties—see Example 5).*

25. $\log_b u^2 v^7$
26. $\log_b u^{1/2} v^{1/3}$

27. $\log_b \dfrac{1}{a}$
28. $\log_b \dfrac{1}{M^3}$

29. $\log_b \dfrac{\sqrt[3]{N}}{p^2 q^3}$
30. $\log_b \dfrac{m^5 n^3}{\sqrt{p}}$

31. $\log_b \sqrt[4]{\dfrac{x^2 y^3}{\sqrt{z}}}$
32. $\log_b \sqrt[5]{\left(\dfrac{x}{y^4 z^9}\right)^3}$

Write each expression in terms of a single logarithm with a coefficient of 1.

33. $2 \log_b x - \log_b y$
34. $\log_b m - \frac{1}{2} \log n$
35. $3 \log_b x + 2 \log_b y - 4 \log_b z$
36. $\frac{1}{4} \log_b w - 3 \log x - 5 \log y$
37. $\frac{1}{5} (2 \log_b x + 3 \log_b y)$
38. $\frac{1}{3} (\log_b x - \log_b y)$

If $\log_b 2 = 0.69$, $\log_b 3 = 1.10$, *and* $\log_b 5 = 1.61$, *find the logarithm to the base b of the following numbers.*

39. $\log_b 7.5$
40. $\log_b 1.5$
41. $\log_b \sqrt[3]{2}$
42. $\log_b \sqrt{3}$
43. $\log_b \sqrt{0.9}$
44. $\log_b \sqrt[3]{\frac{3}{2}}$

C 45. Find x so that $\frac{3}{2} \log_b 4 - \frac{2}{3} \log_b 8 + 2 \log_b 2 = \log_b x$.

46. Find x so that $3 \log_b 2 + \frac{1}{2} \log_b 25 - \log_b 20 = \log_b x$.

47. Write $\log_b y - \log_b c + kt = 0$ in exponential form free of logarithms.

48. Write $\log_e x - \log_e 100 = -0.08t$ in exponential form free of logarithms.

49. Prove that $\log_b (M/N) = \log_b M - \log_b N$ under the hypotheses of Theorem 1.

50. Prove that $\log_b M^p = p \log_b M$ under the hypotheses of Theorem 1.

51. Prove that $\log_b MN = \log_b M + \log_b N$ by starting with $M = b^{\log_b M}$ and $N = b^{\log_b N}$.

52. Prove that $\log_b (M/N) = \log_b M - \log_b N$ by starting with $M = b^{\log_b M}$ and $N = b^{\log_b N}$.

6.4 LOGARITHMS TO THE BASE 10

Of all possible logarithmic bases, the base e and the base 10 are used almost exclusively. Logarithmic functions with base e are of great value in pure and applied mathematics from calculus onward. Logarithmic functions with base 10 (because of our base-10 decimal system) find widespread use as computational tools for evaluating difficult problems such as

$$\frac{(538{,}000)^3 (0.002374)^2}{\sqrt[5]{0.1083}}$$

or solving exponential equations such as

$$2 = (1.05)^x$$

Logarithms of numbers to the base 10 are called *common logarithms*. Since common logarithms will be used extensively in the work that follows, we do not indicate the base 10 unless special emphasis is desired. Thus, we define

$$\log x = \log_{10} x$$

Because of the property

$$\log_b b^x = x$$

we can easily find the common logarithm of any power of 10; just let $b = 10$. Thus,

$$\log_{10} 10^x = \log 10^x = x$$

But how do we find logarithms of numbers such as 53,200 or 0.00876? Recalling that any decimal fraction can be written in a power-of-10 form (see Chap. 2), we see that

$$\log 53{,}200 = \log(5.32 \times 10^4) = \log 5.32 + \log 10^4 = \log 5.32 + 4$$

and that

$$\log 0.00876 = \log(8.76 \times 10^{-3}) = \log 8.76 + \log 10^{-3} = \log 8.76 - 3$$

In general, if N (a positive decimal fraction) is written in power-of-10 form

$$N = r \times 10^k \qquad 1 \le r < 10, \, k \text{ an integer}$$

then

$$\log N = \log(r \times 10^k) = \log r + \log 10^k = \log r + k$$

Thus, if the logarithms of numbers r, $1 \le r < 10$, are known, then we can find the common logarithm of any positive decimal fraction.

Using methods of advanced mathematics, a table of common logarithms of numbers from 1 to 10 can be computed to any decimal accuracy desired. Table 3 in the Appendix is such a table to four-decimal-place accuracy. It is useful to remember that if x is between 1 and 10, then $\log x$ is between 0 and 1 (see Fig. 4).

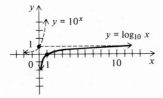

FIGURE 4

To illustrate the use of Table 3, a small portion of it is reproduced in Fig. 5. To find log 3.47, for example, we first locate 3.4 under the x heading; then we move across to the column headed 7, where we find .5403. Thus $\log 3.47 = 0.5403$.

x	0	1	2	3	4	5	6	7	8	9
3.2	.5051	.5065	.5079	.5092	.5105	.5119	.5132	.5145	.5159	.5172
3.3	.5185	.5198	.5211	.5224	.5237	.5250	.5263	.5276	.5289	.5302
3.4	.5315	.5328	.5340	.5353	.5366	.5378	.5391	**.5403**	.5416	.5428
3.5	.5441	.5453	.5465	.5478	.5490	.5502	.5514	.5527	.5539	.5551

log 3.47 = 0.5403

FIGURE 5

Example 8.   (A) $\log 33{,}800 = \log (3.38 \times 10^4) = \log 3.38 + \log 10^4$
$$= 0.5289 + 4$$
$$= 4.5289$$

(B) $\log 0.00351 = \log (3.51 \times 10^{-3}) = \log 3.51 + \log 10^{-3}$
$$= 0.5453 - 3, \text{ or } -2.4547$$

NOTE: The form $0.5453 - 3$ is usually preferred to -2.4547 for reasons that will be made clear later.

Problem 8.   Use the table in Fig. 5 to find (A) $\log 328{,}000$, and (B) $\log 0.000342$.

ANSWER

(A) 5.5159; (B) $0.5340 - 4$.

We see that the log of a positive decimal fraction has two main parts: a nonnegative decimal fraction between 0 and 1 (called the *mantissa*) and an integral part (called the *characteristic*). With a little practice you will be able to write down the characteristic and mantissa directly, omitting the second and third steps in Example 8.

Now we will reverse the problem; that is, given the log of a number, find the number. To find the number, we first write the log of the number in the form $m + c$, where m (the mantissa) is a nonnegative number between 0 and 1, and c (the characteristic) is an integer; then reverse the process illustrated in Example 8.

Example 9.   (A) $\log x = 2.5224$
$$= 0.5224 + 2$$
$$x = 3.33 \times 10^2 \text{ or } 333$$

(B) $\log x = 0.5172 - 4$
$$x = 3.29 \times 10^{-4} \text{ or } 0.000329$$

(C) $\log x = -4.4685$
$$= 0.5315 - 5$$
$$x = 3.4 \times 10^{-5} \text{ or } 0.000034$$

Problem 9.   Use Fig. 5 to find x if (A) $\log x = 5.5378$, (B) $\log x = 0.5289 - 3$, and (C) $\log x = -2.4921$.

ANSWER

(A) 3.45×10^5; (B) 3.38×10^{-3}; (C) 3.22×10^{-3}.

Any printed table is necessarily limited to a finite number of entries. The logarithmic function

$$y = \log x \qquad 1 \le x < 10$$

is defined for an infinite number of values—all real numbers between 1 and 10. What, then, do we do about values of x not in a table? How do we find, for example, log 3.276? If a certain amount of accuracy can be sacrificed, we can round 3.276 to the closest entry in the table and proceed as before. Thus,

$$\log 3.276 \approx \log 3.28 = 0.5159$$

We can do better than this, however, without too much additional work, by using a process called *linear interpolation* (see Fig. 6).

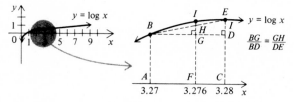

FIGURE 6

The distances $AB = \log 3.27$ and $CE = \log 3.28$ are known from the table, and are 0.5145 and 0.5159, respectively. What we would like to know is FI, the log of 3.276. To this end, we join points B and E with a straight line, and we find FH as an approximation of FI by using proportional parts of the similar triangles BGH and BDE. The work is conveniently set up as follows:

$$
\begin{array}{ccc}
 & x & \log x \\
0.010 \left\{ \begin{array}{l} 3.280 \\ 0.006 \left\{ \begin{array}{l} 3.276 \\ 3.270 \end{array} \right. \end{array} \right. & & \left. \begin{array}{l} 0.5159 \\ n \\ 0.5145 \end{array} \right\} d \left. \right\} 0.0014
\end{array}
$$

$$\frac{BG}{BD} = \frac{GH}{DE}$$

$$\frac{0.006}{0.010} = \frac{d}{0.0014}$$

$$d = 0.0008$$

Thus,

$$\log 3.276 = 0.5145 + 0.0008 = 0.5153$$

In practice, the linear interpolation process is carried out by means of a few key operational steps (often done mentally), as indicated in the next example. Notice how decimal points have been dropped to simplify the arithmetic. This is convenient, and no harm is done as long as the decimal points are properly reintroduced at the end of the calculation. If in doubt, proceed with all the decimal points, as in the example above.

Example 10. Use linear interpolation to find log 3,514.

SOLUTION

$$\log 3{,}514 = \log (3.514 \times 10^3) = \log 3.514 + 3$$

$$
\begin{array}{cc}
x & \log x
\end{array}
$$

$$
10\left\{
\begin{array}{c}
4\left\{
\begin{array}{c}
3.520 \\
3.514 \\
3.510
\end{array}
\right.
\end{array}
\right.
\quad
\left.
\begin{array}{c}
0.5465 \\
n \\
0.5453
\end{array}
\right\}d
\right\}12
$$

$$\frac{4}{10} = \frac{d}{12}$$

$$d = 5$$

Thus,

$$\log 3.514 = 0.5453 + 0.0005 = 0.5458$$

and

$$\log 3{,}514 = 0.5458 + 3 = 3.5458$$

Problem 10. Use linear interpolation to find log 326.6.

ANSWER

2.5140.

The linear interpolation process just described is also used to find x, given log x. The following example illustrates the procedure.

Example 11. Use linear interpolation to find x, if log $x = 2.5333$.

Solution

$\log x = 2.5333$
$\qquad = 0.5333 + 2$

$$
\begin{array}{ccc}
 & x & \log x \\
\end{array}
$$

$$
10\left\{d\left\{\begin{array}{l}
3.420 \quad 0.5340 \\
n \quad\ \ \ \ 0.5333 \\
3.410 \quad 0.5328
\end{array}\right\}5\right\}12
$$

$$\frac{d}{10} = \frac{5}{12}$$

$d = 4$

$n = 3.410 + 0.004 = 3.414$

Thus,

$x = 3.414 \times 10^2$ or 341.4

Problem 11. Use linear interpolation to find x, if $\log x = 7.5230$.

Answer

3.335×10^7.

EXERCISE 46

A *Use Table 3 to find each logarithm.*

1. $\log 2.35$ 2. $\log 7.82$ 3. $\log 5.03$
4. $\log 9.39$ 5. $\log 74$ 6. $\log 123$
7. $\log 3,100,000$ 8. $\log 48,700$ 9. $\log 0.00636$
10. $\log 0.0398$ 11. $\log 0.000049$ 12. $\log 0.72$

Use Table 3 to find x, given $\log x$ as indicated.

13. $\log x = 0.7226$ 14. $\log x = 0.9289$ 15. $\log x = 0.9713$
16. $\log x = 0.4594$ 17. $\log x = 4.9196$ 18. $\log x = 2.8331$
19. $\log x = 0.6096 - 1$ 20. $\log x = 0.6998 - 3$ 21. $\log x = 1.4440$
22. $\log x = 1.3160$ 23. $\log x = 0.9609 - 4$ 24. $\log x = 0.0086 - 2$
25. $\log x = 0.6749 - 3$ 26. $\log x = 3.9523 - 5$ 27. $\log x = -0.1387$
28. $\log x = -0.3696$ 29. $\log x = -3.1675$ 30. $\log x = -2.2958$

B   *Use linear interpolation to find each logarithm.*

31. log 2.317	32. log 5.143	33. log 703,400
34. log 28,430	35. log 65.03	36. log 20.35
37. log 0.004006	38. log 0.03713	39. log 0.9008
40. log 0.6413	41. log 692,300	42. log 84,660

Use linear interpolation to find x.

43. $\log x = 0.7163$	44. $\log x = 0.4085$	45. $\log x = 5.5458$
46. $\log x = 2.4735$	47. $\log x = 3.4303$	48. $\log x = 1.9141$
49. $\log x = 0.6038 - 3$	50. $\log x = 0.2177 - 1$	51. $\log x = 0.8392 - 1$
52. $\log x = 0.8509 - 4$	53. $\log x = -0.8315$	54. $\log x = -2.6651$

Find each logarithm.

55. $\log(42.2)(0.0038)$	56. $\log(352)(0.0218)$	57. $\log(3870/0.05)$
58. $\log(34,000/45.2)$	59. $\log 2^{20}$	60. $\log(39.8)^5$
61. $\log(0.627)^7$	62. $\log(0.00243)^3$	63. $\log \sqrt[5]{0.000053}$
64. $\log \sqrt[3]{(431)^2}$		

C   65. Find y if $y = 10^{1.6138}$.
66. Find y if $y = 10^{3.8627}$.

Evaluate by finding log x, and then x. Use linear interpolation where necessary.

67. $x = 78.12/0.00386$	68. $x = (3.718)(43.8)$
69. $(0.004153)^3$	70. $\sqrt[3]{43.67}$

6.5 COMPUTATION WITH LOGARITHMS

The ability to find common logarithms, together with our knowledge of the properties of logarithms discussed earlier, provides us with a new computational tool. Several detailed examples will illustrate how logarithms are used in this regard.

Example 12.   Find the product $(4,325)(32.94)$ using logarithms.

SOLUTION

Let

$$N = (4,325)(32.94)$$

then

$$\log N = \log(4,325)(32.94)$$
$$= \log 4,325 + \log 32.94$$

The last member of this equation tells us how to proceed. We arrange our work as follows for ease and accuracy of computation:

$$\log 4{,}325 = 3.6360$$
$$\log 32.94 = 1.5177$$
$$\overline{5.1537}$$

$$\log N = 5.1537$$
$$= 0.1537 + 5$$

$$N = 1.427 \times 10^5, \text{ or } 142{,}700 \qquad \text{(to four significant figures using linear interpolation)}$$

NOTE: By direct multiplication we obtain 142,465.5, which when rounded to four significant figures is 142,500. The use of logarithms produced an error of two units in the fourth significant figure.

Problem 12. Find the product $(873.2)(21{,}030)$ using logarithms. Also compute the product directly and compare results.

ANSWER

By logarithms: 1.836×10^7, or 18,360,000; by direct computation: 18,363,396.

Example 13. Find the value of $\sqrt[3]{263.8}/(4.37)^4$ using logarithms.

SOLUTION

Let
$$N = \frac{(263.8)^{1/3}}{(4.37)^4}$$
then
$$\log N = \log (263.8)^{1/3} - \log (4.37)^4 = \tfrac{1}{3} \log 263.8 - 4 \log 4.37$$
$$\tfrac{1}{3} \log 263.8 = \tfrac{1}{3}(2.4213) = 0.8071$$
$$4 \log 4.37 = 4(0.6405) = 2.5620$$

Before subtracting, we note that to be able to find N we must have $\log N$ in the form $m + c$, where m is a mantissa (a positive number between 0 and 1), and c is a characteristic (an integer). To obtain the desired $m + c$ form directly, we simply add, and subtract 2 from 0.8071 before we subtract 2.5620. Thus,

$$2.8071 - 2$$
$$-2.5620$$
$$\log N = \overline{\quad 0.2451 - 2}$$
$$N = 1.758 \times 10^{-2} \text{ or } 0.01758$$

Problem 13.   Find $\sqrt[4]{88.18/(2.09)^6}$ using logarithms.

ANSWER

3.678×10^{-2}.

Example 14.   Find $\sqrt[5]{-0.00627}$ using logarithms.

SOLUTION

Since $\log x$ is defined only for positive x, we first determine the sign of the answer, and then proceed with positive quantities only. In this case, the answer will be negative. Let

$$N = (0.00627)^{1/5}$$

then

$$\log N = \tfrac{1}{5} \log (6.27 \times 10^{-3})$$
$$= \tfrac{1}{5}(0.7973 - 3)$$

To keep the arithmetic as short and as simple as possible, we add and subtract 2 to the second factor, so that the integral part of that factor will be exactly divisible by 5. Thus,

$$\log N = \tfrac{1}{5}(2.7973 - 5)$$
$$= 0.5595 - 1$$
$$N = 3.627 \times 10^{-1} \text{ or } 0.3627$$

Hence,

$$\sqrt[5]{-0.00627} = -0.3627$$

Problem 14.   Find $\sqrt[7]{-0.000418}$ using logarithms.

ANSWER

-0.3291.

Logarithms were first conceived by the Scotsman John Napier (1550–1617) as a computational device to ease the backbreaking calculations required in astronomy studies. The new computational tool was immediately welcomed by the mathematical and scientific world. Now, with the increased availability of electronic calculating devices, logarithms have lost some of their importance as a computational tool. However, the logarithmic concept has been greatly generalized since its first introduction, and logarithmic functions are of great importance in both pure and applied mathematics.

EXERCISE 47

A *Compute, using common logarithms.*

1. $(92.4)(837)$
2. $(4.53)(3,620)$
3. $452/32.7$
4. $65.4/8.03$
5. $(5,172)(32.6)$
6. $(6,632,000)(0.0198)$
7. $43.2/6,405$
8. $0.813/25.13$
9. $(0.064)(382.1)(4.07)$
10. $(45)(3,680)(0.5173)$
11. $(5.138)^5$
12. $(32.72)^4$

B 13. $(0.0304)^7$
14. $(0.143)^6$
15. $\sqrt[4]{408.2}$
16. $\sqrt[3]{32.63}$
17. $\sqrt[8]{0.05903}$
18. $\sqrt[7]{0.0004177}$

19. $\dfrac{(0.0517)^3(0.253)}{0.00183}$
20. $\dfrac{(238.1)(0.704)^2}{4.82}$

21. $\dfrac{(0.03039)^3}{(0.00792)(-444)}$
22. $\dfrac{(6,114,000)^2}{(-738,000)(0.0395)}$

23. $\dfrac{(4.63)^3}{\sqrt{0.431}}$
24. $\dfrac{\sqrt[3]{62.5}}{(0.038)^4}$

25. $\sqrt[3]{\dfrac{42.52}{(0.047)(0.964)}}$
26. $\sqrt{\dfrac{(212)(13.72)}{(0.019)}}$

27. $\dfrac{(-0.0732)^{1/5}}{(6430)^2(0.003214)}$
28. $\dfrac{(-547)\sqrt[3]{0.000365}}{(-3691)}$

29. $\dfrac{(538,000)^3(0.002374)^2}{\sqrt[5]{0.1083}}$
30. $\dfrac{(87.64)^{1/3}(-0.0008240)}{(7.923)(0.6273)}$

31. $18^{-1.27}$
32. $(4.63)^{2.08}$
33. $8 - \sqrt[5]{0.00348}$
34. $5 + \sqrt[3]{(7.320)^2}$
35. The time t it takes a simple pendulum L feet long to complete one oscillation (through a small arc) is given by the formula

$$t = 2\pi\sqrt{\dfrac{L}{g}}$$

Find t for a pendulum 5 ft long. (Use $\pi = 3.14$ and $g = 32.2$.)
36. Find the radius of a sphere whose volume is 25 ft³. [$V = (4\pi r^3)/3$; use $\pi = 3.142$.]
37. Suppose a distant ancestor of yours at the time of the birth of Christ deposited $1 in a bank that paid 3% interest compounded annually. How much could you have collected in 1970 if you had been the designated heir?

(Now you should understand why banks do not allow deposits to remain in an inactive account indefinitely.) $[A = A_0(1 + r)^n.]$

38. If when you were born your parents had deposited \$2,000 in a bank for your college education, how much would you have at age 17 if the bank paid 5% interest compounded annually? $[A = A_0(1 + r)^n.]$

c 39. $\sqrt[5]{\sqrt[4]{13.2} - \sqrt[3]{435}} = ?$

40. $(3.08)^{2.32}(42.5)^{0.03} + 4 \log 33.04 = ?$

41. In a study on learning, the psychologist Thurstone found that the time t required for learning a list of symbols varied directly as the $\frac{3}{2}$ power of the number n of items on the list. (A) Write the equation of variation. (B) If it takes a person 2 hr to learn a list of 25 symbols, approximately how many symbols should he be able to learn in 4 hr? (*Hint:* Obtain $2/25^{3/2} = 4/n^{3/2}$, and solve for n.)

42. The German astronomer J. Kepler (1571–1630) discovered that the time t it takes a planet to travel once around the sun varies directly as the $\frac{3}{2}$ power of its mean distance d from the sun. Using 93 million mi as the mean distance between the earth and the sun, and 141.5 million mi as the mean distance between Mars and the sun, compute the number of days it takes Mars to complete one revolution about the sun.

6.6 EXPONENTIAL AND LOGARITHMIC EQUATIONS: CHANGE OF BASE

Often, when dealing with exponential functions, one must solve exponential equations in which the variable appears in the exponent. Logarithms play an important role in the solution of such equations.

Example 15.   Solve $2^{3x-2} = 5$ for x.

SOLUTION

$$2^{3x-2} = 5$$
$$\log 2^{3x-2} = \log 5$$
$$(3x - 2) \log 2 = \log 5$$
$$(3x - 2) = \frac{\log 5}{\log 2}$$
$$x = \frac{1}{3}\left(2 + \frac{\log 5}{\log 2}\right)$$
$$= \frac{1}{3}\left(2 + \frac{0.6990}{0.3010}\right)$$
$$= 1.441$$

NOTE: $\log A/\log B \neq \log A - \log B$.

Problem 15.   Solve $35^{1-2x} = 7$ for x.

ANSWER

0.2263.

The next example illustrates an approach to solving some types of logarithmic equations.

Example 16.   Solve $\log (x + 3) + \log x = 1$.

SOLUTION

$$\log(x + 3) + \log x = 1$$
$$\log[x(x + 3)] = 1$$
$$x(x + 3) = 10^1$$
$$x^2 + 3x - 10 = 0$$
$$(x + 5)(x - 2) = 0$$
$$x = -5, 2$$

-5 is not a solution (why?). Thus 2 is the only solution.

Problem 16.   Solve $\log (x - 15) = 2 - \log x$.

ANSWER

$x = 20$.

With only a table of common logarithms, is it possible to find the logarithm of a number to a base other than 10? The following example illustrates a procedure that is generalized in the next theorem.

Example 17.   Find $y = \log_5 14$, using the common logarithm table in the Appendix.

SOLUTION

To find the logarithm of 14 to the base 5, we form the equivalent exponential equation

$$14 = 5^y$$

and take the common logarithm of both members. Thus,

$$\log 14 = \log 5^y$$
$$\log 14 = y \log 5$$

$$y = \frac{\log 14}{\log 5} = \frac{1.1461}{0.6990} = 1.639$$

Since y also equals $\log_5 14$, we have

$$\log_5 14 = 1.639$$

This change-of-base procedure is generalized in the following theorem.

Theorem 2.
Change-of-
Base
Formula

For $N, a, b > 0$, and $a, b \neq 1$,

$$\log_b N = \frac{\log_a N}{\log_a b}$$

PROOF

Can you supply the reasons for each of the following steps?

$$y = \log_b N$$
$$N = b^y$$
$$\log_a N = \log_a b^y$$
$$\log_a N = y \log_a b$$

$$y = \frac{\log_a N}{\log_a b}$$

$$\log_b N = \frac{\log_a N}{\log_a b}$$

Problem 17. Use the change-of-base formula to find $\log_7 729$.

ANSWER

3.3874.

EXERCISE 48

A   *Solve to two significant figures.*

1. $23 = 3^x$ 2. $5 = 2^x$
3. $10^{5x-2} = 348$ 4. $10^{3x} = 92$
5. $3^{x-2} = 78.4$ 6. $2^{2x-3} = 435$
7. $0.074 = 3^{-x}$ 8. $0.238 = 2^{-x}$
9. $\log x - \log 8 = 1$ 10. $\log 5 + \log x = 2$

B   *Solve to two significant figures (use $e = 2.718$ and $\log e = 0.4343$).*

11. $3 = 1.06^x$ 12. $2 = 1.05^x$
13. $12 = e^{-x}$ 14. $42.1 = e^x$
15. $438 = 100e^{0.25x}$ 16. $123 = 500e^{-0.12x}$
17. $3 = (1 + x)^{18}$ 18. $2 = (1 + x)^{12}$
19. $\log (x - 9) + \log 100x = 3$ 20. $\log x + \log (x - 3) = 1$
21. $e^{\log_e 4x} = 16$ 22. $\log_e e^{3x} = 12$

Find each to four significant figures (use $e = 2.718$ and $\log e = 0.4343$).

23. $\log_{12} 42.8$ 24. $\log_2 12$
25. $\log_e 235$ 26. $\log_e 10$

27. Radioactive strontium 90 is used in nuclear reactors and decays according to the equation

$$A = Pe^{-0.0248t}$$

where P is the amount present at $t = 0$, and A is the amount remaining after t years. If 500 mg of strontium 90 are placed in a nuclear reactor, how much will be left after 10 years?

28. If 500 mg of strontium 90 are placed in a nuclear reactor, how much will be left after 100 years?

29. Find the half-life (to the nearest year) of strontium 90; that is, find t so that $A = P/2$.

30. How long (to the nearest year) will it take for strontium 90 to decompose so that only 1 percent of the original amount remains. (*Hint:* Find t so that $A = 0.01P$.)

31. If you start with 2 cents and double the amount each day, at the end of n days you will have 2^n cents. How many dollars will you have at the end of 31 days?

C 32. Show that $(\log_e 10)(\log_{10} e) = 1$.

33. Show that $(\log_a b)(\log_b a) = 1$ for $a, b > 0$, $a, b \neq 1$.

34. Earlier we mentioned that e could be approximated to any decimal-place accuracy desired by taking the integer n sufficiently large in $[1 + (1/n)]^n$. Use common logarithms to approximate e for $n = 10$ and $n = 100$.

6.7 ADDITIONAL APPLICATIONS

Logarithmic and exponential functions are widely used in both applied and pure mathematics. The following additional applications illustrate the use of these functions in the social, natural, and physical sciences.

EXERCISE 49

In the following problems use e = 2.718 and log *e = 0.4343 where necessary.*

Archaeology—Carbon-14 Dating

Cosmic-ray bombardment of the atmosphere produces neutrons, which in turn react with nitrogen to produce radioactive carbon 14. In 1946, Willard Libby, the Nobel prize-winning chemist, reasoned that carbon 14 entered all living tissues through the carbon dioxide which is first absorbed by plants. As long as a plant or animal is alive, he found, carbon 14 is maintained at a constant level in its tissues. Once dead, however, it ceases taking in carbon and, to the slow beat of time, the carbon 14 diminishes by radioactive decay at a rate determined by its half-life of 5,600 years. Thus, a piece of old bone or a piece of charcoal from an ancient campfire can be dated by measuring the amount of carbon 14 left. The method is reasonably accurate up to about 40 or 50 thousand years, covering ancient civilizations back to Cro-Magnon man.

Mathematically, if at a given time there is A_0 milligrams of carbon 14 in a nonliving substance, at the end of t years there will be

$$A = A_0(\tfrac{1}{2})^{t/5,600} \qquad \text{milligrams}$$

of carbon 14 in that substance.

1. Graph the exponential equation above for $t = 0$, 5,600, 2(5,600), 3(5,600), 4(5,600), and 5(5,600).
2. The remains of an ancient campfire were discovered in a cave near the site of the discovery of Cro-Magnon man in France. Charcoal from the campfire was tested for its carbon-14 content. Estimate the age of the campfire if it was found that 10 percent of the original amount of carbon 14 was still present.

Astronomy—Brightness of Stars

Ever since the time of the Greek astronomer Hipparchus (second century B.C.), the brightness of stars has been measured in terms of *magnitude*. The brightest stars (excluding the sun) are classed as magnitude 1, and the dimmest visible by the eye are classed as magnitude 6. In 1856, the English astronomer N. R. Pegson showed that first-magnitude stars are 100 times brighter than sixth-magnitude stars. And he concluded that the ratio of brightness between any two consecutive magnitudes is $0.01^{1/5}$.

3. Find the ratio of brightness between two consecutive magnitudes, $0.01^{1/5}$, to three decimal places.
4. An optical instrument is required to observe stars beyond the sixth magnitude, the limit of ordinary vision. However, even optical instruments have their limitations. The limiting magnitude LM of any optical telescope with lens diameter D is given by the formula

$$LM = 8.8 + 51 \log_{10} D$$

Find the limiting magnitude of (A) a homemade 6-in. reflecting telescope, (B) the 200-in. Mt. Palomar telescope in California.

Biology—Bacteria Growth

5. At a given temperature, the number of bacteria in milk double every 3 hr. If we start with A_0 bacteria in a batch of milk, after t hours there will be $A = A_0 2^{t/3}$ bacteria in the milk. Graph this exponential function for $t = 0$, 3, 6, 9, 12, and 15; then join these points with a smooth curve.

6. A single cholera bacterium divides every $\frac{1}{2}$ hr to produce two complete cholera bacteria. If we start with a colony of A_0 bacteria, in t hours (assuming adequate food supply) we will have $A = A_0 2^{2t}$ bacteria. Find A for $A_0 = 5,000$ and $t = 12.6$.

Ecology—Human Population Growth

If a population of A_0 people grows at the constant rate of r percent per year, in t years there will be $A = A_0(1 + r)^t$ people in the population. Use this formula for the following two problems.

7. It is estimated that the population of the world is increasing at the rate of 2 percent per year. At this rate how long will it take the world population to double? To triple?

8. If the world population continues to grow at its present growth rate of 2 percent a year, approximately how many square yards of land will there be for each person 565 years from now? (The earth has approximately 1.7×10^{14} yd^2 of land, and the present population is approximately 4×10^9.)

Biology—Ancestors and Heredity

9. Galton's law of heredity states that the influence of ancestors on an individual is as follows: each parent, $\frac{1}{2}$; each grandparent, $(\frac{1}{2})^2$; each great-grandparent, $(\frac{1}{2})^3$; and so on. How much hereditary influence would an ancestor 20 generations back (approximately 600 years) have had on you?

10. For each generation back, the number of our direct ancestors (parents, grandparents, and so forth) doubles. If we figure 30 years to a generation, then how many ancestors did you have 600 years ago? 1,980 years ago? (Note that at the time of Christ there were an estimated 3.5×10^8 people on the earth.)

Business

11. If a certain amount of money P (called the principal) is invested at r percent interest compounded annually, the amount of money A after t years is given by the equation

$$A = P(1 + r)^t$$

How much will $1,000 be worth in 5 years at 6% interest compounded annually?

12. How long (to the nearest year) will it take for a sum of money to double if invested at 5% interest compounded annually?

13. At what rate of interest (compounded annually) should a sum of money be invested if it is to double in 10 years?

14. Monthly payments p on a loan of L dollars for n months at i percent interest per month on the unpaid balance are determined by the formula

$$p = \frac{Li}{1 - (1+i)^{-n}}$$

What are the monthly payments on a 12-month loan of $500 at 1% interest per month on the unpaid balance?

Earth Science

15. For relatively clear bodies of fresh water or saltwater, light intensity is reduced according to the exponential function

$$I = I_0 e^{-kd}$$

where I is the intensity at d feet below the surface, and I_0 is the intensity at the surface; k is called the coefficient of extinction. Two of the clearest bodies of water in the world are the fresh-water Crystal Lake in Wisconsin ($k = 0.0485$) and the saltwater Sargasso Sea off the West Indies ($k = 0.00942$). Find the depths (to the nearest foot) in these two bodies of water at which the light is reduced to 1 percent of that at the surface.

16. An approximation of atmospheric pressure in pounds per square inch may be calculated from the formula

$$P = 14.7e^{-0.21h}$$

where h is altitude above sea level in miles. (A) What is the pressure 2 miles above sea level? (B) What is the pressure at the bottom of a mine shaft $\frac{1}{3}$ mile below sea level? (Use Table 2 in the Appendix.)

Geometry

17. Find the radius of a sphere with surface area 160 in.^{2}. ($A = 4\pi r^2$; use $\pi = 3.142$.)

18. It is possible to show that for a triangle with sides a, b, and c, the area is given by

$$A = \sqrt{s(s-a)(s-b)(s-c)}$$

where s is the semiperimeter $\frac{1}{2}(a+b+c)$. Find the area of a triangle with sides 16, 28.3, and 23.5 ft.

Physics—Sound

Because of the extraordinary range of sensitivity of the human ear (a range of over 1,000 million million to 1), it is helpful to use a logarithmic scale to measure sound intensity over this range rather than an absolute scale. The unit of measure is called the *decibel*, after the inventor of the telephone, Alexander Graham Bell. If we let N be the number of decibels, I the power of the sound in question in watts per cubic centimeter, and I_0 the power of sound just below the threshold of hearing (approximately 10^{-16} watt per cm^2),

$$I = I_0\, 10^{N/10}$$

19. Starting with the decibel formula above, show that $N = 10\log_{10}(I/I_0)$.
20. Use the formula in Prob. 19 (with $I_0 = 10^{-16}$ watt per cm^2) to find the decibel ratings of the following sounds:
    (A) Whisper (10^{-13} watt per cm^2)
    (B) Normal conversation (3.16×10^{-10} watt per cm^2)
    (C) Heavy traffic (10^{-8} watt per cm^2)
    (D) Jet plane with afterburner (10^{-1} watt per cm^2)

Psychology—Learning

In learning a particular task, such as typing or swimming, one progresses faster at the beginning and then levels off. If you plot the level of performance against time, you will obtain a curve of the type shown in Fig. 7. This is called a learning curve and can be very closely approximated by an exponential equation of the form $y = a(1 - e^{-cx})$, where a and c are positive constants. Curves of this type have applications in psychology, education, and industry.

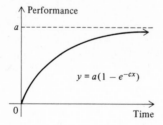

FIGURE 7

21. A particular person's history of learning to type is given by the exponential equation $N = 80(1 - e^{-0.08n})$, where N is the number of words per minute he was able to type after n weeks of instruction. Graph this equation for $n = 0, 5, 10, 15, 20, 25, 30$ (using Table 2 in the Appendix), and join the points with a smooth curve.
22. Approximately how many weeks did it take the person in Prob. 21 to learn to type 60 words per min?

Psychology—Sensation

Professor S. S. Stevens of Harvard University discovered that sensation magnitude y grows as a power function of the stimulus magnitude x, in terms of the formula $y = kx^p$. A law of this form seems to govern our reactions to light, sound, smell, taste, vibration, shock, warmth, and cold.

23. For brightness of light, $y = kx^{0.33}$, where y is the sensed brightness of a light of x candlepower. Approximately what increase in candlepower will double the sensed brightness of a light?

24. For electric shocks, $y = kx^{3.5}$, where y is the sensed magnitude of the shock produced by a current of x amperes. What increase in current will double the sensed magnitude of an electric shock?

Puzzles

25. If a very thin piece of paper 0.001 in. thick is torn in half, and each half is again torn in half, and this process is repeated for a total of 50 times, how high will the paper be if the pieces are stacked one on top of the other? Give the answer to two significant figures in miles (1 mi = 63,360 in.).

26. Find the fallacy.

$$3 > 2$$
$$3 \log \tfrac{1}{2} > 2 \log \tfrac{1}{2}$$
$$\log \left(\tfrac{1}{2}\right)^3 > \log \left(\tfrac{1}{2}\right)^2$$
$$\left(\tfrac{1}{2}\right)^3 > \left(\tfrac{1}{2}\right)^2$$
$$\tfrac{1}{8} > \tfrac{1}{4}$$

EXERCISE 50 CHAPTER-REVIEW EXERCISES

A
1. Write $\log_{10} x = y$ in exponential form.
2. Write $m = 10^n$ in logarithmic form with base 10.

Solve for x without the use of a table.

3. $\log_2 x = 2$ 4. $\log_x 25 = 2$ 5. $\log_2 8 = x$

Use common logarithms to evaluate each problem.

6. $(27{,}300)(0.00418)$ 7. $5.987/0.7904$ 8. $\dfrac{(52.5)(1.33)}{0.079}$

Solve for x to two significant figures.

9. $10^x = 17.5$ 10. $\log 4 + \log x = 2$

B
11. For $f = \{(x, y) \mid y = \log_2 x\}$, graph f and f^{-1} using the same coordinate axes. What are the domains and range of f and f^{-1}?

12. Write $\log_e y = x$ in exponential form.
13. Write $y = e^x$ in logarithmic form with base e.

Solve for x without the use of a table.

14. $\log_{1/4} 16 = x$ 15. $\log_x 9 = -2$ 16. $\log_{16} x = \frac{3}{2}$
17. $\log_x e^5 = 5$ 18. $10^{\log_{10} x} = 33$

Use common logarithms to evaluate each problem.

19. $\dfrac{(0.318)^3}{(0.00457)(328)}$ 20. $\sqrt[7]{0.00004803}$

21. $\sqrt[5]{\dfrac{(0.315)^3}{0.075}}$ 22. $(6.07)^{1.35}$

23. $\sqrt[3]{(752)^2} - 40.32$ 24. If $\log x = -2.6073$, find x.

Solve for x to two significant figures ($e = 2.718$).

25. $25 = 5(2)^x$ 26. $0.01 = e^{-0.05x}$
27. $\log_e x = 0$ 28. $\log(3x^2) - \log 9x = 1$
29. $\log_e e^{x^2} = 4$ 30. $\log_5 23 = x$
31. Many countries in the world have a population growth rate of 3 percent (or more) per year. At this rate how long, to the nearest year, will it take a population to double? [$P = P_0(1.03)^t$.]

c 32. Explain why 1 cannot be used as a logarithmic base.
33. Prove that $\log_b (M/N) = \log_b M - \log_b N$.
34. Write $\log_e y = -5t + \log_e c$ in exponential form free of logarithms.
35. $\log_e 100 = ?$ (*Note: e = 2.718.*)
36. Radioactive argon 39 has a half-life of 4 min. After t minutes the amount A of argon 39 left after starting with A_0 is given by the formula

$$A = A_0(\tfrac{1}{2})^{t/4}$$

Graph this exponential function for $t = 0, 4, 8, 12, 16,$ and 20, and join these points with a smooth curve.
37. How long, to three significant figures, will it take for the carbon 14 to diminish to 1 percent of the original amount after the death of a plant or animal? [$A = A_0(\tfrac{1}{2})^{t/5,600}$.]

Chapter

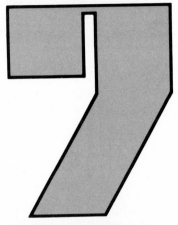

Systems of Equations and Inequalities; Matrices and Determinants

7.1 SYSTEMS OF LINEAR EQUATIONS IN TWO VARIABLES

In elementary algebra you studied systems of linear equations of the type

$$a_1 x + b_1 y = k_1$$
$$a_2 x + b_2 y = k_2$$

(1)

and solved these systems by graphing, substitution, or elimination. In this section we will briefly review these methods.

Recall that the *solution set* of system (1) is the set of all ordered pairs of numbers such that each ordered pair satisfies each equation in the system.

253 | Symbolically,

Solution set of system (1)

$$= \{(x, y) \mid a_1 x + b_1 y = k_1 \text{ and } a_2 x + b_2 y = k_2\}$$
$$= \{(x, y) \mid a_1 x + b_1 y = k_1\} \cap \{(x, y) \mid a_2 x + b_2 y = k_2\}$$

The last expression states that the solution set of system (1) is the intersection of the solution sets of the linear equations in system (1).

Solution by Graphing

Since the graph of each linear equation in system (1) is a straight line, we can look at the intersection of the graphs of these two equations for information about the solutions of the system. Two lines in the same rectangular coordinate system in a plane must be related to each other in one of three ways: (1) they intersect at one and only one point, (2) they are parallel, or (3) they coincide (see Example 1).

Example 1. Solve each of the following systems by graphing.

(A) $2x - 3y = 2$ (B) $4x + 6y = 12$ (C) $2x - 3y = -6$
$\quad\quad x + 2y = 8$ $\quad\quad 2x + 3y = -6$ $\quad\quad -x + \frac{3}{2}y = 3$

SOLUTION

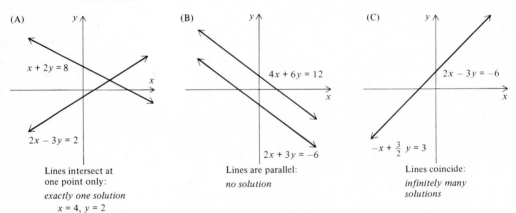

(A)

$x + 2y = 8$

$2x - 3y = 2$

Lines intersect at
one point only:
exactly one solution
$x = 4, y = 2$

(B)

$4x + 6y = 12$

$2x + 3y = -6$

Lines are parallel:
no solution

(C)

$2x - 3y = -6$

$-x + \frac{3}{2}y = 3$

Lines coincide:
infinitely many solutions

Now we know exactly what to expect when solving a system of two linear equations in two unknowns: exactly one pair of numbers as a solution, no solutions, or an infinite number of solutions.

Problem 1. Solve each of the following systems by graphing.

(A) $2x + 3y = 12$ (B) $\quad\quad x - 3y = -3$ (C) $2x - 3y = 12$
$\quad\quad x - 3y = -3$ $-2x + 6y = 12$ $\quad\quad -x + \frac{3}{2}y = -6$

ANSWER

(A) $x = 3$, $y = 2$; (B) no solution; (C) infinitely many solutions.

The graphical method, though yielding useful information, has some limitations. For example, it may be difficult to obtain solutions to more than one- or two-decimal-place accuracy, or if the lines are nearly parallel, the point of intersection may be far from the origin, hence difficult to locate. The following methods provide us with a means of finding solutions (if they exist) to any decimal-place accuracy desired.

Solution by Elimination and by Substitution

The methods of solving systems of equations we are now going to review involve replacing a system of equations with a simpler equivalent system, by use of suitable transformations, and continuing the process until a system is obtained whose solution is obvious. Equivalent systems are, as can be expected, systems with the same solution set. What transformations on systems of equations produce equivalent systems? The following theorem, stated but not proved, partially answers this question.

Theorem 1. A system of equations is transformed into an equivalent system if either equation in the system is replaced by:

(A) An equivalent equation
(B) A nonzero multiple of itself [a special case of (A)]
(C) The sum of it and the other equation

or

(D) The equation resulting from solving one of the equations for one variable in terms of the other and substituting the result into the other equation

Several examples will refresh your memory as to how this theorem is used.

Example 2. Solve the system

$$2x - 3y = 7$$
$$-3x + y = -7$$

Method 1. Elimination

$$(A) \qquad 2x - 3y = 7$$
$$(B) \quad -3x + y = -7$$

$$(A) \qquad 2x - 3y = 7$$
$$3(B) \quad -9x + 3y = -21$$
$$(A) + 3(B) \quad \overline{-7x \qquad = -14} \qquad \text{Eliminate } y \text{ by addition.}$$
$$x = 2$$

$$2 \cdot 2 - 3y = 7 \qquad \text{Substitute } x = 2 \text{ into either}$$
$$-3y = 3 \qquad \text{(A) or (B), the simpler of the}$$
$$y = -1 \qquad \text{two, and solve for } y.$$

Thus, $(2, -1)$ is the solution to the original system, as the reader can readily check.

Method 2. Substitution

$$(A) \qquad 2x - 3y = 7$$
$$(B) \quad -3x + y = -7$$

$$y = 3x - 7 \qquad \text{Solve (B), the simplest choice, for } y$$
$$\text{in terms of } x.$$

$$2x - 3(3x - 7) = 7 \qquad \text{Replace } y \text{ in (A) with } 3x - 7,$$
$$x = 2 \qquad\qquad \text{and solve for } x.$$

$$(-3)(2) + y = -7 \qquad \text{Substitute } x = 2 \text{ into either}$$
$$y = -1 \qquad\qquad \text{(A) or (B) and solve for } y.$$

Problem 2. Solve the following system by elimination, and also by substitution.

$$3x - 4y = 18$$
$$2x + y = 1$$

Answer

$(2, -3)$.

Example 3. Solve the system

$$x + 3y = 2$$
$$2x + 6y = -3$$

SOLUTION

$$
\begin{array}{rl}
\text{(A)} & x + 3y = 2 \\
\text{(B)} & 2x + 6y = -3 \\
-2\text{(A)} & -2x - 6y = -4 \\
\text{(B)} & \underline{2x + 6y = -3} \\
-2\text{(A)} + \text{(B)} & 0 = -7 \qquad \text{(a contradiction)}
\end{array}
$$

Our assumption that there are values for x and y that satisfy (A) and (B) simultaneously must be false (otherwise, we have proved that $0 = -7$). If you check the slope of each line, you will find they are the same (but the y intercepts are different); hence, the lines are parallel, and the system has no solution. Systems of this type are called *inconsistent*—conditions have been placed on the variables x and y that are impossible to meet.

Problem 3. Solve the system

$$
\begin{array}{l}
3x - 4y = -2 \\
-6x + 8y = 1
\end{array}
$$

ANSWER

No solution.

Example 4. Solve the system

$$
\begin{array}{l}
-2x + y = -8 \\
x - \tfrac{1}{2}y = 4
\end{array}
$$

SOLUTION

$$
\begin{array}{rl}
\text{(A)} & -2x + y = -8 \\
\text{(B)} & x - \tfrac{1}{2}y = 4 \\
\text{(A)} & -2x + y = -8 \\
2\text{(B)} & \underline{2x - y = 8} \\
\text{(A)} + 2\text{(B)} & 0 = 0
\end{array}
$$

Both sides have been eliminated. Actually, if we had multiplied (B) by -2, we would have obtained (A). When one equation is a constant multiple of the other, the system is said to be *dependent*, and the graphs will coincide. There are infinitely many solutions to the system—any solution of one equation will be a solution of the other.

Problem 4. Solve the system

$$6x - 3y = -2$$
$$-2x + y = \tfrac{2}{3}$$

ANSWER

Infinitely many solutions.

Applications

Many applications can be solved using two-equations-two-unknowns methods. The following example illustrates the process.

Example 5. A jeweler has two bars of gold alloy in stock, one 12 carat and the other 18 carat (24-carat gold is pure gold, 12-carat gold is $\tfrac{12}{24}$ pure, 18-carat gold is $\tfrac{18}{24}$ pure, and so on). How many grams of each alloy must be mixed to obtain 10 grams of 14-carat gold?

SOLUTION

Let

$x =$ number of grams of 12-carat gold used

$y =$ number of grams of 18-carat gold used

$x + y = 10$	Amount of new alloy.
$\tfrac{12}{24}x + \tfrac{18}{24}y = \tfrac{14}{24}(10)$	Pure gold present before mixing equals pure gold present after mixing.
$x + y = 10$ $6x + 9y = 70$	Multiply second equation by $\tfrac{24}{2}$ to simplify, and then solve using methods described above. (We use elimination here.)

$$
\begin{aligned}
-6x - 6y &= -60 \\
\underline{6x + 9y} &= \underline{70} \\
3y &= 10 \\
y &= 3\tfrac{1}{3} \qquad \text{grams of 18-carat alloy}
\end{aligned}
$$

$$
\begin{aligned}
x + 3\tfrac{1}{3} &= 10 \\
x &= 6\tfrac{2}{3} \qquad \text{grams of 12-carat alloy}
\end{aligned}
$$

The checking of solutions is left to the reader.

Problem 5. Repeat Example 5 using the fact that the jeweler has only 10-carat and pure gold in stock.

ANSWER

$2\frac{6}{7}$ grams of pure gold and $7\frac{1}{7}$ grams of 10-carat gold.

EXERCISE 51

A *Solve by graphing.*

1. $3x - 2y = 12$
   $7x + 2y = 8$
2. $x + 5y = -10$
   $-5x + y = 24$
3. $3x + 5y = 15$
   $6x + 10y = -5$
4. $3x - 5y = 15$
   $x - \frac{5}{3}y = 5$

Solve by elimination

5. $3p + 8q = 4$
   $15p + 10q = -10$
6. $3x - y = -3$
   $5x + 3y = -19$
7. $6x - 2y = 18$
   $-3x + y = -9$
8. $4m + 6n = 2$
   $6m - 9n = 15$

Solve by substitution.

9. $2x + y = 6$
   $y = x + 3$
10. $m - 2n = 0$
    $-3m + 6n = 8$
11. $3x - y = -3$
    $5x + 3y = -19$
12. $2m - 3n = 9$
    $m + 2n = -13$
13. A bank gave you \$1.50 in change consisting of only nickels and dimes. If there were 22 coins in all, how many of each type of coin did you receive?
14. A friend of yours came out of a post office having spent \$1.32 on thirty 4-cent and 5-cent stamps. How many of each type did he buy?
15. If the sum of two angles in a right triangle is 90° and their difference is 14°, find the two angles.
16. Find the dimensions of a rectangle with perimeter 72 in., if its length is 25 percent greater than its width.

B *Solve each system by graphing, elimination, and by substitution.*

17. $x - 3y = -11$
    $2x + 5y = 11$
18. $5x + y = 4$
    $x - 2y = 3$
19. $11x + 2y = 1$
    $9x - 3y = 24$
20. $2x + y = 0$
    $3x + y = 2$

Use any of the methods discussed in this section to solve each system.

21. $y = 3x - 3$
    $6x = 8 + 3y$
22. $3m = 2n$
    $n = -7 - 2m$
23. $\frac{1}{2}x - y = -3$
    $-x + 2y = 6$
24. $y = 2x - 1$
    $6x - 3y = -1$

25. $2x + 3y = 2y - 2$
    $3x + 2y = 2x + 2$

26. $2u - 3v = 1 - 3u$
    $4v = 7u - 2$

27. $0.2x - 0.5y = 0.07$
    $0.8x - 0.3y = 0.79$

28. $0.5m + 0.2n = 0.54$
    $0.3m - 0.6n = 0.18$

29. $(x/4) - (2y/3) = -2$
    $(x/2) - \quad y \quad = -2$

30. $\frac{2}{3}a + \frac{1}{2}b = 2$
    $\frac{1}{2}a + \frac{1}{3}b = 1$

31. $(5/u) - (2/v) = -\frac{7}{2}$
    $-(3/u) + (4/v) = \frac{7}{2}$

32. $(2/x) - (4/y) = -2$
    $(3/x) + (5/y) = -\frac{1}{4}$

33. A packing carton contains 144 small packages, some weighing $\frac{1}{4}$ lb each and the others $\frac{1}{2}$ lb each. How many of each type are in the carton if the total contents of the carton weighs 51 lb?

34. A biologist, in a nutrition experiment, wants to prepare a special diet for his experimental animals. He requires a food mixture that contains, among other things, 20 oz of protein and 6 oz of fat. He is able to purchase food mixes of the following composition:

	Protein (%)	Fat (%)
Mix A	20	2
Mix B	10	6

How many ounces of each mix should he use to prepare the diet mix? Solve graphically and algebraically.

35. A chemist has two concentrations of hydrochloric acid in stock, a 50% solution and an 80% solution. How much of each should he mix to obtain 100 cc of a 68% solution?

36. A newspaper printing plant has two folding machines for the final assembling of the evening newspaper—circulation, 29,000. The slower machine can fold papers at the rate of 6,000 per hour, and the faster machine at the rate of 10,000 per hour. If the use of the slower machine is delayed $\frac{1}{2}$ hr because of a minor breakdown, how much total time is required to fold all the papers? How much time does each machine spend on the job?

37. A ship using sound-sensing devices above and below water recorded a surface explosion 6 sec sooner by its underwater device than its above-water device. Sound travels in air at about 1,100 fps and in sea water at about 5,000 fps. (A) How long did it take each sound wave to reach the ship? (B) How far was the explosion from the ship?

38. An earthquake emits a primary wave and a secondary wave. Near the surface of the earth the primary wave travels at about 5 mi per sec, and the secondary wave at about 3 mi per sec. From the time lag between the two waves arriving at a given station, it is possible to estimate the distance to the quake. (The *epicenter* can be located by obtaining distance bearings at three or more stations.) Suppose a station measured a time difference of 16 sec between the arrival of the two waves. How long did each wave travel, and how far was the earthquake from the station?

39. Two companies have offered you a sales position. Both jobs are essentially the same, but one company pays a straight 8% commission and the other

pays $51 per week plus a 5% commission. The best salesmen with either company rarely have sales greater than $4,000 in any 1 week. Before accepting either offer, it would be helpful to know at what point both companies pay the same, and which of the companies pays more on either side of this point. Solve graphically and algebraically.

40. Solve Prob. 39 with the straight-commission company paying 7% commission and the salary-plus-commission company paying $75 per week plus 4% commission.

C 41. What is the relationship of the graphs of $m(Ax + By + C) + n(Dx + Ey + F) = 0$, m and n any real numbers (not both zero), and the intersection of the graphs of $Ax + By + C = 0$ and $Dx + Ey + F = 0$, assuming they intersect?

42. In a particular city the weekly supply and demand for popular stereo records, relative to average price per record p, are given by the equations

$$d = 5,000 - 1,000p \qquad \$1 \leq p \leq \$4$$
$$s = -3,000 + 3,000p \qquad \$1 \leq p \leq \$4$$

At what price does the supply equal the demand (equilibrium point)? (A) Solve graphically. (B) Solve algebraically.

43. A psychologist trained a group of rats (in an experiment on motivation and avoidance) to run down a narrow passage in a cage to receive food in a goal box. He put a harness on each rat, and connected it to an overhead wire attached to a scale. In this way he could place the rat different distances from the food and measure the pull (in grams) of the rat toward the food. He found that a relation between motivation and distance was given approximately by the equation $p = -\frac{1}{5}d + 70$, $30 \leq d \leq 175$, where p is pull in grams, and d is distance from the goal box in centimeters.

The psychologist then replaced the food with a mild electric shock, and with the same apparatus he was able to measure the avoidance strength relative to the distance from the object to be avoided. He found that the avoidance strength was given approximately by $a = -\frac{4}{3}d + 230$, $30 \leq d \leq 175$, where a is avoidance measured in grams, and d is distance from the goal box in centimeters.

If the rat were trained in both experiments, at what distance from the goal box would the approach and avoidance strengths be the same? Solve algebraically and graphically. What do you predict that the rat would do if placed to the right of this point (assume the goal box is on the right)? To the left of this point?

44. The management of a small plant that manufactures high-performance surfboards estimates fixed costs (rent, labor, insurance, and so on) to be $120 per day, and variable costs (materials, packaging, and so on) to be $60 per board. (A) If the company sells each board for $90, how many must be sold each day to break even? What are the costs and returns for this number? (B) Graph the cost equation and the return equation on the same coordinate system, assuming a plant capacity of 12 boards per day, and interpret the regions between the lines to the left of the breakeven point and to the right of the breakeven point.

7.2 SYSTEMS OF LINEAR INEQUALITIES IN TWO VARIABLES

Single-Inequality Statements

We know how to graph first-degree equations such as

$$y = 2x - 3$$

or

$$2x - 3y = 5$$

but how do we graph

$$y \le 2x - 3$$

or

$$2x - 3y > 5$$

We will find that graphing these inequalities is almost as easy as graphing the equalities. The following discussion leads to a simple solution to the problem.

A line in a Cartesian coordinate system divides the plane into two *half planes*. A vertical line divides the plane into left and right half planes; a nonvertical line divides the plane into upper and lower half planes, according to the location of each point as indicated in Fig. 1. Now let us compare the graphs of

$$y < 2x - 3$$
$$y = 2x - 3$$

and

$$y > 2x - 3$$

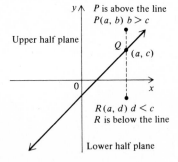

FIGURE 1

Consider the vertical line $x = x_0$, and ask what the relationship of y is to $2x_0 - 3$ as we move (x_0, y) up and down this vertical line (see Fig. 2). If we are at point Q, then $y = 2x_0 - 3$; if we move up the vertical line to P, the ordinate of (x_0, y) increases and $y > 2x_0 - 3$; if we move down the line to R, the ordinate of (x_0, y) decreases and $y < 2x_0 - 3$. Since the same results are obtained for each point on the x axis, we conclude that the graph of $y > 2x - 3$ is the upper half plane determined by $y = 2x - 3$, and $y < 2x - 3$ is the lower half plane.

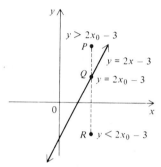

FIGURE 2

In graphing $y > 2x - 3$, we show the line $y = 2x - 3$ as a broken line, indicating that it is not part of the graph; in graphing $y \geq 2x - 3$, we show the line $y = 2x - 3$ as a solid line, indicating that it is part of the graph. Figure 3 illustrates four typical cases.

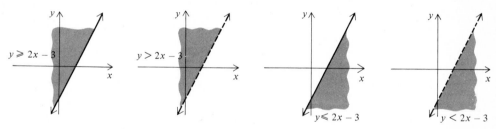

FIGURE 3

The preceding discussion suggests the following important theorem, which we state without proof.

Theorem 2. The graph of a linear inequality

$$Ax + By < C$$

or

$$Ax + By > C$$

with $B \neq 0$, is either the upper half plane or the lower half plane (but not both) determined by the line $Ax + By = C$. If $B = 0$, the graph of

$$Ax < C$$

or

$$Ax > C$$

is either the left half plane or the right half plane (but not both) as determined by the line $Ax = C$.

This theorem leads to a simple, fast procedure for graphing linear inequalities in two variables:

1. First, graph $Ax + By = C$
   As a broken line if equality is not included in original statement
   As a solid line if equality is included in original statement
2. Choose a test point in the plane not on the line—the origin is the best choice if it is not on the line—and substitute the coordinates into the inequality.
3. The graph of the original inequality includes
   The half plane containing the test point, if the inequality is satisfied by that point
   The half plane not containing the test point, if the inequality is not satisfied by that point

Example 6. Graph $3x - 4y \leq 12$.

SOLUTION

First graph the line $3x - 4y = 12$. Pick a convenient test point above or below the line. The origin requires the least computation. We see that $3 \cdot 0 - 4 \cdot 0 \leq 12$ is true; hence, the graph of the inequality is the upper half plane.

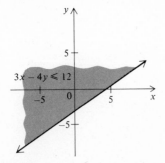

Problem 6.   Graph $2x + 3y \leq 6$.

ANSWER

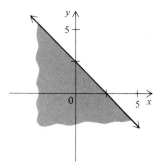

Example 7.   Graph (A) $y > -3$, (B) $2x < 5$, and (C) $-2 \leq x \leq 4$.

SOLUTION

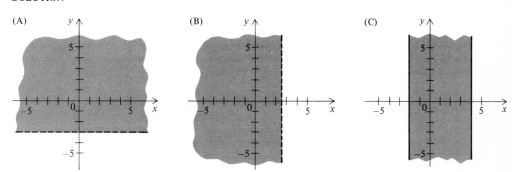

Problem 7.   Graph (A) $y < 2$, (B) $3x > -8$, and (C) $1 \leq y \leq 5$.

ANSWER

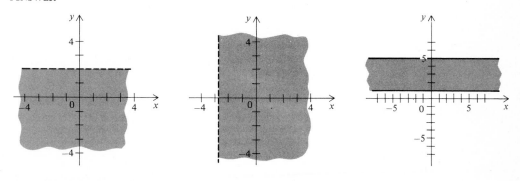

Systems of Inequality Statements

As in systems of linear equations in two variables, we say that the ordered pair of numbers (x_0, y_0) is a solution of a system of linear inequalities in two variables if the ordered pair satisfies each inequality in the system. Thus, the graph of a system of linear inequalities is the intersection of the graphs of each inequality in the system. In this book we will limit our investigation of solutions of systems of inequalities to graphical methods. An example will illustrate the process.

Example 8.   Find the solution set of the system graphically.

$$3x + 5y \geq 60$$
$$4x + 2y \geq 40$$
$$2 \leq x \leq 14$$
$$6 \leq y \leq 18$$

SOLUTION

To find the solution set, we graph each of the inequalities in the system and find the intersection of all these sets of points. Thus,

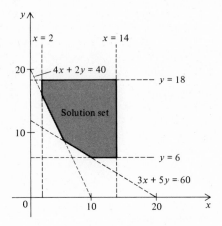

Problem 8.   Find the solution set of the system graphically:

$$2x + 3y \leq 18$$
$$0 \leq x < 6$$
$$0 \leq y < 4$$

ANSWER

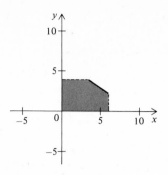

EXERCISE 52

A *Graph each inequality.*

1. $2x - 3y < 6$
3. $3x + 2y \geq 18$
5. $y \leq \frac{2}{3}x + 5$
7. $y < 8$
9. $-3 \leq y < 2$

2. $3x + 4y < 12$
4. $3y - 2x \geq 24$
6. $y \geq (x/3) - 2$
8. $x > -5$
10. $-1 < x \leq 3$

B *Find the solution set of each system graphically.*

11. $-2 \leq x < 2$
    $-1 < y \leq 6$
13. $2x + y \leq 8$
    $0 \leq x \leq 3$
    $0 \leq y \leq 5$
15. $2x + y \leq 8$
    $x + 3y \leq 12$
    $x \geq 0$
    $y \geq 0$

12. $-4 \leq x < -1$
    $-2 < y \leq 5$
14. $x + 3y \leq 12$
    $0 \leq x \leq 8$
    $0 \leq y \leq 3$
16. $x + 2y \leq 10$
    $3x + y \leq 15$
    $x \geq 0$
    $y \geq 0$

C 17. Graph $\{(x, y) | 4x + 3y \leq 24, 0 \leq x \leq 4, \text{ and } 0 \leq y \leq 5\}$.

18. Graph $\{(x, y) | y \leq x + 6, 0 \leq x \leq 7, \text{ and } y \geq 0\}$.

19. A sports car dealer has display and storage facilities for a maximum of 30 cars. He must decide how many of each of two models to stock. His company produces a standard and a deluxe model. He knows from past experience that he cannot sell more than 15 deluxe models and 25 standard models. If s is the number of standard models and d is the number of deluxe models the dealer is willing to order, write a system of inequalities indicating the restrictions on s and d. Graph this system, showing the permissible values for s and d.

20. A manufacturer of surfboards makes a standard model and a competition model. The pertinent manufacturing data is summarized in the table:

	Standard model (man-hours per board)	Competition model (man-hours per board)	Maximum man-hours available per week
Fabricating	6	8	120
Finishing	1	3	30

If x is the number of standard models and y is the number of competition models produced per week, write a system of inequalities indicating the restrictions on x and y. Graph this system, showing the region of permissible values for x and y.

Linear Programming

Several of the problems in Exercise 68 are actually related to a more general type of problem. Take, for example, the surfboard problem, which we will repeat here in part and extend.

Example 9. A manufacturer of surfboards makes a standard model and a competition model. The relevant manufacturing data are:

	Standard model (man-hours per board)	Competition model (man-hours per board)	Maximum man-hours available per week
Fabricating	6	8	120
Finishing	1	3	30
Profit per board sold	$20	$40	

How many boards of each type should be manufactured each week to produce a maximum profit (assuming that all boards made can be sold)?

SOLUTION

Let x and y be the respective number of standard and competition boards produced per week. These variables are restricted as follows:

$$6x + 8y \leq 120$$
$$x + 3y \leq 30$$
$$x \geq 0$$
$$y \geq 0$$

The solution set of this system of inequalities is the shaded area in Fig. 4. The problem now is to see what combination of x and y in this shaded area produces a maximum profit.

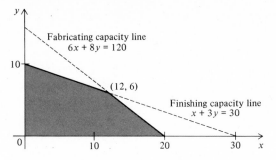

FIGURE 4

Each standard model sold produces a profit of $20, and each competition model a profit of $40. If we let P represent the total weekly profit, then

$$P = 20x + 40y$$

Plotting *constant-profit* lines, we see (Fig. 5) that we obtain a family of parallel lines which move away from the origin as the profit increases. (To see this, write the profit equation in slope-intercept form and observe how the y intercept increases as the profit increases.) The maximum profit occurs at a point where a constant-profit line is furthest from the origin but still in contact with the shaded area. This occurs at (12, 6) in this example. If the manufacturer makes 12 standard and 6 competition surfboards per week, he will realize a maximum profit of

$$P = 20 \cdot 12 + 40 \cdot 6$$
$$= \$480$$

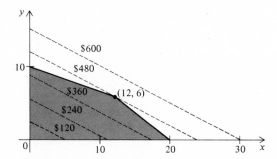

FIGURE 5

The procedure used to solve this problem falls under the general heading of *linear programming*. Linear programming is a mathematical method used to find an optimum policy relative to the attainment of certain well-defined objectives or goals. Its widespread use by the government and industry since World War II has been possible only because of the development of electronic computers. Many linear programming problems now involve the use of several thousand variables and almost as many inequalities.

Problem 9.   Repeat Example 9 using 5 hr for fabricating a standard board in place of 6 hr, and a maximum of 31 man-hours for finishing in place of 30 hr.

ANSWER

16 standard models, 5 competition models.

EXERCISE 53

1. Work Example 9 with the company making a profit of $10 on the standard model and $40 on the competition model.
2. Work Example 9 with the company making a profit of $30 on each board.
3. A sports car dealer has display and storage facilities for a maximum of 30 cars. He must decide how many of each of two models to stock. His company produces a standard and a deluxe model. He knows from past experience that he cannot sell more than 15 deluxe models and 25 standard models. A profit of $250 is made on each standard model, and $500 on each deluxe model. Assuming that the dealer is fairly certain of selling any combination of models that meets these conditions, how many of each model should he order if he is to make a maximum profit?
4. A small manufacturing company makes two types of radios, a transistor model and a vacuum tube model. The relevant manufacturing data is:

	Transistor (man-hours per radio)	Tube (man-hours per radio)	Maximum man-hours available per week
Fabricating	4	1	16
Assembling	1	3	15
Profit per radio sold	$12	$10	

How many radios of each type should be manufactured each day to produce a maximum profit (assuming that all radios made can be sold)?

7.3 SYSTEMS INVOLVING SECOND-DEGREE EQUATIONS IN TWO VARIABLES

In this section we will investigate nonlinear systems of the type

$$ax^2 + bxy + cy^2 = d$$
$$ex + fy = g$$

and

$$a_1 x^2 + b_1 xy + c_1 y^2 = d_1$$
$$a_2 x^2 + b_2 xy + c_2 y^2 = d_2$$

The methods used will be similar to those used to solve linear systems. Several examples should make the process clear.

Example 10. Solve the system

$$4x^2 + y^2 = 25$$
$$2x + y = 7$$

SOLUTION

The substitution principle is effective. Solve the linear equation for one variable in terms of the other, and then substitute into the nonlinear equation to obtain a quadratic equation in one variable. Thus,

$$y = 7 - 2x$$

is substituted into the second-degree equation to obtain

$$4x^2 + (7 - 2x)^2 = 25$$

Now we solve for x:

$$8x^2 - 28x + 24 = 0$$
$$2x^2 - 7x + 6 = 0$$
$$(2x - 3)(x - 2) = 0$$
$$x = \tfrac{3}{2}, 2$$

These values are substituted back into the linear equation to find the corresponding values for y. (Note that if we substitute these values back into the second-degree equations, we may obtain "extraneous" roots; try it and see why.)

For $x = \frac{3}{2}$,

$$2(\tfrac{3}{2}) + y = 7$$
$$y = 4$$

For $x = 2$,

$$2(2) + y = 7$$
$$y = 3$$

Thus $(\frac{3}{2}, 4)$ and $(2, 3)$ are solutions to the system, as can easily be checked.

Problem 10.   Solve

$$2x^2 - y^2 = 1$$
$$3x + y = 2$$

ANSWER

$(1, -1), (\frac{5}{7}, -\frac{1}{7})$.

Example 11.   Solve

$$x^2 - y^2 = 5$$
$$x^2 + 2y^2 = 17$$

SOLUTION

$$x^2 - y^2 = 5$$
$$\underline{x^2 + 2y^2 = 17}$$
$$-3y^2 = -12$$
$$y = \pm 2$$

Proceed as with linear equations—subtract to eliminate x.

For $y = 2$,

$$x^2 - (2)^2 = 5$$
$$x = \pm 3$$

For $y = -2$,

$$x^2 - (-2)^2 = 5$$
$$x = \pm 3$$

Thus $(3, -2), (3, 2), (-3, -2)$, and $(-3, 2)$ are the four solutions to the system. The checking of the solutions is left to the reader.

Problem 11. Solve

$$2x^2 - 3y^2 = 5$$
$$3x^2 + 4y^2 = 16$$

ANSWER

$(2, 1), (2, -1), (-2, 1), (-2, -1).$

Example 12. Solve

$$x^2 + 3xy + y^2 = 20 \tag{1}$$
$$xy - y^2 = 0 \tag{2}$$

SOLUTION

$$y(x - y) = 0 \qquad \text{Factor Eq. (2).}$$

$y = 0 \qquad \text{or} \qquad x - y = 0 \qquad$ Substitute each of these in turn
$$\qquad\qquad\qquad\qquad y = x \qquad$$ into Eq. (1), and proceed as before.

For $y = 0$,

$$x^2 + 3x(0) + (0)^2 = 20$$
$$x = \pm 2\sqrt{5}$$

For $y = x$,

$$y^2 + 3yy + y^2 = 20$$
$$\qquad\qquad y = \pm 2 \qquad$$ Substitute these values back into $y = x$
$$\qquad\qquad\qquad\qquad$$ to find corresponding values of x.

For $y = 2$, $x = 2$; for $y = -2$, $x = -2$.

Thus $(2\sqrt{5}, 0), (-2\sqrt{5}, 0), (2, 2),$ and $(-2, -2)$ are the four solutions to the system. The checking of the solutions is left to the reader.

Problem 12. Solve

$$x^2 + xy - y^2 = 4$$
$$2x^2 - xy = 0$$

ANSWER

$(0, 2i), (0, -2i), (2i, 4i), (-2i, -4i)$.

Example 12 is somewhat specialized. However, it suggests a procedure that, when used alone or in combination with other procedures, is effective for some problems.

To obtain an idea of how many solutions one might expect from a system of second-degree equations in two variables, one has only to look at the number of ways two conics can intersect. This gives us information about real solutions. Actually, it turns out that a system of one linear and one quadratic equation can have at most two solutions, and a system of two quadratic equations can have at most four solutions. Of course, some of the solutions may be complex.

EXERCISE 54

A *Solve each system.*

1. $x^2 + y^2 = 169$
   $x = -12$

2. $x^2 + y^2 = 25$
   $y = -4$

3. $8x^2 - y^2 = 16$
   $y = 2x$

4. $y^2 = 2x$
   $x = y - \frac{1}{2}$

5. $2x^2 - 3y^2 = 25$
   $x + y = 0$

6. $x^2 + 4y^2 = 32$
   $x + 2y = 0$

7. $y^2 = -x$
   $x - 2y = 5$

8. $x^2 = 2y$
   $3x = y + 5$

9. $2x^2 + y^2 = 24$
   $x^2 - y^2 = -12$

10. $x^2 - y^2 = 3$
    $x^2 + y^2 = 5$

11. $x^2 + y^2 = 10$
    $16x^2 + y^2 = 25$

12. $x^2 - 2y^2 = 1$
    $x^2 + 4y^2 = 25$

B 13. $xy = -4$
     $y - x = 2$

14. $xy - 6 = 0$
    $x - y = 4$

15. $x^2 - 2xy + y^2 = 1$
    $x - 2y = 2$

16. $x^2 + xy - y^2 = -5$
    $y - x = 3$

17. $2x^2 + 3y^2 = -4$
    $4x^2 + 2y^2 = 8$

18. $2x^2 - 3y^2 = 10$
    $x^2 + 4y^2 = 17$

19. $x^2 - y^2 = 2$
    $y^2 = x$

20. $x^2 + y^2 = 20$
    $x^2 = y$

21. $x^2 + y^2 = 5$
    $x^2 = 4(2 - y)$

22. $x^2 + y^2 = 16$
    $y^2 = 4 - x$

23. $x^2 - y^2 = 3$
    $xy = 2$

24. $2x^2 + y^2 = 18$
    $xy = 4$

25. $2x^2 - xy + y^2 = 8$
    $(x - y)(x + y) = 0$

26. $x^2 + 2xy + y^2 = 36$
    $x^2 - xy = 0$

27. $x^2 + xy - 3y^2 = 3$ 28. $x^2 - 2xy + 2y^2 = 16$
    $x^2 + 4xy + 3y^2 = 0$ $x^2 \qquad - y^2 = 0$

29. Find two numbers such that their sum is 1 and their product is 1.
30. Find the dimensions of a rectangle with an area of 32 ft^2 and perimeter 36 ft.

c   *Solve Probs. 31 to 34 graphically for all real solutions.*

31. The system in Prob. 3
32. The system in Prob. 4
33. The system in Prob. 11
34. The system in Prob. 12
35. Find the dimensions of a rectangle with an area of 60 in.^{2} if its diagonal is 13 in.
36. The daily demand equation for a certain brand of ballpoint pen in a given city is $dp = 1,000$, and the supply equation is $s = 5p - 50$, where d is the number of pens shoppers are willing to buy at p cents each, and s is the number the supplier is willing to sell at p cents each. At what price will supply equal demand; that is, at what price will $s = d$?

7.4 SYSTEMS OF LINEAR EQUATIONS IN MORE THAN TWO VARIABLES; ROW-EQUIVALENT MATRICES

In Sec. 9.1 we solved systems of linear equations in two variables. There is no reason to stop there. Systems of the form

$$
\begin{aligned}
a_1 x + b_1 y + c_1 z &= k_1 \\
a_2 x + b_2 y + c_2 z &= k_2 \\
a_3 x + b_3 y + c_3 z &= k_3
\end{aligned} \tag{1}
$$

as well as higher-order systems, are encountered frequently and are worth studying.

An ordered triple of numbers (x_0, y_0, z_0) is a *solution* of system (1) if the ordered triple satisfies each equation in system (1). The set of all such ordered triples of numbers is called the *solution set* of system (1). Symbolically,

Solution set of system (1)

$$
\begin{aligned}
&= \{(x, y, z) \mid a_1 x + b_1 y + c_1 z = k_1\} \\
&\cap \{(x, y, z) \mid a_2 x + b_2 y + c_2 z = k_2\} \\
&\cap \{(x, y, z) \mid a_3 x + b_3 y + c_3 z = k_3\}
\end{aligned}
$$

Two systems are said to be *equivalent* if they have the same solution set. Similar definitions hold for fourth-order and higher systems.

If we were given a system to solve of the form

$$3x \qquad\qquad = -9$$
$$x + y \qquad = -2$$
$$-x - 3y + z = -2$$

we would consider ourselves lucky since the solution is almost obvious. [From the first equation we find that $x = -3$. This value is substituted into the second equation, and we find that $y = 1$. These two values are substituted into the third equation, and z is found to be 2. Hence $(-3, 1, 2)$ is the solution of the system.]

The above system is an example of a triangular system. In general, a system is a *triangular system* if

1. One of the equations in the system yields the value of one of the unknowns directly.
2. After substituting this value into a second equation, the value of a second unknown is determined.
3. After substituting these two values into a third equation, a third unknown is determined.

and so on.

Unfortunately, most of the systems one encounters are not triangular systems. By the use of suitable transformations, however, one is often able to change a complicated system into an equivalent triangular system whose solution is easily determined. The next theorem, a slight modification of Theorem 1 in Sec. 9.1, provides us with the means of carrying out these transformations.

Theorem 3. A system of equations is transformed into an equivalent system if:

(A) The position of any two equations is interchanged.
(B) Any equation in the system is multiplied by a nonzero constant.
(C) Any equation is replaced by the sum of it and a nonzero constant multiple of another equation in the system.

Example 13. Solve by transforming into an equivalent triangular system.

$$2x - 3y + z = 10$$
$$x + 2y + 4z = 12$$
$$3x - y - 2z = 1$$

SOLUTION

$$\begin{aligned} 3x - y - 2z &= 1 \\ x + 2y + 4z &= 12 \\ 2x - 3y + z &= 10 \end{aligned}$$

Interchange the first and last equations (Theorem 3A).

$$\begin{aligned} 7x - 7y &= 21 \\ x + 2y + 4z &= 12 \\ 2x - 3y + z &= 10 \end{aligned}$$

Replace the first equation with the sum of it and 2 times the third equation (Theorem 3C).

$$\begin{aligned} x - y &= 3 \\ -7x + 14y &= -28 \\ 2x - 3y + z &= 10 \end{aligned}$$

Multiply the first equation by $\frac{1}{7}$ (Theorem 3B); replace the second equation by the sum of it and -4 times the third equation (Theorem 3C).

$$\begin{aligned} x - y &= 3 \\ x - 2y &= 4 \\ 2x - 3y + z &= 10 \end{aligned}$$

Multiply the second equation by $-\frac{1}{7}$ (Theorem 3B).

$$\begin{aligned} x - y &= 3 \\ -y &= 1 \\ 2x - 3y + z &= 10 \end{aligned}$$

Replace the second equation with the sum of it and -1 times the first equation (Theorem 3C).

We now have a triangular system whose solution is

$(2, -1, 3)$

Problem 13. Solve by transforming into an equivalent triangular system.

$$\begin{aligned} 2x - y + z &= 0 \\ x + 2y - 2z &= 5 \\ 3x - 4y - 3z &= -5 \end{aligned}$$

ANSWER

$(1, 2, 0)$.

If we encounter, in the process of transforming a system of equations into an equivalent triangular system, an equation that states a contradiction, such as $0 = -2$, then we must conclude that the system has no solution (that is, the system is inconsistent). If, on the other hand, one of the equations turns out to be $0 = 0$, then the system is either dependent or inconsistent. It is generally easy to determine which it is at this stage of the solution process.

The above process can be speeded up substantially by the introduction of matrices. A *matrix* is a rectangular array of numbers written within a bracket. Thus,

$$\begin{bmatrix} 2 & 0 \\ -3 & 1 \end{bmatrix} \qquad \begin{bmatrix} 4 \\ 0 \\ -3 \end{bmatrix} \qquad [1 \quad 1 \quad 5]$$

$$\begin{bmatrix} 1 & -2 & 0 & 3 \\ 3 & 8 & 6 & -1 \end{bmatrix} \qquad \begin{bmatrix} 1 & 0 & 0 \\ 0 & 1 & 0 \\ 0 & 0 & 1 \end{bmatrix}$$

are matrices. Associated with each linear system of the form

$$a_1 x + b_1 y + c_1 z = k_1$$
$$a_2 x + b_2 y + c_2 z = k_2 \qquad\qquad (2)$$
$$a_3 x + b_3 y + c_3 z = k_3$$

is a matrix called the *augmented matrix* of the system:

$$\begin{bmatrix} a_1 & b_1 & c_1 & k_1 \\ a_2 & b_2 & c_2 & k_2 \\ a_3 & b_3 & c_3 & k_3 \end{bmatrix}$$

This array of numbers contains the essential parts of system (2). We will say that two augmented matrices are *row-equivalent* if they are augmented matrices of equivalent systems of equations. The following transformations transform augmented matrices into row-equivalent forms. These operations come, of course, directly from Theorem 3.

Theorem 4. Augmented matrices are transformed into row-equivalent forms by the following operations if:

(A) Two rows are interchanged.
(B) Any row is multiplied by a nonzero constant.
(C) Any row is replaced by the sum of it and a nonzero constant multiple of another row.

Proofs of parts of this theorem are left as exercises. To solve a system using an augmented matrix, we write the augmented matrix of a given system, transform it into an augmented matrix of an equivalent triangle system, and proceed as before. The matrix saves a lot of writing of unnecessary symbols. We will now repeat Example 13, using augmented matrix methods.

Example 14. Solve the system in Example 13, using augmented matrix methods. NOTE: $\sim$ means "is equivalent to."

SOLUTION

$$2x - 3y + z = 10$$
$$x + 2y + 4z = 12 \qquad \text{(system)}$$
$$3x - y - 2z = 1$$

$$\begin{bmatrix} 2 & -3 & 1 & 10 \\ 1 & 2 & 4 & 12 \\ 3 & -1 & -2 & 1 \end{bmatrix} \qquad \text{(augmented matrix)}$$

$$\begin{bmatrix} 2 & -3 & 1 & 10 \\ 1 & 2 & 4 & 12 \\ 3 & -1 & -2 & 1 \end{bmatrix} \overset{\textcircled{1}}{\sim} \begin{bmatrix} 3 & -1 & -2 & 1 \\ 1 & 2 & 4 & 12 \\ 2 & -3 & 1 & 10 \end{bmatrix} \overset{\textcircled{2}}{\sim}$$

$$\begin{bmatrix} 7 & -7 & & 21 \\ 1 & 2 & 4 & 12 \\ 2 & -3 & 1 & 10 \end{bmatrix} \overset{\textcircled{3}}{\sim} \begin{bmatrix} 1 & -1 & & 3 \\ -7 & 14 & & -28 \\ 2 & -3 & 1 & 10 \end{bmatrix} \overset{\textcircled{4}}{\sim}$$

$$\begin{bmatrix} 1 & -1 & & 3 \\ 1 & -2 & & 4 \\ 2 & -3 & 1 & 10 \end{bmatrix} \overset{\textcircled{5}}{\sim} \begin{bmatrix} 1 & -1 & & 3 \\ & -1 & & 1 \\ 2 & -3 & 1 & 10 \end{bmatrix}$$

① Interchange the first and last rows (Theorem 4A).
② Replace the first row by the sum of it and 2 times the last row (Theorem 4C).
③ Multiply the first row by $\frac{1}{7}$ (Theorem 4B); replace the second row by the sum of it and -4 times the third row (Theorem 4C).
④ Multiply the second row by $-\frac{1}{7}$ (Theorem 4B).
⑤ Replace the second row by the sum of it and -1 times the first row (Theorem 4C).

The last matrix is the augmented matrix of the triangular system

$$x - y = 3$$
$$ -y = 1$$
$$2x - 3y + z = 10$$

which has the solution $(2, -1, 3)$.

Problem 14. Solve the system in Prob. 13, using augmented matrix methods.

ANSWER

(1, 2, 0).

With a little practice, the augmented matrix method of solving linear systems of higher order turns out to be a fairly efficient method. After you understand the transformations, arithmetical errors account for the major difficulties in the process.

EXERCISE 55

A *Solve each triangular system.*

1. $5x - 2y = -3$
   $3y = 12$

2. $2x = -6$
   $-x + 4y = -1$

3. $-2x = 2$
   $x - 3y = 2$
   $-x + 2y + 3z = -7$

4. $2v + w = -4$
   $u - 3v + 2w = 9$
   $-v = 3$

Solve, using augmented matrix methods.

5. $7s - 2t = -1$
   $-s + 3t = -8$

6. $u - 2v = -4$
   $5u + 6v = -4$

7. $4s + t = -3$
   $3s + 2t = 4$
   $6r - 5s - 2t = 0$

8. $x - 4y = 11$
   $2x + y = 4$
   $-x - 3y + z = 3$

B 9. $x - 3y + z = 4$
   $-x + 4y - 4z = 1$
   $2x - y + 5z = -3$

10. $2a + 4b + 3c = 6$
   $a - 3b + 2c = -7$
   $-a + 2b - c = 5$

11. $x - 8y + 2z = -1$
   $x - 3y + z = 1$
   $2x - 11y + 3z = 2$

12. $-x + 2y - z = -4$
   $4x + y - 2z = 1$
   $x + y - z = -1$

13. $(1/u) + (3/v) + (1/w) = 9$
   $(2/u) - (1/v) - (4/w) = 9$
   $-(1/u) - (1/v) + (5/w) = -15$

14. $(2/x) + (1/y) + (3/z) = -9$
   $(1/x) - (4/y) - (2/z) = 15$
   $(1/x) + (6/y) + (1/z) = -14$

15. A circle in a rectangular coordinate system can be written in the form $x^2 + y^2 + Dx + Ey + F = 0$. Find D, E, and F so that the circle passes through $(-2, -1)$, $(-1, -2)$, and $(6, -1)$.

16. Solve Prob. 15 if the circle is required to pass through $(0, 3)$, $(3, 1)$, and $(6, -1)$.

17. A zoologist, in an experiment involving mice, finds he needs a food mix that contains, among other things, 23 grams of protein, 6.2 grams of fat,

and 16 grams of moisture. He has on hand mixes of the following compositions:

	Protein (%)	Fat (%)	Moisture (%)
Mix A	20	2	15
Mix B	10	6	10
Mix C	15	5	5

How many grams of each mix should he use to obtain the desired diet mix?

18. A newspaper firm uses three printing presses, of different ages and capacities, to print the evening paper. With all three presses running, the paper can be printed in 2 hr. If the newest press breaks down, then the older two presses can print the paper in 4 hr; if the middle press breaks down, the newest and oldest together can print the paper in 3 hr. How long would it take each press alone to print the paper? [*Hint:* Use $(2/x) + (2/y) + (2/z) = 1$ as one of the equations.]

C *Solve, using augmented matrix methods.*

19.
$$2r - s + 2t - u = 5$$
$$r - 2s + t + u = 1$$
$$-r + s - 3t - u = -1$$
$$-r - 2s + t + 2u = -4$$

20.
$$4w - x = 5$$
$$-3w + 2x - y = -5$$
$$2w - 5x + 4y + 3z = 13$$
$$2w + 2x - 2y - z = -2$$

It is clear that $(0, 0, 0)$ *is a solution to each of the following two systems. Do the systems have any other solutions?*

21.
$$x - 4y + 9z = 0$$
$$4x - y + 6z = 0$$
$$x - y + 3z = 0$$

22.
$$3x - y + 3z = 0$$
$$5x + 5y - 9z = 0$$
$$-2x + y - 3z = 0$$

23. Prove Theorem 4A.

24. Prove Theorem 4B.

7.5 MATRICES AND MATRIX ADDITION

In the last section an important new mathematical concept was introduced, namely, that of a matrix. In this section and those following, we will develop this concept further.

Recall that we defined a *matrix* as any rectangular array of numbers enclosed within brackets. The size or *dimension* of a matrix is important relative to operations on matrices. We define an *m × n matrix* (read "*m*-by-*n* matrix") to be one with *m* rows and *n* columns—the number of rows is always given first. If a matrix has the same number of rows and columns, it is called a *square matrix*. A matrix with only one column is called a *column matrix*, and one with only one row, a *row matrix*. These definitions are illustrated by the following matrices:

$$
\begin{array}{cccc}
2 \times 3 & 3 \times 3 & 4 \times 1 & 1 \times 3 \\
\begin{bmatrix} -2 & 3 & 0 \\ 1 & 5 & -6 \end{bmatrix} &
\begin{bmatrix} 1 & -3 & 0 \\ -2 & 1 & 5 \\ 3 & 0 & 2 \end{bmatrix} &
\begin{bmatrix} -2 \\ 0 \\ 3 \\ 5 \end{bmatrix} &
\begin{bmatrix} 6 & 0 & -3 \end{bmatrix}
\end{array}
$$

Square matrix (below the 3×3) · Row matrix (below the 1×3) · Column matrix (below the 4×1)

Two matrices are *equal* if they have the same dimensions and the corresponding elements are equal. For example,

$$
\begin{bmatrix} w & x \\ y & z \end{bmatrix} = \begin{bmatrix} a & b \\ c & d \end{bmatrix} \Leftrightarrow \begin{cases} w = a \\ x = b \\ y = c \\ z = d \end{cases}
$$

The *sum of two matrices* of the same dimension is a matrix whose elements are the sum of the corresponding elements of the two given matrices. Addition is not defined on matrices with different dimensions.

Example 15. (A) $\begin{bmatrix} w & x \\ y & z \end{bmatrix} + \begin{bmatrix} a & b \\ c & d \end{bmatrix} = \begin{bmatrix} w+a & x+b \\ y+c & z+d \end{bmatrix}$

(B) $\begin{bmatrix} -3 & 0 & 1 \\ 5 & 2 & -4 \end{bmatrix} + \begin{bmatrix} 5 & 3 & -2 \\ -2 & 0 & 5 \end{bmatrix} = \begin{bmatrix} 2 & 3 & -1 \\ 3 & 2 & 1 \end{bmatrix}$

Problem 15. Add

$$
\begin{bmatrix} 2 & -3 & 0 \\ 0 & 5 & -1 \\ 2 & -1 & 3 \end{bmatrix} + \begin{bmatrix} -1 & 2 & 3 \\ 1 & -6 & -1 \\ 2 & 1 & -3 \end{bmatrix}
$$

ANSWER

$$
\begin{bmatrix} 1 & -1 & 3 \\ 1 & -1 & -2 \\ 4 & 0 & 0 \end{bmatrix}.
$$

A matrix whose elements are all zeros is called a *zero matrix*. For example,

$$
\begin{bmatrix} 0 & 0 & 0 \\ 0 & 0 & 0 \end{bmatrix} \qquad \begin{bmatrix} 0 \\ 0 \\ 0 \end{bmatrix} \qquad \begin{bmatrix} 0 & 0 \\ 0 & 0 \end{bmatrix}
$$

are zero matrices of different dimensions. The *negative of a matrix M*, denoted by $-M$, is a matrix whose elements are the negative of the corresponding elements in M. Thus, if

$$M = \begin{bmatrix} a & b \\ c & d \end{bmatrix}$$

then

$$-M = \begin{bmatrix} -a & -b \\ -c & -d \end{bmatrix}$$

Note that $M + (-M) = 0$ (a zero matrix).

Finally, we define *subtraction* as follows: If A and B are matrices of the same dimension, then

$$A - B = A + (-B)$$

Example 16.

$$\begin{bmatrix} 5 & 3 \\ -2 & 1 \end{bmatrix} - \begin{bmatrix} 2 & -2 \\ 0 & 5 \end{bmatrix} = \begin{bmatrix} 5 & 3 \\ -2 & 1 \end{bmatrix} + \begin{bmatrix} -2 & 2 \\ 0 & -5 \end{bmatrix} = \begin{bmatrix} 3 & 5 \\ -2 & -4 \end{bmatrix}$$

Problem 16. Subtract

$$\begin{bmatrix} -3 & 0 & 1 \\ 5 & 2 & -4 \end{bmatrix} - \begin{bmatrix} 5 & 3 & -2 \\ -2 & 0 & 5 \end{bmatrix}$$

ANSWER

$$\begin{bmatrix} -8 & -3 & 3 \\ 7 & 2 & -9 \end{bmatrix}.$$

Group Structure*

The following structure should look familiar to you from your experience with real numbers:

Group Let S be a set of elements, with the binary operation $*$ satisfying the following properties: If A, B, and C are elements of S, then:

1. CLOSURE PROPERTY: $A * B$ is a unique element in S
2. ASSOCIATIVE PROPERTY: $(A * B) * C = A * (B * C)$
3. COMMUTATIVE PROPERTY: $A * B = B * A$

* May be omitted without loss of continuity.

4. IDENTITY: There is a unique element I in S such that for every element A in S, $A * I = A$

5. INVERSE: For each element A in S, there exists a unique element $-A$ in S such that $A * (-A) = I$

Any set of elements with a binary operation that satisfies properties 1, 2, 4, and 5 is called a *group*. If, in addition, condition 3 is satisfied, then the set of elements under the given binary operation is called a *commutative group*.

Recall that, under the operation of addition, the set of real numbers satisfies the above five conditions; hence, it is called a commutative group relative to addition. You should not find it difficult to check that the set of all matrices of the same dimension and with real-number elements also forms a commutative group relative to the operation of addition. We can conclude, because of these observations, that symbols that name real numbers and symbols that name matrices of the same dimension can be manipulated in essentially the same way relative to the operation of addition.

EXERCISE 56

A Problems 1 to 18 refer to the following matrices:

$$A = \begin{bmatrix} 2 & -1 \\ -5 & 0 \end{bmatrix} \quad B = \begin{bmatrix} -3 & -2 \\ 0 & 4 \end{bmatrix} \quad C = \begin{bmatrix} 6 \\ -1 \\ 0 \end{bmatrix}$$

$$D = \begin{bmatrix} -3 & 2 & 0 & 1 \\ 0 & 1 & 5 & -1 \\ 4 & -2 & 2 & 0 \end{bmatrix} \quad E = \begin{bmatrix} -3 & 2 & 0 & 4 \end{bmatrix} \quad F = \begin{bmatrix} -3 & 4 \\ 0 & 5 \\ 2 & -1 \end{bmatrix}$$

1. What are the dimensions of matrices B, D, and E?
2. What are the dimensions of matrices A, C, and F?
3. What element is in the third row and first column of matrix F?
4. What element is in the second row and fourth column of matrix D?
5. Write a zero matrix of the same dimension as matrix E.
6. Write a zero matrix of the same dimension as matrix D.
7. Identify all column matrices.
8. Identify all row matrices.
9. Identify all 3×3 square matrices.
10. Identify all 2×2 square matrices.
11. Write the negative of matrix F.
12. Write the negative of matrix B.
13. Add A and B.
14. Why cannot D and F be added?

15. Subtract A from B.

16. Subtract B from A.

B 17. Is $A - B = -(B - A)$?

18. Does $-(-A) = A$?

In Probs. 19 to 24 add or subtract as indicated.

19. $[-6 \quad 8] + [2 \quad -3]$

20. $\begin{bmatrix} 3 & -2 \\ -1 & 0 \end{bmatrix} + \begin{bmatrix} -2 & -1 \\ 3 & 4 \end{bmatrix}$

21. $\begin{bmatrix} 6 & -3 & 1 \\ -2 & 0 & 5 \end{bmatrix} + \begin{bmatrix} 2 & -5 & -1 \\ 2 & 3 & -2 \end{bmatrix}$

22. $\begin{bmatrix} -1 & 0 & 2 \\ 3 & -2 & 5 \\ 1 & 7 & 0 \end{bmatrix} + \begin{bmatrix} 4 & -3 & -1 \\ 0 & 4 & -8 \\ 2 & 5 & -4 \end{bmatrix}$

23. $\begin{bmatrix} -5 & 2 \\ 0 & -3 \end{bmatrix} - \begin{bmatrix} -2 & 2 \\ -3 & -1 \end{bmatrix}$

24. $\begin{bmatrix} 6 & -1 \\ 0 & -3 \\ -2 & 5 \end{bmatrix} - \begin{bmatrix} 4 & 3 \\ 2 & -1 \\ -1 & -3 \end{bmatrix}$

25. Find w, x, y, and z so that

$$\begin{bmatrix} w & x \\ y & z \end{bmatrix} + \begin{bmatrix} 3 & 0 \\ -1 & 5 \end{bmatrix} = \begin{bmatrix} 2 & 1 \\ 6 & -3 \end{bmatrix}$$

26. Find a, b, c, d, e, and f so that

$$\begin{bmatrix} a & b & c \\ d & e & f \end{bmatrix} - \begin{bmatrix} 3 & -2 & 1 \\ 5 & 0 & -4 \end{bmatrix} = \begin{bmatrix} -1 & -2 & 3 \\ -2 & 4 & 6 \end{bmatrix}$$

C 27. Which of the following sets form a commutative group under the operation of addition?

(A) The set of positive integers

(B) The set of integers

(C) The set of rational numbers

28. Which of the following sets form a commutative group under the operation of addition?

(A) The set of real numbers

(B) The set of complex numbers

29. If

$$A = \begin{bmatrix} a & b \\ c & d \end{bmatrix}$$

what is the additive inverse of A?

30. What is the additive identity in the set of all 2×2 matrices whose elements are real numbers?

31. Let S be the set of all 2×2 matrices with real-number elements. Show that the matrices of S form a commutative group under the operation of addition. (Assume the real numbers form a commutative group under the operation of addition.)

7.6 MATRIX MULTIPLICATION

Any element from the set of real numbers is also called a *scalar*. We define the *product of a matrix M and a scalar k*, denoted by kM, to be the matrix formed by multiplying each element of M by k. This definition is partially motivated by the fact that, if M is a matrix, then we would like $M + M$ to equal $2M$.

Example 17.
$$(-3)\begin{bmatrix} -2 & 1 \\ -4 & 3 \\ 0 & 6 \end{bmatrix} = \begin{bmatrix} 6 & -3 \\ 12 & -9 \\ 0 & -18 \end{bmatrix}$$

Problem 17. Find
$$(-2)\begin{bmatrix} -2 & 0 & 1 \\ 3 & -2 & 5 \end{bmatrix}$$

ANSWER
$$\begin{bmatrix} 4 & 0 & -2 \\ -6 & 4 & -10 \end{bmatrix}.$$

Preliminary to defining the product of two matrices, we define the *scalar product* of two special matrices, a $1 \times n$ row matrix and an $n \times 1$ column matrix, as follows:

$$[a_1 \quad a_2 \quad \cdots \quad a_n] \cdot \begin{bmatrix} b_1 \\ b_2 \\ \vdots \\ b_n \end{bmatrix} = a_1 b_1 + a_2 b_2 + \cdots + a_n b_n \qquad \text{(a scalar)}$$

The dot between the two matrices is important, since it indicates a scalar product; if the dot is omitted, the multiplication is of another type, which we will consider below.

Example 18.
$$[-1 \quad 0 \quad 3] \cdot \begin{bmatrix} -2 \\ 3 \\ -1 \end{bmatrix} = (-1)(-2) + 0(3) + 3(-1) = 2 + 0 - 3 = -1$$

Problem 18.

$$[2 \quad -1 \quad 0 \quad 3] \cdot \begin{bmatrix} -1 \\ 2 \\ 3 \\ 4 \end{bmatrix} = ?$$

ANSWER

8.

We are now ready to define the product of two matrices.

Definition 1.
Product of
Two Matrices
The product of two matrices A and B is defined only on the assumption that the number of columns of A is equal to the number of rows of B. If A is an $m \times p$ matrix and B is a $p \times n$ matrix, the product of A and B, denoted by AB, is an $m \times n$ matrix whose element in the ith row and jth column is the scalar product of the ith-row matrix of A and the jth-column matrix of B.

It is important to check dimensions before starting multiplication; that is, if matrix A has the dimension $a \times b$ and matrix B has the dimension $c \times d$, for AB to be defined, b must be equal to c. Under these conditions AB can be found, and will have the dimension $a \times d$. To fix ideas, we multiply a 2×3 matrix by a 3×2 matrix and obtain a 2×2 matrix as follows:

$$\overset{2 \times 3}{\begin{bmatrix} 2 & -1 & 3 \\ 1 & 2 & -1 \end{bmatrix}} \overset{3 \times 2}{\begin{bmatrix} 3 & 2 \\ 0 & -1 \\ 1 & -2 \end{bmatrix}} =$$

$$\begin{bmatrix} [2 \quad -1 \quad 3] \cdot \begin{bmatrix} 3 \\ 0 \\ 1 \end{bmatrix} & [2 \quad -1 \quad 3] \cdot \begin{bmatrix} 2 \\ -1 \\ -2 \end{bmatrix} \\ [1 \quad 2 \quad -1] \cdot \begin{bmatrix} 3 \\ 0 \\ 1 \end{bmatrix} & [1 \quad 2 \quad -1] \cdot \begin{bmatrix} 2 \\ -1 \\ -2 \end{bmatrix} \end{bmatrix} \overset{2 \times 2}{=} \begin{bmatrix} 9 & -1 \\ 2 & 2 \end{bmatrix}$$

Example 19.

$$\overset{3 \times 2}{\begin{bmatrix} 3 & 2 \\ 0 & -1 \\ 1 & -2 \end{bmatrix}} \overset{2 \times 4}{\begin{bmatrix} 2 & -1 & 3 & 0 \\ 1 & 2 & -1 & -5 \end{bmatrix}} = \overset{3 \times 4}{\begin{bmatrix} 8 & 1 & 7 & -10 \\ -1 & -2 & 1 & 5 \\ 0 & -5 & 5 & 10 \end{bmatrix}}$$

Problem 19. Find the product

$$\begin{bmatrix} -1 & 1 & -2 \\ 0 & 3 & 1 \end{bmatrix} \begin{bmatrix} 1 & -1 \\ 2 & 3 \\ 0 & -2 \end{bmatrix}$$

ANSWER

$$\begin{bmatrix} 1 & 8 \\ 6 & 7 \end{bmatrix}.$$

Compare Example 19 with the illustration that precedes it. We note that interchanging the order of multiplication makes a difference; that is, in general, multiplication of matrices is not commutative. Matrices do, however, have other general properties. We state three here, leaving the proofs to the exercises. Assuming all products and sums involved are defined,

$$(AB)C = A(BC) \qquad \text{(associative property)}$$
$$A(B + C) = AB + AC \qquad \text{(left-hand distributive property)}$$
$$(B + C)A = BA + CA \qquad \text{(right-hand distributive property)}$$

Matrices are used extensively in both the social sciences and physical sciences. A simplified application of matrices to a business problem is as follows.

A manufacturer of skis produces two models: standard and competition. Standard skis require 5, 1, and 0.2 man-hours, respectively, for fabricating, finishing, and packaging, and competition skis 7, 2, and 0.2 man-hours, respectively. The management can keep track of weekly labor costs using matrix multiplication. Thus,

Pairs of skis   Man-hours
per wk   per pair   Man-hours per wk

$$[100 \quad 10] \begin{bmatrix} 5 & 1 & 0.2 \\ 7 & 2 & 0.2 \end{bmatrix} = [570 \quad 120 \quad 22]$$

Stan-   Compe- Fabri-   Finish-   Pack-   Fabri-   Finish-   Pack-
dard   tition   cating   ing   aging   cating   ing   aging
skis   skis   dept.   dept.   dept.   dept.   dept.   dept.

Now, if labor costs are given in dollars per man-hour for each department by the column matrix

$$\begin{bmatrix} \$8 \\ \$10 \\ \$3 \end{bmatrix} \qquad \begin{array}{l} \text{(fabricating dept.)} \\ \text{(finishing dept.)} \\ \text{(packaging dept.)} \end{array}$$

then we can multiply this matrix by the man-hours-per-week matrix above to obtain the weekly labor costs for running all three departments.

$$[570 \quad 120 \quad 22] \begin{bmatrix} \$8 \\ \$10 \\ \$3 \end{bmatrix} = [\$5,826]$$

More realistic problems require the use of much larger matrices, and electronic computers are used to store the relevant data and to carry out the matrix multiplications.

EXERCISE 57

A *Perform the operations as indicated, where*

$$A = \begin{bmatrix} 3 & 0 \\ -2 & 1 \end{bmatrix} \quad and \quad B = \begin{bmatrix} -2 & 1 \\ 4 & -1 \end{bmatrix}$$

1. $4B$
3. $3A + B$

2. $3A$
4. $A + 2B$

Find the scalar products.

5.
$$[3 \quad 1] \cdot \begin{bmatrix} 2 \\ 4 \end{bmatrix}$$

6.
$$[2 \quad 4] \cdot \begin{bmatrix} 3 \\ 1 \end{bmatrix}$$

7.
$$[-4 \quad -1] \cdot \begin{bmatrix} 3 \\ -2 \end{bmatrix}$$

8.
$$[-3 \quad 2] \cdot \begin{bmatrix} -1 \\ -2 \end{bmatrix}$$

Find the matrix products.

9.
$$[1 \quad 3] \begin{bmatrix} 2 & 3 \\ 1 & -4 \end{bmatrix}$$

10.
$$[2 \quad 5] \begin{bmatrix} 1 & -1 \\ 2 & 3 \end{bmatrix}$$

11.
$$\begin{bmatrix} -1 & 1 \\ 2 & -3 \end{bmatrix} \begin{bmatrix} 4 \\ -2 \end{bmatrix}$$

12.
$$\begin{bmatrix} 3 & 4 \\ -1 & -2 \end{bmatrix} \begin{bmatrix} -1 \\ 2 \end{bmatrix}$$

13.
$$\begin{bmatrix} -3 & 2 \\ 4 & -1 \end{bmatrix} \begin{bmatrix} -2 & 5 \\ -1 & 3 \end{bmatrix}$$

14.
$$\begin{bmatrix} 2 & -3 \\ 1 & 2 \end{bmatrix} \begin{bmatrix} 1 & -1 \\ 0 & -2 \end{bmatrix}$$

15.
$$\begin{bmatrix} -2 & 1 \\ 0 & -3 \end{bmatrix} \begin{bmatrix} -5 & -2 \\ 1 & -3 \end{bmatrix}$$

16.
$$\begin{bmatrix} -5 & -2 \\ 1 & -3 \end{bmatrix} \begin{bmatrix} -2 & 1 \\ 0 & -3 \end{bmatrix}$$

B *Perform the operations as indicated, where*

$$C = \begin{bmatrix} -1 & 2 \\ 0 & -4 \\ 2 & -3 \end{bmatrix} \quad and \quad D = \begin{bmatrix} 5 & -2 \\ 3 & 5 \\ -1 & 0 \end{bmatrix}$$

17. $-3D$
19. $3D - C$

18. $-2C$
20. $2C - 3D$

Find the scalar products.

21.
$$[-1 \quad -3 \quad 2] \cdot \begin{bmatrix} -2 \\ 4 \\ 0 \end{bmatrix}$$

22.
$$[2 \quad -1 \quad 3] \cdot \begin{bmatrix} -1 \\ -2 \\ 2 \end{bmatrix}$$

23.
$$[3 \quad -2 \quad 0 \quad 4] \cdot \begin{bmatrix} -1 \\ 2 \\ 3 \\ -2 \end{bmatrix}$$

24.
$$[4 \quad -3 \quad -1 \quad 2] \cdot \begin{bmatrix} -1 \\ -3 \\ 0 \\ 5 \end{bmatrix}$$

Find the matrix products.

25.
$$\begin{bmatrix} -1 & -4 & 3 \\ 2 & 0 & 1 \end{bmatrix} \begin{bmatrix} 2 & -3 \\ 1 & 2 \\ 0 & -1 \end{bmatrix}$$

26.
$$\begin{bmatrix} 2 & -1 & 1 \\ 1 & 3 & -2 \end{bmatrix} \begin{bmatrix} 1 & 3 \\ 0 & -1 \\ -2 & 2 \end{bmatrix}$$

27.
$$\begin{bmatrix} 2 & -3 \\ 1 & 2 \\ 0 & -1 \end{bmatrix} \begin{bmatrix} -1 & -4 & 3 \\ 2 & 0 & 1 \end{bmatrix}$$

28.
$$\begin{bmatrix} 1 & 3 \\ 0 & -1 \\ -2 & 2 \end{bmatrix} \begin{bmatrix} 2 & -1 & 1 \\ 1 & 3 & -2 \end{bmatrix}$$

29.
$$[1 \quad -2 \quad 2] \begin{bmatrix} 2 \\ -1 \\ 1 \end{bmatrix}$$

30.
$$[3 \quad -2 \quad -4] \begin{bmatrix} 1 \\ 2 \\ -3 \end{bmatrix}$$

31.
$$\begin{bmatrix} 2 \\ -1 \\ 1 \end{bmatrix} [1 \quad -2 \quad 2]$$

32.
$$\begin{bmatrix} 1 \\ 2 \\ -3 \end{bmatrix} [3 \quad -2 \quad -4]$$

In Probs. 33 to 38 verify each statement, using

$$A = \begin{bmatrix} 4 & 2 \\ 0 & 0 \end{bmatrix} \qquad B = \begin{bmatrix} 2 & 1 \\ -2 & 4 \end{bmatrix} \qquad C = \begin{bmatrix} -1 & 2 \\ 4 & 2 \end{bmatrix}$$

33. $AB \neq BA$

34. $(AB)C = A(BC)$

35. $(B + C)A = BA + CA$

36. $A(B + C) = AB + AC$

37. $(B + C)(B - C) \neq B^2 - C^2$

38. $AB = AC$ (Could this happen in the real numbers with $A \neq 0$ and $B \neq C$?)

C 39. Prove that $(AB)C = A(BC)$ for all 2×2 matrices.

40. Prove that $A(B + C) = AB + AC$ for all 2×2 matrices.

41. Show that the linear system

$$2x - 3y = 5$$
$$x + 2y = -1$$

can be written as a matrix equation $AX = D$ where

$$A = \begin{bmatrix} 2 & -3 \\ 1 & 2 \end{bmatrix} \qquad X = \begin{bmatrix} x \\ y \end{bmatrix} \qquad D = \begin{bmatrix} 5 \\ -1 \end{bmatrix}$$

42. Write the system

$$x - 2y + 3z = -1$$
$$2x \quad\;\; - z = 3$$
$$-x + 2y \quad\quad = -2$$

in matrix form (see Prob. 41).

43. (A) If $\begin{matrix} u = 2x + y \\ v = 3x - 2y \end{matrix}$, find u and v if $x = 1$ and $y = -2$.

(B) Show that the matrix equation

$$\begin{bmatrix} u \\ v \end{bmatrix} = \begin{bmatrix} 2 & 1 \\ 3 & -2 \end{bmatrix} \begin{bmatrix} x \\ y \end{bmatrix}$$

is equivalent to the system in part (A). Use the matrix equation to find u and v for $x = 1$ and $y = -2$.

(C) The equations in parts (A) and (B) are examples of linear transformations. Under such a transformation, a point in the xy plane is "mapped" into a point in the uv plane. Consider the pair of transformations

$$\begin{matrix} u = 2x + y \\ v = 3x - 2y \end{matrix} \quad \text{and} \quad \begin{matrix} m = u - v \\ n = u + 2v \end{matrix}$$

Find m and n in terms of x and y. Write the result as a matrix equation, and compare the coefficient matrix with the product of the coefficient matrices of the two transformations, that is, with the product

$$\begin{bmatrix} 1 & -1 \\ 1 & 2 \end{bmatrix} \begin{bmatrix} 2 & 1 \\ 3 & -2 \end{bmatrix}$$

This result provides additional insight into the definition of the product of two matrices. (See Fig. 6 for a geometric interpretation.)

$$\begin{bmatrix} m \\ n \end{bmatrix} = \begin{bmatrix} 1 & -1 \\ 1 & 2 \end{bmatrix} \begin{bmatrix} 2 & 1 \\ 3 & -2 \end{bmatrix} \begin{bmatrix} x \\ y \end{bmatrix} = \begin{bmatrix} -1 & 3 \\ 8 & -3 \end{bmatrix} \begin{bmatrix} x \\ y \end{bmatrix}$$

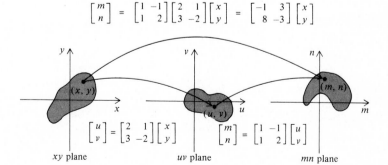

$$\begin{bmatrix} u \\ v \end{bmatrix} = \begin{bmatrix} 2 & 1 \\ 3 & -2 \end{bmatrix} \begin{bmatrix} x \\ y \end{bmatrix} \qquad \begin{bmatrix} m \\ n \end{bmatrix} = \begin{bmatrix} 1 & -1 \\ 1 & 2 \end{bmatrix} \begin{bmatrix} u \\ v \end{bmatrix}$$

xy plane $\qquad\qquad uv$ plane $\qquad\qquad mn$ plane

FIGURE 6

Cliques and Communication Nets*

A fairly recent and interesting use of matrices is to be found in studies on communication nets and cliques within groups of people, such as legislative bodies, neighborhood groups, and administrative groups in business or government. Matrix multiplication can show us quickly and accurately when cliques exist, who belongs to them, and which individuals have the greatest number of "connections" within a group. In short, we can obtain a fairly clear picture of the power or communication structure within a group.

We define a *clique* to be all (but minimally three) persons in a group who choose each other mutually. Individual alliances within a group can be conveniently exhibited using a square matrix. For example, in a group of five members alliances might be exhibited by

$$M = \begin{array}{c} \\ a \\ b \\ c \\ d \\ e \end{array} \begin{array}{ccccc} a & b & c & d & e \\ \left[\begin{array}{ccccc} 0 & 0 & 1 & 1 & 0 \\ 1 & 0 & 0 & 1 & 0 \\ 1 & 0 & 0 & 1 & 1 \\ 1 & 1 & 1 & 0 & 1 \\ 1 & 0 & 0 & 1 & 0 \end{array}\right] \end{array}$$

where 1 in the ith row and jth column means that the person associated with the ith row chooses the person associated with the jth column; a zero entry means "does not choose." Thus, a chooses c, but does not choose b; c chooses a, but does not choose b; and so on. By convention, zeros are always chosen for the main diagonal.

We now convert matrix M to a symmetric matrix S; that is, to one in which the element in the ith row and jth column is made zero if the element in the jth row and ith column is zero. Thus,

$$S = \left[\begin{array}{ccccc} 0 & 0 & 1 & 1 & 0 \\ 0 & 0 & 0 & 1 & 0 \\ 1 & 0 & 0 & 1 & 0 \\ 1 & 1 & 1 & 0 & 1 \\ 0 & 0 & 0 & 1 & 0 \end{array}\right]$$

Several interesting and useful theorems can be proved about the entries in various powers of S. We state three here without proof.†

Theorem 5.   In S^2, the ith diagonal entry has a value of m if and only if person i is in a symmetric relation with m members of the group.

---

* May be omitted without loss of continuity.
† The interested reader might want to pursue the subject further by consulting P. F. Lazarsfeld and N. W. Henry's "Readings in Mathematical Social Science," Science Research Associates, Inc., Chicago, 1966, p. 111.

Theorem 6. A person i is in a clique if and only if the ith entry in the main diagonal of S^3 is not zero.

Theorem 7. In S^3, if n entries on the main diagonal have the value $(n-1)(n-2)$ and all other entries on the main diagonal are zero, the n people associated with these n diagonal values form a clique of n members.

We now apply these theorems to matrix S above. First we compute S^2 and find this to be

$$S^2 = \begin{array}{c} \\ a \\ b \\ c \\ d \\ e \end{array} \begin{array}{ccccc} a & b & c & d & e \\ \left[\begin{array}{ccccc} 2 & 1 & 1 & 1 & 1 \\ 1 & 1 & 1 & 0 & 1 \\ 1 & 1 & 2 & 1 & 1 \\ 1 & 0 & 1 & 4 & 0 \\ 1 & 1 & 1 & 0 & 1 \end{array}\right] \end{array}$$

By Theorem 5 we see that person a is in a symmetric relationship with two members of the group, b with one, c with two, d with four, and e with one. Clearly, person d gets along with the most people in the group. We now look at S^3:

$$S^3 = \begin{array}{c} \\ a \\ b \\ c \\ d \\ e \end{array} \begin{array}{ccccc} a & b & c & d & e \\ \left[\begin{array}{ccccc} 2 & 1 & 3 & 5 & 1 \\ 1 & 0 & 1 & 4 & 0 \\ 3 & 1 & 2 & 5 & 1 \\ 5 & 4 & 5 & 2 & 4 \\ 1 & 0 & 1 & 4 & 0 \end{array}\right] \end{array}$$

Thus, by Theorems 6 and 7, persons a, c, and d form the only clique.

The above mathematical model can be applied equally well to "perfect communication groups" simply by replacing "chooses" with "communicates with," and "clique" with "perfect communication group." Other interpretations are also possible. This is just a brief glimpse into a subject that has received considerable attention in recent years.

EXERCISE 58

Let the choice matrix for a five-person group be given by

$$M = \begin{array}{c} \\ a \\ b \\ c \\ d \\ e \end{array} \begin{array}{ccccc} a & b & c & d & e \\ \left[\begin{array}{ccccc} 0 & 0 & 1 & 1 & 0 \\ 1 & 0 & 0 & 1 & 1 \\ 0 & 0 & 0 & 1 & 0 \\ 1 & 1 & 0 & 0 & 1 \\ 0 & 1 & 1 & 1 & 0 \end{array}\right] \end{array}$$

(A) Which people does b choose?

(B) Transform M into a symmetric matrix S.

(C) Compute S^2, and indicate how many symmetric relationships exist for each person.

(D) Compute S^3, and indicate who is in a clique.

7.7 DETERMINANT FUNCTION

In this section we are going to define a new function, called a determinant function. Its domain will be the set of all square matrices with real elements, and its range the set of all real numbers. If A is a square matrix, then

det A

read "the determinant of A," will be used to denote the unique real number in the range of the determinant function which corresponds to the matrix A in its domain.

A square matrix of order n is one with dimension $n \times n$. The determinant of a matrix of order 2 is defined as follows:

$$\det \begin{bmatrix} a_{11} & a_{12} \\ a_{21} & a_{22} \end{bmatrix} = \begin{vmatrix} a_{11} & a_{12} \\ a_{21} & a_{22} \end{vmatrix} = a_{11}a_{22} - a_{21}a_{12}$$

We use a single letter with a double subscript for convenience of generalization. The first number in the subscript indicates the row in which the element lies, and the second number indicates the column. Thus, a_{21} is the element in the second row and first column, and a_{12} is the element in the first row and second column.

Example 20. $\det \begin{bmatrix} -1 & 2 \\ -3 & -4 \end{bmatrix} = \begin{vmatrix} -1 & 2 \\ -3 & -4 \end{vmatrix} = (-1)(-4) - (-3)(2) = 10$

Problem 20. Find

$$\det \begin{bmatrix} 3 & -5 \\ 4 & -2 \end{bmatrix}$$

ANSWER

14.

A determinant of a square matrix of order n, denoted by

$$\det \begin{bmatrix} a_{11} & a_{12} & \cdots & a_{1n} \\ a_{21} & a_{22} & \cdots & a_{2n} \\ \cdots\cdots\cdots\cdots\cdots \\ a_{n1} & a_{n2} & \cdots & a_{nn} \end{bmatrix} = \begin{vmatrix} a_{11} & a_{12} & \cdots & a_{1n} \\ a_{21} & a_{22} & \cdots & a_{2n} \\ \cdots\cdots\cdots\cdots\cdots \\ a_{n1} & a_{n2} & \cdots & a_{nn} \end{vmatrix}$$

is called a *determinant of order n*. The *minor of an element* of a determinant of order n is a determinant of order $n - 1$, which is obtained by deleting the row and column in the original determinant which contains the element. For example, in the third-order determinant

$$\begin{vmatrix} a_{11} & a_{12} & a_{13} \\ a_{21} & a_{22} & a_{23} \\ a_{31} & a_{32} & a_{33} \end{vmatrix}$$

the minor of a_{23} is

$$\begin{vmatrix} a_{11} & a_{12} \\ a_{31} & a_{32} \end{vmatrix}$$

and the minor of a_{32} is

$$\begin{vmatrix} a_{11} & a_{13} \\ a_{21} & a_{23} \end{vmatrix}$$

A quantity closely associated with the minor of an element is the cofactor of an element. The *cofactor of an element* a_{ij} (from the ith row and jth column) is the product of the minor of a_{ij} and $(-1)^{i+j}$. Thus, using the third-order determinant above,

$$\text{The cofactor of } a_{23} = (-1)^{2+3} \begin{vmatrix} a_{11} & a_{12} \\ a_{31} & a_{32} \end{vmatrix}$$

$$\text{The cofactor of } a_{11} = (-1)^{1+1} \begin{vmatrix} a_{22} & a_{23} \\ a_{32} & a_{33} \end{vmatrix}$$

Example 21. Find the cofactor of -2 and of 5 in the determinant

$$\begin{vmatrix} -2 & 0 & 3 \\ 1 & -6 & 5 \\ -1 & 2 & 0 \end{vmatrix}$$

SOLUTION

$$\text{The cofactor of } -2 = (-1)^{1+1} \begin{vmatrix} -6 & 5 \\ 2 & 0 \end{vmatrix} = \begin{vmatrix} -6 & 5 \\ 2 & 0 \end{vmatrix} = -10$$

$$\text{The cofactor of } 5 = (-1)^{2+3} \begin{vmatrix} -2 & 0 \\ -1 & 2 \end{vmatrix} = -\begin{vmatrix} -2 & 0 \\ -1 & 2 \end{vmatrix} = 4$$

Problem 21. Find the cofactor of 2 and of 3 in the determinant in Example 21.

ANSWER

$137 - 4$.

NOTE: $(-1)^{i+j}$ in any particular case can easily be determined rather mechanically by using a checkerboard pattern of $+$ and $-$ signs over the determinant, starting with a $+$ in the upper left-hand corner.

We are now ready to define a determinant of a matrix of order n. The *determinant of a matrix* of order n, $n > 2$, is defined to be the sum of the n products obtained by multiplying each element of the first row by its cofactor. Symbolically,

$$
\begin{vmatrix}
a_{11} & a_{12} & \cdots & a_{1n} \\
a_{21} & a_{22} & \cdots & a_{2n} \\
\hdotsfor{4} \\
a_{n1} & a_{n2} & \cdots & a_{nn}
\end{vmatrix} = \sum_{k=1}^{n} (a_{1k})(\text{cofactor of } a_{1k})
$$

We often refer to the process described in the definition as the expansion of a determinant by the first row. The following important theorem tells us that we can also expand a determinant by using any other row or column.

Theorem 8. The determinant of a matrix of order n, $n > 2$, is the sum of the n products obtained by multiplying each element of any one row (or each element of any one column) by its cofactor.

The proof of this theorem is long and involved, so it is omitted here. In the case of a third-order determinant, you should not find it difficult to show, by expanding by any row or column, that

$$
D = \begin{vmatrix}
a_{11} & a_{12} & a_{13} \\
a_{21} & a_{22} & a_{23} \\
a_{31} & a_{32} & a_{33}
\end{vmatrix}
$$

$$
= a_{11}a_{22}a_{33} - a_{11}a_{23}a_{32} + a_{12}a_{23}a_{31} - a_{12}a_{21}a_{33} \\
+ a_{13}a_{21}a_{32} - a_{13}a_{22}a_{31}
$$

It should be clear that we can greatly reduce the work involved in evaluating a determinant by choosing to expand by the row or column with the greatest number of zeros.

Example 22. Evaluate

$$
\begin{vmatrix}
2 & -3 & 1 \\
-2 & 1 & -3 \\
0 & 2 & -1
\end{vmatrix}
$$

SOLUTION

Expand by the first column since it contains a zero (we could also use the third row).

$$\begin{vmatrix} 2 & -3 & 1 \\ -2 & 1 & -3 \\ 0 & 2 & -1 \end{vmatrix} = 2\binom{\text{cofactor}}{\text{of } a_{11}} + (-2)\binom{\text{cofactor}}{\text{of } a_{21}} + 0\binom{\text{cofactor}}{\text{of } a_{31}}$$

$$= 2\left((-1)^{1+1}\begin{vmatrix} 1 & -3 \\ 2 & -1 \end{vmatrix}\right)$$

$$+ (-2)\left((-1)^{2+1}\begin{vmatrix} -3 & 1 \\ 2 & -1 \end{vmatrix}\right) + 0$$

$$= 2(1)[(1)(-1) - (2)(-3)]$$
$$+ (-2)(-1)[(-3)(-1) - (2)(1)]$$

$$= 2(1)(5) + (-2)(-1)(1)$$

$$= 12$$

Problem 22. Evaluate

$$\begin{vmatrix} 2 & 1 & -1 \\ -2 & -3 & 0 \\ -1 & 2 & 1 \end{vmatrix}$$

ANSWER

3.

EXERCISE 59

A *Evaluate each second-order determinant.*

1. $\det\begin{bmatrix} 2 & 2 \\ -3 & 1 \end{bmatrix}$ 2. $\begin{vmatrix} 2 & 4 \\ 3 & -1 \end{vmatrix}$ 3. $\det\begin{bmatrix} 6 & -2 \\ -1 & -3 \end{bmatrix}$

4. $\det\begin{bmatrix} 5 & -4 \\ -2 & 2 \end{bmatrix}$ 5. $\begin{vmatrix} 1.8 & -1.6 \\ -1.9 & 1.2 \end{vmatrix}$ 6. $\det\begin{bmatrix} 0.5 & -3.2 \\ 1.4 & -6.7 \end{bmatrix}$

Given the determinant

$$\begin{vmatrix} a_{11} & a_{12} & a_{13} \\ a_{21} & a_{22} & a_{23} \\ a_{31} & a_{32} & a_{33} \end{vmatrix}$$

write the minor of each of the following elements.

7. a_{11} 8. a_{33} 9. a_{23} 10. a_{22}

Write the cofactor of each of the following elements.

11. a_{11} 12. a_{33} 13. a_{23} 14. a_{22}

Given the determinant

$$\begin{vmatrix} -2 & 3 & 0 \\ 5 & 1 & -2 \\ 7 & -4 & 8 \end{vmatrix}$$

write the minor of each of the following elements. (Leave the answer in determinant form.)

15. a_{11} 16. a_{22} 17. a_{32} 18. a_{21}

Write the cofactor of each of the following elements and evaluate each.

19. a_{11} 20. a_{22} 21. a_{32} 22. a_{21}

Evaluate each of the following determinants.

23. $\begin{vmatrix} 1 & 0 & 0 \\ -2 & 4 & 3 \\ 5 & -2 & 1 \end{vmatrix}$

24. $\begin{vmatrix} 2 & -3 & 5 \\ 0 & -3 & 1 \\ 0 & 6 & 2 \end{vmatrix}$

25. $\det \begin{bmatrix} 0 & 1 & 5 \\ 3 & -7 & 6 \\ 0 & -2 & -3 \end{bmatrix}$

26. $\det \begin{bmatrix} 4 & -2 & 0 \\ 9 & 5 & 4 \\ 1 & 2 & 0 \end{bmatrix}$

27. $\begin{vmatrix} -1 & 2 & -3 \\ -2 & 0 & -6 \\ 4 & -3 & 2 \end{vmatrix}$

28. $\begin{vmatrix} 0 & 2 & -1 \\ -6 & 3 & 1 \\ 7 & -9 & -2 \end{vmatrix}$

B *Given the determinant*

$$\begin{vmatrix} a_{11} & a_{12} & a_{13} & a_{14} \\ a_{21} & a_{22} & a_{23} & a_{24} \\ a_{31} & a_{32} & a_{33} & a_{34} \\ a_{41} & a_{42} & a_{43} & a_{44} \end{vmatrix}$$

write the cofactor (in determinant form) of each of the following elements.

29. a_{11} 30. a_{44} 31. a_{43} 32. a_{23}

Evaluate each of the following determinants.

33. $\begin{vmatrix} 3 & -2 & -8 \\ -2 & 0 & -3 \\ 1 & 0 & -4 \end{vmatrix}$

34. $\begin{vmatrix} 4 & -4 & 6 \\ 2 & 8 & -3 \\ 0 & -5 & 0 \end{vmatrix}$

35. $\begin{vmatrix} 1 & 4 & 1 \\ 1 & 1 & -2 \\ 2 & 1 & -1 \end{vmatrix}$

36. $\begin{vmatrix} 3 & 2 & 1 \\ -1 & 5 & 1 \\ 2 & 3 & 1 \end{vmatrix}$

37.
$$\begin{vmatrix} 1 & 4 & 3 \\ 2 & 1 & 6 \\ 3 & -2 & 9 \end{vmatrix}$$

38.
$$\begin{vmatrix} 4 & -6 & 3 \\ -1 & 4 & 1 \\ 5 & -6 & 3 \end{vmatrix}$$

39.
$$\begin{vmatrix} 2 & 6 & 1 & 7 \\ 0 & 3 & 0 & 0 \\ 3 & 4 & 2 & 5 \\ 0 & 9 & 0 & 2 \end{vmatrix}$$

40.
$$\begin{vmatrix} 0 & 1 & 0 & 1 \\ 2 & 4 & 7 & 6 \\ 0 & 3 & 0 & 1 \\ 0 & 6 & 2 & 5 \end{vmatrix}$$

C 41.
$$\begin{vmatrix} -2 & 0 & 0 & 0 & 0 \\ 9 & -1 & 0 & 0 & 0 \\ 2 & 1 & 3 & 0 & 0 \\ -1 & 4 & 2 & 2 & 0 \\ 7 & -2 & 3 & 5 & 5 \end{vmatrix}$$

42.
$$\begin{vmatrix} 2 & 0 & 0 & 0 & 0 \\ 0 & 3 & 0 & 0 & 0 \\ 0 & 0 & 2 & 0 & 0 \\ 0 & 0 & 0 & 1 & 0 \\ 0 & 0 & 0 & 0 & 4 \end{vmatrix}$$

If all the letters in Probs. 43 through 46 represent real numbers, show that each statement is true.

43.
$$\begin{vmatrix} a & b \\ ka & kb \end{vmatrix} = 0$$

44.
$$\begin{vmatrix} a & b \\ c & d \end{vmatrix} = - \begin{vmatrix} b & a \\ d & c \end{vmatrix}$$

45.
$$\begin{vmatrix} a & b \\ c & d \end{vmatrix} = \begin{vmatrix} a & c \\ b & d \end{vmatrix}$$

46.
$$\begin{vmatrix} ka & kb \\ c & d \end{vmatrix} = k \begin{vmatrix} a & b \\ c & d \end{vmatrix}$$

47. Show that the expansion of the determinant

$$\begin{vmatrix} a_{11} & a_{12} & a_{13} \\ a_{21} & a_{22} & a_{23} \\ a_{31} & a_{32} & a_{33} \end{vmatrix}$$

by the first column is the same as its expansion by the third row.

48. Repeat Prob. 47, using the second row and the third column.

49. If

$$A = \begin{bmatrix} 2 & 3 \\ 1 & -2 \end{bmatrix} \quad \text{and} \quad B = \begin{bmatrix} -1 & 3 \\ 2 & 1 \end{bmatrix}$$

show that $\det(AB) = \det A \cdot \det B$.

50. If

$$A = \begin{bmatrix} a & b \\ c & d \end{bmatrix} \quad \text{and} \quad B = \begin{bmatrix} w & x \\ y & z \end{bmatrix}$$

show that $\det(AB) = \det A \cdot \det B$.

7.8 PROPERTIES OF DETERMINANTS

The following theorems greatly facilitate the task of evaluating determinants of order 3 or greater. Because the proofs for the general case are involved and notationally difficult, we will only sketch informal proofs for determinants of order 3.

Theorem 9. If each element of any row (or column) of a determinant is multiplied by a constant k, the new determinant is k times the original.

PARTIAL PROOF

Let C_{ij} be the cofactor of a_{ij}. Then

$$\begin{vmatrix} ka_{11} & ka_{12} & ka_{13} \\ a_{21} & a_{22} & a_{23} \\ a_{31} & a_{32} & a_{33} \end{vmatrix} = ka_{11}C_{11} + ka_{12}C_{12} + ka_{13}C_{13}$$

$$= k(a_{11}C_{11} + a_{12}C_{12} + a_{13}C_{13})$$

$$= k\begin{vmatrix} a_{11} & a_{12} & a_{13} \\ a_{21} & a_{22} & a_{23} \\ a_{31} & a_{32} & a_{33} \end{vmatrix}$$

This theorem also states that a factor common to all elements of a row (or column) can be taken out as a factor of the determinant. It is important not to confuse the process of multiplying a determinant by a scalar with the process of multiplying a matrix by a scalar. How do the two processes differ?

Example 23.
$$\begin{vmatrix} 6 & 1 & 3 \\ -2 & 7 & -2 \\ 4 & 5 & 0 \end{vmatrix} = 2\begin{vmatrix} 3 & 1 & 3 \\ -1 & 7 & -2 \\ 2 & 5 & 0 \end{vmatrix}$$

where 2 is a common factor of the first column.

Problem 23. Take out factors common to any row or any column.

$$\begin{vmatrix} 3 & 2 & 1 \\ 6 & 3 & -9 \\ 1 & 0 & -5 \end{vmatrix}$$

ANSWER

$$3\begin{vmatrix} 3 & 2 & 1 \\ 2 & 1 & -3 \\ 1 & 0 & -5 \end{vmatrix}.$$

Theorem 10. If every element in a row (or column) is zero, the value of the determinant is zero.

This theorem is an immediate consequence of the preceding theorem, and its proof is left as an exercise. It is illustrated in the following example:

$$\begin{vmatrix} 3 & -2 & 5 \\ 0 & 0 & 0 \\ -1 & 4 & 9 \end{vmatrix} = 0$$

Theorem 11. If two rows (or two columns) of a determinant are interchanged, the new determinant is the negative of the old.

A proof of this theorem even for a determinant of order 3 is notationally involved. We suggest that you partially prove the theorem by direct expansion of the determinants before and after the interchange of two rows (or columns). The theorem is illustrated by the following example:

$$\begin{vmatrix} 1 & 0 & 9 \\ -2 & 1 & 5 \\ 3 & 0 & 7 \end{vmatrix} = - \begin{vmatrix} 1 & 9 & 0 \\ -2 & 5 & 1 \\ 3 & 7 & 0 \end{vmatrix}$$

Theorem 12. If the corresponding elements are equal in two rows (or columns), the value of the determinant is zero.

PROOF

The general proof of this theorem is easy, making direct use of the preceding theorem. If we start with a determinant D having two rows (or columns) equal, and we interchange the equal rows (or columns), the new determinant will be the same as the old. But by the preceding theorem,

$$D = -D$$

hence,

$$D = 0$$

Theorem 13. If a multiple of any row (or column) of a determinant is added to any other row (or column), the value of the determinant is not changed.

PARTIAL PROOF

If, in a general third-order determinant, we add a k multiple of the second column to the first, we obtain (where C_{ij} is the cofactor of a_{ij} in the original determinant)

$$\begin{vmatrix} a_{11}+ka_{12} & a_{12} & a_{13} \\ a_{21}+ka_{22} & a_{22} & a_{23} \\ a_{31}+ka_{32} & a_{32} & a_{33} \end{vmatrix} = (a_{11}+ka_{12})C_{11} + (a_{21}+ka_{22})C_{21} \\ + (a_{31}+ka_{32})C_{31}$$

$$= (a_{11}C_{11} + a_{21}C_{21} + a_{31}C_{31}) \\ + k(a_{12}C_{11} + a_{22}C_{21} + a_{32}C_{31})$$

$$= \begin{vmatrix} a_{11} & a_{12} & a_{13} \\ a_{21} & a_{22} & a_{23} \\ a_{31} & a_{32} & a_{33} \end{vmatrix} + k \begin{vmatrix} a_{12} & a_{12} & a_{13} \\ a_{22} & a_{22} & a_{23} \\ a_{32} & a_{32} & a_{33} \end{vmatrix}$$

$$= \begin{vmatrix} a_{11} & a_{12} & a_{13} \\ a_{21} & a_{22} & a_{23} \\ a_{31} & a_{32} & a_{33} \end{vmatrix}$$

since the determinant following k is zero (why?).

Note the similarity in the process described in this theorem to that used to obtain row-equivalent matrices. We use this theorem to transform a determinant without zero elements into one that contains a row or column with all elements zero but one. The determinant can then be easily expanded by this row (or column). An example best illustrates the process.

Example 24. Evaluate the determinant

$$\begin{vmatrix} 3 & -1 & 2 \\ -2 & 4 & -3 \\ 4 & -2 & 5 \end{vmatrix}$$

SOLUTION

We use Theorem 13 to obtain two zeros in the first row, and then expand the determinant by this row. To start, we replace the third column with the sum of it and 2 times the second column to obtain a zero in the a_{13} position.

$$\begin{vmatrix} 3 & -1 & 2 \\ -2 & 4 & -3 \\ 4 & -2 & 5 \end{vmatrix} = \begin{vmatrix} 3 & -1 & 0 \\ -2 & 4 & 5 \\ 4 & -2 & 1 \end{vmatrix}$$

Next, to obtain a zero in the a_{11} position, we replace the first column with the sum of it and 3 times the second column.

$$\begin{vmatrix} 0 & -1 & 0 \\ 10 & 4 & 5 \\ -2 & -2 & 1 \end{vmatrix}$$

Now it is an easy matter to expand this determinant by the first row to obtain

$$0 + (-1)\left((-1)^{1+2}\begin{vmatrix} 10 & 5 \\ -2 & 1 \end{vmatrix}\right) + 0 = 20$$

Problem 24. Evaluate the following determinant by first using Theorem 13 to obtain zeros in the a_{11} and a_{31} positions, and then expand by the first column.

$$\begin{vmatrix} 3 & 10 & -5 \\ 1 & 6 & -3 \\ 2 & 3 & 4 \end{vmatrix}$$

ANSWER

44.

EXERCISE 60

A *For each statement, identify the theorem from this section that justifies it. Do not evaluate.*

1. $\begin{vmatrix} 16 & 8 \\ 0 & -1 \end{vmatrix} = 8\begin{vmatrix} 2 & 1 \\ 0 & -1 \end{vmatrix}$

2. $\begin{vmatrix} 1 & -9 \\ 0 & -6 \end{vmatrix} = -3\begin{vmatrix} 1 & 3 \\ 0 & 2 \end{vmatrix}$

3. $-2\begin{vmatrix} 2 & 1 \\ -3 & 4 \end{vmatrix} = \begin{vmatrix} -4 & 1 \\ 6 & 4 \end{vmatrix}$

4. $4\begin{vmatrix} -1 & 3 \\ 2 & 1 \end{vmatrix} = \begin{vmatrix} -4 & 12 \\ 2 & 1 \end{vmatrix}$

5. $\begin{vmatrix} 3 & 0 \\ -2 & 0 \end{vmatrix} = 0$

6. $\begin{vmatrix} 5 & -7 \\ 0 & 0 \end{vmatrix} = 0$

7. $\begin{vmatrix} 5 & -1 \\ 8 & 0 \end{vmatrix} = -\begin{vmatrix} -1 & 5 \\ 0 & 8 \end{vmatrix}$

8. $\begin{vmatrix} 6 & 9 \\ 0 & 1 \end{vmatrix} = -\begin{vmatrix} 0 & 1 \\ 6 & 9 \end{vmatrix}$

9. $\begin{vmatrix} 4 & 3 \\ 1 & 2 \end{vmatrix} = \begin{vmatrix} 4-4 & 3-8 \\ 1 & 2 \end{vmatrix}$

10. $\begin{vmatrix} 3 & 2 \\ 5 & 1 \end{vmatrix} = \begin{vmatrix} 3+4 & 2 \\ 5+2 & 1 \end{vmatrix}$

Theorem 13 was used to transform the determinant on the left to that on the right. Replace each letter x with an appropriate numeral to complete the transformation.

11. $\begin{vmatrix} -1 & 3 \\ 2 & -4 \end{vmatrix} = \begin{vmatrix} -1 & x \\ 2 & 2 \end{vmatrix}$

12. $\begin{vmatrix} -1 & 3 \\ 5 & -2 \end{vmatrix} = \begin{vmatrix} -1 & 3 \\ x & 13 \end{vmatrix}$

13. $\begin{vmatrix} -1 & 2 & 3 \\ 2 & 1 & 4 \\ 1 & 3 & 2 \end{vmatrix} = \begin{vmatrix} -1 & 2 & 0 \\ 2 & 1 & 10 \\ 1 & 3 & x \end{vmatrix}$

14. $\begin{vmatrix} -1 & 2 & 3 \\ 2 & 1 & 4 \\ 1 & 3 & 2 \end{vmatrix} = \begin{vmatrix} -1 & 0 & 3 \\ 2 & x & 4 \\ 1 & 5 & 2 \end{vmatrix}$

Use Theorem 13 to transform each determinant into one that contains a row (or column) with all elements zero but one (if possible); then expand the transformed determinant by this row (or column).

15. $\begin{vmatrix} -1 & 0 & 3 \\ 2 & 5 & 4 \\ 1 & 5 & 2 \end{vmatrix}$

16. $\begin{vmatrix} -1 & 2 & 0 \\ 2 & 1 & 10 \\ 1 & 3 & 5 \end{vmatrix}$

17. $\begin{vmatrix} 3 & 5 & 0 \\ 1 & 1 & -2 \\ 2 & 1 & -1 \end{vmatrix}$

18. $\begin{vmatrix} 2 & 0 & 1 \\ -1 & -3 & 4 \\ 1 & 2 & 3 \end{vmatrix}$

B   *For each statement, identify the theorem from this section that justifies it.*

19. $-2 \begin{vmatrix} 1 & 0 & 2 \\ 3 & -2 & 4 \\ 0 & 1 & 1 \end{vmatrix} = \begin{vmatrix} 1 & 0 & 2 \\ -6 & 4 & -8 \\ 0 & 1 & 1 \end{vmatrix}$

20. $\begin{vmatrix} 8 & 0 & 1 \\ 12 & -1 & 0 \\ 4 & 3 & 2 \end{vmatrix} = 4 \begin{vmatrix} 2 & 0 & 1 \\ 3 & -1 & 0 \\ 1 & 3 & 2 \end{vmatrix}$

21. $\begin{vmatrix} 1 & 2 & 0 \\ -1 & 3 & 0 \\ 0 & 1 & 0 \end{vmatrix} = 0$

22. $\begin{vmatrix} -2 & 5 & 13 \\ 1 & 7 & 12 \\ 0 & 8 & 15 \end{vmatrix} = -\begin{vmatrix} 5 & -2 & 13 \\ 7 & 1 & 12 \\ 8 & 0 & 15 \end{vmatrix}$

23. $\begin{vmatrix} 4 & 2 & -1 \\ 2 & 0 & 2 \\ -3 & 5 & -2 \end{vmatrix} = \begin{vmatrix} 4-4 & 2 & -1 \\ 2+8 & 0 & 2 \\ -3-8 & 5 & -2 \end{vmatrix}$

24. $\begin{vmatrix} 7 & 7 & 1 \\ -3 & -3 & 11 \\ 2 & 2 & 0 \end{vmatrix} = 0$

Theorem 13 was used to transform the determinant on the left to that on the right. Replace each letter with an appropriate numeral to complete the transformation.

25. $\begin{vmatrix} 2 & 1 & -1 \\ 3 & 4 & 1 \\ 1 & 2 & -2 \end{vmatrix} = \begin{vmatrix} 0 & 0 & -1 \\ x & 5 & 1 \\ -3 & y & -2 \end{vmatrix}$

26. $\begin{vmatrix} 3 & -1 & 1 \\ -2 & 4 & 3 \\ 1 & 5 & 2 \end{vmatrix} = \begin{vmatrix} 0 & -1 & 0 \\ 10 & 4 & 7 \\ x & 5 & y \end{vmatrix}$

27. $\begin{vmatrix} 7 & 9 & 4 \\ 2 & 3 & 1 \\ 3 & 4 & -2 \end{vmatrix} = \begin{vmatrix} -1 & x & 0 \\ 2 & 3 & 1 \\ 7 & y & 0 \end{vmatrix}$

28. $\begin{vmatrix} 5 & 2 & 3 \\ 3 & 1 & 2 \\ -4 & -3 & 5 \end{vmatrix} = \begin{vmatrix} x & 0 & -1 \\ 3 & 1 & 2 \\ 5 & 0 & y \end{vmatrix}$

Use Theorem 13 to transform each determinant into one that contains a row (or column) with all elements zero but one (if possible); then expand the transformed determinant by this row (or column).

29. $\begin{vmatrix} 1 & 5 & 3 \\ 4 & 2 & 1 \\ 3 & 1 & 2 \end{vmatrix}$

30. $\begin{vmatrix} -1 & 5 & 1 \\ 2 & 3 & 1 \\ 3 & 2 & 1 \end{vmatrix}$

31. $\begin{vmatrix} 5 & 2 & -3 \\ -2 & 4 & 4 \\ 1 & -1 & 3 \end{vmatrix}$

32. $\begin{vmatrix} 5 & 3 & -6 \\ -1 & 1 & 4 \\ 4 & 3 & -6 \end{vmatrix}$

33. $\begin{vmatrix} 3 & -4 & 1 \\ 6 & -1 & 2 \\ 9 & 2 & 3 \end{vmatrix}$

34. $\begin{vmatrix} 2 & 3 & -1 \\ 5 & 4 & 7 \\ -4 & -6 & 2 \end{vmatrix}$

35. $\begin{vmatrix} 0 & 1 & 0 & 1 \\ 1 & -2 & 4 & 3 \\ 2 & 1 & 5 & 4 \\ 1 & 2 & 1 & 2 \end{vmatrix}$

36. $\begin{vmatrix} 2 & 3 & 1 & -1 \\ 3 & 1 & 2 & 1 \\ 0 & 5 & 4 & 0 \\ -1 & 2 & 3 & 0 \end{vmatrix}$

C 37. $\begin{vmatrix} 3 & 2 & 3 & 1 \\ 3 & -2 & 8 & 5 \\ 2 & 1 & 3 & 1 \\ 4 & 5 & 4 & -3 \end{vmatrix}$

38. $\begin{vmatrix} -1 & 4 & 2 & 1 \\ 5 & -1 & -3 & -1 \\ 2 & -1 & -2 & 3 \\ -3 & 3 & 3 & 3 \end{vmatrix}$

Prove each of the following statements.

39. $\begin{vmatrix} a & b & a \\ d & e & d \\ g & h & g \end{vmatrix} = 0$

40. $\begin{vmatrix} a & b & c \\ kd & ke & kf \\ g & h & i \end{vmatrix} = k \begin{vmatrix} a & b & c \\ d & e & f \\ g & h & i \end{vmatrix}$

41. $\begin{vmatrix} a_1 & b_1 & c_1 \\ a_2 & b_2 & c_2 \\ a_3 & b_3 & c_3 \end{vmatrix} = - \begin{vmatrix} b_1 & a_1 & c_1 \\ b_2 & a_2 & c_2 \\ b_3 & a_3 & c_3 \end{vmatrix}$

42. $\begin{vmatrix} a_1 & b_1 & c_1 \\ a_2 & b_2 & c_2 \\ a_3 & b_3 & c_3 \end{vmatrix} = \begin{vmatrix} a_1 + kc_1 & b_1 & c_1 \\ a_2 + kc_2 & b_2 & c_2 \\ a_3 + kc_3 & b_3 & c_3 \end{vmatrix}$

43. Show, without expanding, that $(2, 5)$ and $(-3, 4)$ satisfy the equation

$$\begin{vmatrix} x & y & 1 \\ 2 & 5 & 1 \\ -3 & 4 & 1 \end{vmatrix} = 0$$

44. Show that

$$\begin{vmatrix} x & y & 1 \\ 2 & 3 & 1 \\ -1 & 2 & 1 \end{vmatrix} = 0$$

is the equation of a line that passes through $(2, 3)$ and $(-1, 2)$.

45. Show that

$$\begin{vmatrix} x & y & 1 \\ x_1 & y_1 & 1 \\ x_2 & y_2 & 1 \end{vmatrix} = 0$$

is the equation of a line that passes through (x_1, y_1) and (x_2, y_2).

46. In analytic geometry it is shown that the area of a triangle with vertices (x_1, y_1), (x_2, y_2), and (x_3, y_3) is the absolute value of

$$\frac{1}{2} \begin{vmatrix} x_1 & y_1 & 1 \\ x_2 & y_2 & 1 \\ x_3 & y_3 & 1 \end{vmatrix}$$

Use this result to find the area of a triangle with vertices $(-1, 4)$, $(4, 8)$, and $(1, 1)$.

47. What can we say about the three points (x_1, y_1), (x_2, y_2), and (x_3, y_3) if

$$\begin{vmatrix} x_1 & y_1 & 1 \\ x_2 & y_2 & 1 \\ x_3 & y_3 & 1 \end{vmatrix} = 0$$

(*Hint:* See Prob. 46.)

48. If the three points (x_1, y_1), (x_2, y_2), and (x_3, y_3) are all on the same line, what can we say about the value of the determinant

$$\begin{vmatrix} x_1 & y_1 & 1 \\ x_2 & y_2 & 1 \\ x_3 & y_3 & 1 \end{vmatrix}$$

7.9 INVERSE OF A SQUARE MATRIX

Multiplicative Identity

What real number x has the property that

$$ax = a$$

for all real numbers a? The answer, of course, is 1. This number is called the multiplicative identity for the set of real numbers. Does the set of all matrices of a given dimension have a multiplicative identity? The answer, in general, is no; however, the set of all square matrices of order n does.

The *multiplicative identity* of the set of square matrices of order n, denoted by I, is the square matrix of order n with 1s along the main diagonal (from upper left to lower right) and zeros elsewhere.

Example 25.

$$M \qquad\qquad I \qquad = \qquad M$$

$$\begin{bmatrix} a_{11} & a_{12} & a_{13} \\ a_{21} & a_{22} & a_{23} \\ a_{31} & a_{32} & a_{33} \end{bmatrix} \begin{bmatrix} 1 & 0 & 0 \\ 0 & 1 & 0 \\ 0 & 0 & 1 \end{bmatrix} = \begin{bmatrix} a_{11} & a_{12} & a_{13} \\ a_{21} & a_{22} & a_{23} \\ a_{31} & a_{32} & a_{33} \end{bmatrix}$$

Problem 25. Find IM for I and M as given in Example 25.

ANSWER

M.

In general, we can show that if M is a square matrix of order n, and if I is the multiplicative identity of order n, then

---

$$MI = IM = M$$

Transpose of a Matrix

We digress from the main topic of this section to introduce the transpose of a matrix, a transformation of a matrix that has many uses, one of which will be apparent below. The *transpose of a matrix M*, denoted by M^t, is the matrix formed from M by interchanging corresponding rows and columns; that is, the first row becomes the first column, the second row the second column, and so on.

Example 26.
$$\begin{bmatrix} 6 & 1 \\ 8 & 0 \end{bmatrix}^t = \begin{bmatrix} 6 & 8 \\ 1 & 0 \end{bmatrix} \qquad \text{and} \qquad \begin{bmatrix} a & b & c \\ d & e & f \end{bmatrix}^t = \begin{bmatrix} a & d \\ b & e \\ c & f \end{bmatrix}$$

Problem 26. Find
$$\begin{bmatrix} 2 & -3 & 1 \\ 1 & 5 & -2 \end{bmatrix}^t$$

ANSWER

$$\begin{bmatrix} 2 & 1 \\ -3 & 5 \\ 1 & -2 \end{bmatrix}.$$

Multiplicative Inverse

In the set of real numbers we know that for each real number a (except zero) there exists a real number a^{-1} such that

$$aa^{-1} = 1$$

The number a^{-1} is called the multiplicative inverse of a. Does each square matrix M have a *multiplicative inverse* M^{-1} such that

$$M^{-1}M = MM^{-1} = I$$

The answer is yes, as long as det $M \neq 0$. (It is surprising that the commutative property holds for M and M^{-1}, when it does not hold for square matrices of the same order in general.) The following theorem shows us how an inverse is found if it exists.

Theorem 14. If

$$M = \begin{bmatrix} a_{11} & a_{12} & \cdots & a_{1n} \\ a_{21} & a_{22} & \cdots & a_{2n} \\ \cdots\cdots\cdots\cdots\cdots \\ a_{n1} & a_{n2} & \cdots & a_{nn} \end{bmatrix}$$

and if C_{ij} is the cofactor of a_{ij} and det $M \neq 0$, then

$$M^{-1} = \frac{1}{\det M} \begin{bmatrix} C_{11} & C_{12} & \cdots & C_{1n} \\ C_{21} & C_{22} & \cdots & C_{2n} \\ \cdots\cdots\cdots\cdots\cdots \\ C_{n1} & C_{n2} & \cdots & C_{nn} \end{bmatrix}^{t}$$

Here, we will only show that $MM^{-1} = I$ for $n = 2$. Let det $M = D$, then

$$MM^{-1} = \begin{bmatrix} a_{11} & a_{12} \\ a_{21} & a_{22} \end{bmatrix} \left(\frac{1}{D} \begin{bmatrix} C_{11} & C_{12} \\ C_{21} & C_{22} \end{bmatrix}^{t} \right)$$

$$= \begin{bmatrix} a_{11} & a_{12} \\ a_{21} & a_{22} \end{bmatrix} \begin{bmatrix} \dfrac{C_{11}}{D} & \dfrac{C_{21}}{D} \\ \dfrac{C_{12}}{D} & \dfrac{C_{22}}{D} \end{bmatrix}$$

$$= \begin{bmatrix} \dfrac{a_{11}C_{11} + a_{12}C_{12}}{D} & \dfrac{a_{11}C_{21} + a_{12}C_{22}}{D} \\ \dfrac{a_{21}C_{11} + a_{22}C_{12}}{D} & \dfrac{a_{21}C_{21} + a_{22}C_{22}}{D} \end{bmatrix}$$

$$= \begin{bmatrix} \dfrac{D}{D} & \dfrac{0}{D} \\ \dfrac{0}{D} & \dfrac{D}{D} \end{bmatrix} = \begin{bmatrix} 1 & 0 \\ 0 & 1 \end{bmatrix} = I$$

In the following examples and exercises, we will often use the fact that for any scalar k and square matrices A and B of the same dimension,

---

$$(kA)B = A(kB) = k(AB)$$

Proofs of special cases of this property are left as exercises.

Example 27. Find M^{-1} for

$$M = \begin{bmatrix} 2 & -6 \\ 1 & -2 \end{bmatrix}$$

and show that $M^{-1}M = I$.

SOLUTION

First note that det $M = 2 \neq 0$; hence M^{-1} exists.

$$M^{-1} = \frac{1}{\det M} \begin{bmatrix} C_{11} & C_{12} \\ C_{21} & C_{22} \end{bmatrix}^t$$

$$= \frac{1}{2} \begin{bmatrix} -2 & -1 \\ 6 & 2 \end{bmatrix}^t = \frac{1}{2} \begin{bmatrix} -2 & 6 \\ -1 & 2 \end{bmatrix}$$

Showing that $M^{-1}M = I$ provides a check:

$$M^{-1}M = \frac{1}{2} \begin{bmatrix} -2 & 6 \\ -1 & 2 \end{bmatrix} \begin{bmatrix} 2 & -6 \\ 1 & -2 \end{bmatrix} = \frac{1}{2} \begin{bmatrix} 2 & 0 \\ 0 & 2 \end{bmatrix} = \begin{bmatrix} 1 & 0 \\ 0 & 1 \end{bmatrix} = I$$

Problem 27. Find M^{-1} for

$$M = \begin{bmatrix} 3 & -1 \\ -4 & 2 \end{bmatrix}$$

and show that $M^{-1}M = I$.

ANSWER

$$M^{-1} = \frac{1}{2} \begin{bmatrix} 2 & 1 \\ 4 & 3 \end{bmatrix}.$$

Example 28. Find A^{-1} for

$$A = \begin{bmatrix} 1 & 1 & 1 \\ -2 & 1 & 0 \\ 0 & -1 & 1 \end{bmatrix}$$

SOLUTION

Note that $\det A = 5 \neq 0$; hence A^{-1} exists.

$$A^{-1} = \frac{1}{\det A} \begin{bmatrix} C_{11} & C_{12} & C_{13} \\ C_{21} & C_{22} & C_{23} \\ C_{31} & C_{32} & C_{33} \end{bmatrix}^t$$

$$= \frac{1}{5} \begin{bmatrix} 1 & 2 & 2 \\ -2 & 1 & 1 \\ -1 & -2 & 3 \end{bmatrix}^t = \frac{1}{5} \begin{bmatrix} 1 & -2 & -1 \\ 2 & 1 & -2 \\ 2 & 1 & 3 \end{bmatrix}$$

Problem 28. Find A^{-1} for

$$A = \begin{bmatrix} -1 & 0 & 1 \\ 2 & -1 & 3 \\ 0 & 1 & 2 \end{bmatrix}$$

ANSWER

$$\frac{1}{7} \begin{bmatrix} -5 & 1 & 1 \\ -4 & -2 & 5 \\ 2 & 1 & 1 \end{bmatrix}.$$

The multiplicative inverse of a square matrix has many uses. In the next section we will see how to use it in the matrix solution of systems of linear equations. Finding inverses for matrices of order greater than 3 by hand is a long and tedious task. More efficient methods than those discussed above are available for determining A^{-1}, but such techniques are subject matter for a more thorough treatment of the subject than we intend to give here.

EXERCISE 61

A *Perform the indicated operations.*

1. $\begin{bmatrix} -1 & 4 \\ 2 & 7 \end{bmatrix} \begin{bmatrix} 1 & 0 \\ 0 & 1 \end{bmatrix}$

2. $\begin{bmatrix} 2 & -3 \\ 1 & 5 \end{bmatrix} \begin{bmatrix} 1 & 0 \\ 0 & 1 \end{bmatrix}$

3. $\begin{bmatrix} 1 & 0 & 0 \\ 0 & 1 & 0 \\ 0 & 0 & 1 \end{bmatrix} \begin{bmatrix} 2 & -1 & 3 \\ 5 & 6 & 1 \\ 4 & 0 & 2 \end{bmatrix}$

4. $\begin{bmatrix} 1 & 0 & 0 \\ 0 & 1 & 0 \\ 0 & 0 & 1 \end{bmatrix} \begin{bmatrix} 3 & 4 & 5 \\ 2 & 0 & 1 \\ -1 & 1 & 7 \end{bmatrix}$

5. $\begin{bmatrix} -2 & 5 \\ 1 & 0 \end{bmatrix}^t$

6. $\begin{bmatrix} 3 & 2 \\ 0 & 1 \end{bmatrix}^t$

7. $\begin{bmatrix} 6 & -5 & 2 \\ 3 & -1 & 4 \\ 1 & 4 & 7 \end{bmatrix}^t$

8. $\begin{bmatrix} 2 & 1 & -3 \\ 1 & 0 & 5 \\ 4 & 3 & -2 \end{bmatrix}^t$

Given M as indicated, find M^{-1} and show that $M^{-1}M = I$. If the inverse does not exist, it should be indicated.

9. $\begin{bmatrix} 2 & 1 \\ 5 & 3 \end{bmatrix}$ 10. $\begin{bmatrix} 1 & 2 \\ 1 & 3 \end{bmatrix}$ 11. $\begin{bmatrix} 1 & 3 \\ 2 & 8 \end{bmatrix}$ 12. $\begin{bmatrix} -2 & 6 \\ 1 & -3 \end{bmatrix}$

B 13. $\begin{bmatrix} 1 & 3 & 1 \\ 0 & 2 & 2 \\ 0 & 1 & 0 \end{bmatrix}$ 14. $\begin{bmatrix} 1 & 0 & 0 \\ 2 & 3 & 1 \\ 0 & 1 & 1 \end{bmatrix}$

15. $\begin{bmatrix} 2 & 1 & 1 \\ 1 & 1 & 0 \\ -1 & -1 & 0 \end{bmatrix}$ 16. $\begin{bmatrix} 1 & -1 & 0 \\ 2 & -1 & 1 \\ 0 & 1 & 1 \end{bmatrix}$

17. $\begin{bmatrix} 1 & 0 & -1 \\ 2 & -1 & 0 \\ 1 & 1 & 1 \end{bmatrix}$ 18. $\begin{bmatrix} 1 & 1 & 0 \\ 0 & 2 & 1 \\ -1 & 0 & 1 \end{bmatrix}$

C 19. Find a, b, c, and d (without the use of Theorem 14), so that

$$\begin{bmatrix} 2 & 1 \\ 5 & 3 \end{bmatrix}\begin{bmatrix} a & b \\ c & d \end{bmatrix} = \begin{bmatrix} 1 & 0 \\ 0 & 1 \end{bmatrix}$$

20. Repeat Prob. 19 for

$$\begin{bmatrix} 1 & 2 \\ 1 & 3 \end{bmatrix}\begin{bmatrix} a & b \\ c & d \end{bmatrix} = \begin{bmatrix} 1 & 0 \\ 0 & 1 \end{bmatrix}$$

21. In Theorem 14, show that $M^{-1}M = I$ for $n = 2$.
22. Let $S = \{M \mid M$ is a matrix of order 2, det $M \neq 0\}$.
    (A) Is set S closed under matrix multiplication?
    (B) If A, B, $C \in S$, does $(AB)C = A(BC)$?
    (C) Does S have a multiplicative identity?
    (D) Does each element of S have a multiplicative inverse?
    (E) If A, $B \in S$, does $AB = BA$?
    (*Conclusion:* Set S is a noncommutative group.)
23. If

$$A = \begin{bmatrix} 2 & 1 \\ 5 & 3 \end{bmatrix} \quad \text{and} \quad B = \begin{bmatrix} 1 & 3 \\ 2 & 8 \end{bmatrix}$$

    show that $(AB)^{-1} = B^{-1}A^{-1}$.
24. If A and B are square matrices of order 2, and det $A \neq$ det $B \neq 0$, show that

$$(AB)^{-1} = B^{-1}A^{-1}$$

25. If

$$M = \begin{bmatrix} 2 & 1 \\ 5 & 3 \end{bmatrix}$$

    show that $(M^{-1})^t = (M^t)^{-1}$.
26. If M is an arbitrary 2×2 matrix, det $M \neq 0$, show that $(M^{-1})^t = (M^t)^{-1}$.

7.10 MATRIX SOLUTIONS OF LINEAR SYSTEMS; CRAMER'S RULE

Example 29. Consider the linear system

$$x - 3y = 5$$
$$2x - 5y = 9 \tag{1}$$

Written in matrix form, system (1) becomes

$$\begin{bmatrix} 1 & -3 \\ 2 & -5 \end{bmatrix} \begin{bmatrix} x \\ y \end{bmatrix} = \begin{bmatrix} 5 \\ 9 \end{bmatrix} \tag{2}$$

If we let

$$A = \begin{bmatrix} 1 & -3 \\ 2 & -5 \end{bmatrix} \qquad X = \begin{bmatrix} x \\ y \end{bmatrix} \qquad D = \begin{bmatrix} 5 \\ 9 \end{bmatrix}$$

we can write Eq. (2) in the form

$$AX = D \tag{3}$$

If A^{-1} exists, both members of Eq. (3) can be multiplied (on the left) by A^{-1} to obtain

$$A^{-1}(AX) = A^{-1}D$$
$$(A^{-1}A)X = A^{-1}D$$
$$IX = A^{-1}D$$
$$X = A^{-1}D$$

Using the methods of the last section, we find

$$A^{-1} = \begin{bmatrix} -5 & 3 \\ -2 & 1 \end{bmatrix}$$

Thus,

$$X = A^{-1} \quad D$$
$$\begin{bmatrix} x \\ y \end{bmatrix} = \begin{bmatrix} -5 & 3 \\ -2 & 1 \end{bmatrix} \begin{bmatrix} 5 \\ 9 \end{bmatrix}$$
$$= \begin{bmatrix} 2 \\ -1 \end{bmatrix}$$

Hence, $x = 2$ and $y = -1$.

The method just described generalizes completely. It is clear that the main problem in solving a system of n linear equations in n variables is that of finding the inverse of the coefficient matrix. (If the inverse does not exist, there is either no solution or an infinite number of solutions.)

Problem 29. Use the matrix method described above to solve the system

$$x + 3y = -1$$
$$2x + 8y = -6$$

NOTE: $\begin{bmatrix} 1 & 3 \\ 2 & 8 \end{bmatrix}^{-1} = \frac{1}{2}\begin{bmatrix} 8 & -3 \\ -2 & 1 \end{bmatrix}$

ANSWER

$x = 5, y = -2.$

Example 30. Solve the following system using the matrix method described above.

$$x + y = 1$$
$$3y - z = -4$$
$$x + z = 3$$

SOLUTION

First, write the following system as a matrix equation:

$$\begin{matrix} A & X & = & D \end{matrix}$$
$$\begin{bmatrix} 1 & 1 & 0 \\ 0 & 3 & -1 \\ 1 & 0 & 1 \end{bmatrix}\begin{bmatrix} x \\ y \\ z \end{bmatrix} = \begin{bmatrix} 1 \\ -4 \\ 3 \end{bmatrix} \qquad (4)$$

Next note that $\det A = 2 \neq 0$; hence A^{-1} exists. Find A^{-1} using the methods of the last section.

$$A^{-1} = \frac{1}{2}\begin{bmatrix} 3 & -1 & -1 \\ -1 & 1 & 1 \\ -3 & 1 & 3 \end{bmatrix}$$

Now multiply both members of Eq. (4) by A^{-1} to obtain

$$\begin{matrix} X & = & A^{-1} & D \end{matrix}$$
$$\begin{bmatrix} x \\ y \\ z \end{bmatrix} = \frac{1}{2}\begin{bmatrix} 3 & -1 & -1 \\ -1 & 1 & 1 \\ -3 & 1 & 3 \end{bmatrix}\begin{bmatrix} 1 \\ -4 \\ 3 \end{bmatrix} = \frac{1}{2}\begin{bmatrix} 4 \\ -2 \\ 2 \end{bmatrix} = \begin{bmatrix} 2 \\ -1 \\ 1 \end{bmatrix}$$

Hence, $x = 2, y = -1,$ and $z = 1.$

Problem 30.   Solve the following system using methods described above.

$$3x - z = 5$$
$$x - y + z = 0$$
$$x + y = 0$$

ANSWER

$x = 1, y = -1, z = -2.$

Cramer's Rule

Another method of finding solutions to n linear equations with n unknowns is by the use of Cramer's rule. This rule is of more importance as a theoretical tool than as a practical way of actually finding solutions to systems of equations.

Theorem 15.
Cramer's
Rule

Given the system

$$a_{11}x_1 + a_{12}x_2 + \cdots + a_{1n}x_n = k_1$$
$$a_{21}x_1 + a_{22}x_2 + \cdots + a_{2n}x_n = k_2$$
$$\cdots\cdots\cdots\cdots\cdots\cdots\cdots\cdots\cdots\cdots\cdots$$
$$a_{n1}x_1 + a_{n2}x_2 + \cdots + a_{nn}x_n = k_2$$

with

$$A = \begin{bmatrix} a_{11} & a_{12} & \cdots & a_{1n} \\ \cdots\cdots\cdots\cdots\cdots\cdots \\ a_{n1} & a_{n2} & \cdots & a_{nn} \end{bmatrix} \quad \text{and} \quad \det A \neq 0$$

then

$$x_i = \frac{\begin{bmatrix} a_{11} & a_{12} & \cdots & k_1 & \cdots & a_{1n} \\ \cdots\cdots\cdots\cdots\cdots\cdots\cdots\cdots \\ a_{n1} & a_{n2} & \cdots & k_n & \cdots & a_{nn} \end{bmatrix}}{\det A} \qquad i = 1, 2, \ldots, n$$

ith column

PROOF (FOR $n = 3$ ONLY)

Let $D = \det A$; then from the first part of this section

$$
\begin{bmatrix} x_1 \\ x_2 \\ x_3 \end{bmatrix} = \frac{1}{D} \begin{bmatrix} C_{11} & C_{12} & C_{13} \\ C_{21} & C_{22} & C_{23} \\ C_{31} & C_{32} & C_{33} \end{bmatrix}^t \begin{bmatrix} k_1 \\ k_2 \\ k_3 \end{bmatrix}
$$

$$
= \frac{1}{D} \begin{bmatrix} C_{11} & C_{21} & C_{31} \\ C_{12} & C_{22} & C_{32} \\ C_{13} & C_{23} & C_{33} \end{bmatrix} \begin{bmatrix} k_1 \\ k_2 \\ k_3 \end{bmatrix} = \begin{bmatrix} \dfrac{k_1 C_{11} + k_2 C_{21} + k_3 C_{31}}{D} \\[2mm] \dfrac{k_1 C_{12} + k_2 C_{22} + k_3 C_{32}}{D} \\[2mm] \dfrac{k_1 C_{13} + k_2 C_{23} + k_3 C_{33}}{D} \end{bmatrix}
$$

The elements in the last matrix are simply the expansions of det A about the first, second, and third columns, respectively, with the columns involved in each particular expansion being replaced by the k's. Thus

$$
x_1 = \frac{\begin{vmatrix} k_1 & a_{12} & a_{13} \\ k_2 & a_{22} & a_{23} \\ k_3 & a_{32} & a_{33} \end{vmatrix}}{D} \qquad x_2 = \frac{\begin{vmatrix} a_{11} & k_1 & a_{13} \\ a_{21} & k_2 & a_{23} \\ a_{31} & k_3 & a_{33} \end{vmatrix}}{D} \qquad x_3 = \frac{\begin{vmatrix} a_{11} & a_{12} & k_1 \\ a_{21} & a_{22} & k_2 \\ a_{31} & a_{32} & k_3 \end{vmatrix}}{D}
$$

Example 31. Solve the following system using Cramer's rule.

$$
\begin{aligned}
x + y &= 1 \\
3y - z &= -4 \\
x + z &= 3
\end{aligned}
$$

SOLUTION

$$ D = 2 $$

$$
x = \frac{\begin{vmatrix} 1 & 1 & 0 \\ -4 & 3 & -1 \\ 3 & 0 & 1 \end{vmatrix}}{2} = \frac{4}{2} = 2 \qquad
y = \frac{\begin{vmatrix} 1 & 1 & 0 \\ 0 & -4 & -1 \\ 1 & 3 & 1 \end{vmatrix}}{2} = \frac{-2}{2} = -1
$$

$$
z = \frac{\begin{vmatrix} 1 & 1 & 1 \\ 0 & 3 & -4 \\ 1 & 0 & 3 \end{vmatrix}}{2} = \frac{2}{2} = 1
$$

Problem 31. Solve the following system using Cramer's rule.

$$3x - z = 5$$
$$x - y + z = 0$$
$$x + y = 0$$

ANSWER

$x = 1, y = -1, z = -2.$

EXERCISE 62

A *Write each system in the form $AX = D$, where A, X, and D are matrices.*

1. $x + 2y = 1$
    $x + 3y = -1$

2. $x - 5y = 3$
    $-x + 2y = 5$

Write each as a system of equations free of matrices.

3. $\begin{bmatrix} 2 & -3 \\ -1 & 4 \end{bmatrix} \begin{bmatrix} x \\ y \end{bmatrix} = \begin{bmatrix} -1 \\ 0 \end{bmatrix}$

4. $\begin{bmatrix} -3 & -5 \\ 2 & -1 \end{bmatrix} \begin{bmatrix} x \\ y \end{bmatrix} = \begin{bmatrix} -2 \\ 3 \end{bmatrix}$

Given that

$$\begin{bmatrix} 1 & 2 \\ 1 & 3 \end{bmatrix}^{-1} = \begin{bmatrix} 3 & -2 \\ -1 & 1 \end{bmatrix}$$

solve each system by finding $X = A^{-1}D$.

5. $x + 2y = 1$
    $x + 3y = -1$

6. $x + 2y = 3$
    $x + 3y = 5$

Solve by finding $X = A^{-1}D$.

7. $2x + y = 1$
    $5x + 3y = 2$

8. $x + 3y = 1$
    $2x + 8y = 0$

9. $2x - y = -3$
    $-x + 3y = 4$

10. $2x + y = 1$
    $5x + 3y = 2$

Solve, using Cramer's rule.

11. The system in Prob. 7
12. The system in Prob. 8
13. The system in Prob. 9
14. The system in Prob. 10

B *Given that*

$$\begin{bmatrix} 1 & 1 & 0 \\ 0 & 2 & 1 \\ -1 & 0 & 1 \end{bmatrix}^{-1} = \begin{bmatrix} 2 & -1 & 1 \\ -1 & 1 & -1 \\ 2 & -1 & 2 \end{bmatrix}$$

solve each system by finding $X = A^{-1}D.$

15. $\begin{aligned} x + y &= 0 \\ 2y + z &= -5 \\ -x + z &= -3 \end{aligned}$
16. $\begin{aligned} x + y &= -4 \\ 2y + z &= 0 \\ -x + z &= 5 \end{aligned}$

17. $\begin{aligned} x + y &= 1 \\ 2y + z &= 0 \\ -x + z &= 0 \end{aligned}$
18. $\begin{aligned} x + y &= -4 \\ 2y + z &= 3 \\ -x + z &= 7 \end{aligned}$

Solve by finding $X = A^{-1}D.$

19. $\begin{aligned} y + z &= -4 \\ x + 2z &= 0 \\ x - y &= 5 \end{aligned}$
20. $\begin{aligned} x - z &= 2 \\ 2x - y &= 8 \\ x + y + z &= 2 \end{aligned}$

21. $\begin{aligned} 2y - z &= -4 \\ x - y - z &= 0 \\ x - y + 2z &= 6 \end{aligned}$
22. $\begin{aligned} 2x + y &= 2 \\ x - y + z &= -1 \\ x + y + z &= -1 \end{aligned}$

Solve, using Cramer's rule.

23. The system in Prob. 19
24. The system in Prob. 20
25. The system in Prob. 21
26. The system in Prob. 22

C 27. Prove Cramer's rule for $n = 2$.
28. Prove that, if a determinant is expanded by any row (or column) using corresponding cofactors of another row (or column), the result is always zero.

EXERCISE 63   CHAPTER-REVIEW EXERCISE

A 1. Solve $2x + y = 7$
$3x - 2y = 0$
2. Graph $4x - 5y \le 20$.

3. Solve $x^2 = y$
$y = 2x - 2$
4. Solve $x^2 + y^2 = 2$
$2x - y = 3$

Perform the indicated operations.

5. $2\begin{bmatrix} 3 & -1 \\ 0 & 2 \end{bmatrix} - \begin{bmatrix} 2 & -1 \\ 1 & -2 \end{bmatrix}$
6. $\begin{bmatrix} 2 & -1 \\ 3 & 2 \end{bmatrix}\begin{bmatrix} 1 & -1 \\ 2 & 3 \end{bmatrix}$

7. $\begin{bmatrix} 1 & 0 \\ 0 & 1 \end{bmatrix}\begin{bmatrix} -1 & 4 \\ 2 & 7 \end{bmatrix}$

8. $\begin{bmatrix} 2 & -3 & 1 \\ 4 & 5 & 0 \end{bmatrix} + \begin{bmatrix} 2 & -1 \\ 1 & -2 \end{bmatrix}\begin{bmatrix} 1 & 2 & 0 \\ 3 & 1 & -1 \end{bmatrix}$

9. $\begin{bmatrix} u & v \\ x & y \end{bmatrix}^t$
10. $\begin{bmatrix} -2 & 1 \\ 5 & 2 \end{bmatrix}^{-1}$

11. $\begin{vmatrix} 2 & -3 \\ -5 & -1 \end{vmatrix}$

12. $\det \begin{bmatrix} 2 & 3 & -4 \\ 0 & 5 & 0 \\ 1 & -4 & -2 \end{bmatrix}$

13. If a 2×3 matrix is multiplied by a 5×2 matrix on the left, what will be the dimension of the product?

14. Solve the system

$$3x - 2y = 8$$
$$x + 3y = -1$$

by using

(A) Graphing   (B) Elimination
(C) Substitution   (D) Row-equivalent matrices
(E) $X = A^{-1}D$ (F) Cramer's rule

B 15. Solve the system

$$4x - 3y = -8$$
$$-2x + \tfrac{3}{2}y = 4$$

using any method.

16. A container contains 120 packages. Some of the packages weigh $\frac{1}{2}$ lb each, and the rest weigh $\frac{1}{3}$ lb each. If the total contents of the container weighs 48 lb, how many are there of each type of package? Solve using two-equations-two-unknowns methods.

17. Solve the following system graphically.

$$2x + y \geq 9$$
$$x + 3y > 12$$
$$y \leq 7$$
$$x \leq 9$$

18. Solve $x^2 - y^2 = 2$
$$y^2 = x$$

19. Solve $3x^2 - y^2 = -6$
$$2x^2 + 3y^2 = 29$$

20. Find two numbers such that their difference is 1 and their product is also 1.

Perform the indicated operations.

21. $\begin{bmatrix} 6 & 3 & -2 \\ 5 & -4 & 1 \\ 0 & 2 & -1 \end{bmatrix} \begin{bmatrix} 1 & 0 & 0 \\ 0 & 1 & 0 \\ 0 & 0 & 1 \end{bmatrix}$

22. $\dfrac{1}{2} \begin{bmatrix} 2 & 0 & 0 \\ -2 & 1 & -1 \\ 2 & -1 & 3 \end{bmatrix} \begin{bmatrix} 1 & 0 & 0 \\ 2 & 3 & 1 \\ 0 & 1 & 1 \end{bmatrix}$

23. $\begin{bmatrix} 2 & 5 & 7 \\ -1 & 0 & 1 \\ 3 & 2 & 4 \end{bmatrix}^t$

24. $\begin{vmatrix} -\frac{1}{4} & \frac{3}{8} \\ \frac{1}{2} & \frac{2}{3} \end{vmatrix}$

25.
$$\det \begin{bmatrix} 2 & -1 & 1 \\ -3 & 5 & 2 \\ 1 & -2 & 4 \end{bmatrix}$$

26.
$$\begin{vmatrix} 1 & 2 & 3 \\ 2 & 0 & 1 \\ -1 & -3 & 4 \end{vmatrix}$$

27.
$$\begin{bmatrix} -3 & 1 \\ 6 & -2 \end{bmatrix}^{-1}$$

28.
$$\begin{bmatrix} 0 & 1 & 0 \\ 2 & 1 & 1 \\ 1 & 0 & -1 \end{bmatrix}^{-1}$$

29. What is the additive identity for the set of all 3×3 matrices?

30. What is the multiplicative identity for the set of all 2×2 matrices?

31.
$$\frac{a_1 k_2 - a_2 k_1}{a_1 b_2 - a_2 b_1} = \frac{\begin{vmatrix} ? & k_1 \\ ? & k_2 \end{vmatrix}}{\begin{vmatrix} a_1 & ? \\ a_2 & ? \end{vmatrix}}$$

32. Solve $y + 2z = 4$
$x - z = -2$ using
$x + y = 1$

(A) Row-equivalent matrices
(B) $X = A^{-1}D$
(C) Cramer's rule

c 33. Solve the system $x^2 - y^2 = 7$
$x^2 + y^2 = 25$
graphically.

34. Solve $2x^2 - xy + y^2 = 8$
$x^2 - y^2 = 0$

35. If the hypotenuse of a right triangle is 15 in. and its area is 54 in.^{2}, what are the lengths of the two sides?

36. Three pipes, A, B, and C, are used to fill a swimming pool. If all three pipes are used together, the pool can be filled in 3 hr. If A and B are used without C, the pool can be filled in 6 hr; if B and C are used without A, the pool can be filled in 4 hr. How long would it take each pipe alone to fill the pool?

37.
$$\begin{vmatrix} 0 & -1 & 5 & 4 \\ 0 & 2 & 6 & 3 \\ -2 & 6 & 8 & -5 \\ 0 & 1 & 0 & -1 \end{vmatrix} = ?$$

38.
$$\det \begin{bmatrix} -1 & 4 & 1 & 1 \\ 5 & -1 & 2 & -1 \\ 2 & -1 & 0 & 3 \\ -3 & 3 & 0 & 3 \end{bmatrix} = ?$$

39. Show that
$$\begin{vmatrix} u & v \\ w & x \end{vmatrix} = - \begin{vmatrix} w & x \\ u & v \end{vmatrix}$$

40. Show that
$$\begin{vmatrix} u & v \\ w & x \end{vmatrix} = \begin{vmatrix} u + kv & v \\ w + kx & x \end{vmatrix}$$

41. Show that the expansion of

$$\begin{vmatrix} a_{11} & a_{12} & a_{13} \\ a_{21} & a_{22} & a_{23} \\ a_{31} & a_{32} & a_{33} \end{vmatrix}$$

by the second column is the same as its expansion by the second row.

42. If A and B are 2×2 matrices whose determinants are not zero, show that $(AB)^{-1} = A^{-1}B^{-1}$.

43. Solve $\begin{aligned} 3x - 2y - 7z &= -6 \\ -x + 3y + 2z &= -1 \\ x + 5y + 3z &= 3 \end{aligned}$ using $\begin{cases} \text{(A)} & \text{Row-equivalent matrices} \\ \text{(B)} & X = A^{-1}D \\ \text{(C)} & \text{Cramer's rule} \end{cases}$

Chapter

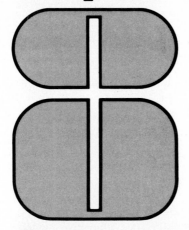

Sequences and Series; Mathematical Induction

In this chapter we are going to consider functions whose domains are the set of natural numbers or a subset of the natural numbers. These special functions, called sequences, are encountered with increased frequency as one progresses in mathematics.

8.1 SEQUENCES AND SERIES

An *infinite sequence* is a function a whose domain is the set of all natural numbers $N = \{1, 2, 3, \ldots, n, \ldots\}$. The range of the function a is the set $\{a(1), a(2), a(3), \ldots, a(n), \ldots\}$, which is usually written

$$a_1, a_2, a_3, \ldots, a_n, \ldots$$

where

$$a_n = a(n)$$

The elements in the range are called the *terms of the sequence*; a_1 is the first term, a_2 the second term, and a_n the nth term. For example, if

$$a_n = \frac{n-1}{n} \qquad n \in N$$

the function a is a sequence with terms

$$0, \frac{1}{2}, \frac{2}{3}, \frac{3}{4}, \ldots, \frac{n-1}{n}, \ldots$$

If the domain of a function a is the set of positive integers $\{1, 2, 3, \ldots, n\}$ for some fixed n, then a is called a *finite sequence*. Thus, if

$$a_1 = 5$$

and

$$a_n = a_{n-1} + 2 \qquad n \in \{2, 3, 4\}$$

the function a is a finite sequence with terms

5, 7, 9, 11

These two examples also illustrate two common ways in which sequences are specified:

1. The nth term a_n is expressed in terms of n.
2. One or more terms are given, and the nth term is expressed in terms of preceding terms.

Example 1.   Find the first four terms of a sequence whose nth term is

$$a_n = \frac{1}{2^n}$$

SOLUTION

$$a_1 = \frac{1}{2^1} = \frac{1}{2} \qquad a_2 = \frac{1}{2^2} = \frac{1}{4} \qquad a_3 = \frac{1}{2^3} = \frac{1}{8} \qquad a_4 = \frac{1}{2^4} = \frac{1}{16}$$

Problem 1. Find the first four terms of a sequence whose nth term is

$$a_n = \frac{n}{n^2 + 1}$$

ANSWER

$\frac{1}{2}, \frac{2}{5}, \frac{3}{10}, \frac{4}{17}.$

Example 2. Find the first five terms of a sequence specified by

$$a_1 = 5$$
$$a_n = \tfrac{1}{2}a_{n-1} \qquad n \geq 2$$

SOLUTION

$$a_1 = 5$$
$$a_2 = \tfrac{1}{2}a_{2-1} = \tfrac{1}{2}a_1 = \tfrac{5}{2}$$
$$a_3 = \tfrac{1}{2}a_{3-1} = \tfrac{1}{2}a_2 = \tfrac{5}{4}$$
$$a_4 = \tfrac{1}{2}a_{4-1} = \tfrac{1}{2}a_3 = \tfrac{5}{8}$$
$$a_5 = \tfrac{1}{2}a_{5-1} = \tfrac{1}{2}a_4 = \tfrac{5}{16}$$

Problem 2. Find the first five terms of a sequence specified by

$$a_1 = 3$$
$$a_n = a_{n-1} + 4$$

ANSWER

3, 7, 11, 15, 19.

Now let us look at the problem in reverse. That is, given the first few terms of a sequence (and assuming the sequence continues in the indicated pattern), find a_n in terms of n.

Example 3. Find a_n in terms of n for the sequences whose first four terms are

(A) 5, 6, 7, 8, ...
(B) 2, −4, 8, −16, ...

SOLUTION

(A) $a_n = n + 4$

(B) $a_n = (-1)^{n+1} 2^n$

NOTE: These representations are not unique.

Problem 3. Find a_n in terms of n for

(A) 3, 5, 7, 9, ...   (B) $1, -\frac{1}{2}, \frac{1}{4}, -\frac{1}{8}, \ldots$

ANSWER

(A) $a_n = 2n + 1$; (B) $a_n = (-1)^{n+1}/2^{n-1}$.

The indicated sum of the terms of a sequence is called a *series*. Thus, if $a_1, a_2, a_3, \ldots, a_n$ are the terms of a sequence,

$$S_n = a_1 + a_2 + a_3 + \cdots + a_n$$

is called a series. If the sequence is infinite, the corresponding series is called an *infinite series*. We will restrict our attention to finite series in this section.

A series is often represented in a compact form using *sigma notation*, as follows:

$$S_n = \sum_{k=1}^{n} a_k = a_1 + a_2 + a_3 + \cdots + a_n$$

where the terms of the series on the right are obtained from the middle expression by successively replacing k in a_k with integers, starting with 1 and ending with n. Thus, if a sequence is given by

$$\frac{1}{2}, \frac{1}{4}, \frac{1}{8}, \ldots, \frac{1}{2^n}$$

the corresponding series is given by

$$S_n = \frac{1}{2} + \frac{1}{4} + \frac{1}{8} + \cdots + \frac{1}{2^n}$$

or

$$S_n = \sum_{k=1}^{n} \frac{1}{2^k}$$

Example 4. Write $S_5 = \sum\limits_{k=1}^{5} \dfrac{k-1}{k}$ without sigma notation.

SOLUTION

$$S_5 = \sum_{k=1}^{5} \frac{k-1}{k} = \frac{1-1}{1} + \frac{2-1}{2} + \frac{3-1}{3} + \frac{4-1}{4} + \frac{5-1}{5}$$

$$= 0 + \tfrac{1}{2} + \tfrac{2}{3} + \tfrac{3}{4} + \tfrac{4}{5}$$

Problem 4. Write $S_6 = \sum\limits_{k=1}^{6} \dfrac{(-1)^{k+1}}{2k-1}$ without sigma notation.

ANSWER

$$S_6 = 1 - \tfrac{1}{3} + \tfrac{1}{5} - \tfrac{1}{7} + \tfrac{1}{9} - \tfrac{1}{11}.$$

Example 5. Write the following series using sigma notation.

$$S_6 = 1 - \tfrac{1}{2} + \tfrac{1}{3} - \tfrac{1}{4} + \tfrac{1}{5} - \tfrac{1}{6}$$

SOLUTION

We first note that the nth term of the series is given by

$$a_n = (-1)^{n+1} \frac{1}{n}$$

hence,

$$S_6 = \sum_{k=1}^{6} (-1)^{k+1} \frac{1}{k}$$

Problem 5. Write the following series using sigma notation

$$S_5 = 1 - \tfrac{2}{3} + \tfrac{4}{9} - \tfrac{8}{27} + \tfrac{16}{81}$$

ANSWER

$$S_5 = \sum_{k=1}^{5} (-\tfrac{2}{3})^{k-1}.$$

Exercise 64

A *Write the first four terms for each sequence.*

1. $a_n = n - 2$

2. $a_n = n + 3$

3. $a_n = \dfrac{n-1}{n+1}$

4. $a_n = \left(1 + \dfrac{1}{n}\right)^n$

5. $a_n = (-2)^{n+1}$

6. $a_n = (-1)^{n+1}/n^2$

7. Write the eighth term in the sequence in Prob. 1.
8. Write the tenth term in the sequence in Prob. 2.
9. Write the one-hundredth term in the sequence in Prob. 3.
10. Write the two-hundredth term in the sequence in Prob. 4.

Write each series in expanded form without sigma notation.

11. $S_5 = \displaystyle\sum_{k=1}^{5} k$

12. $S_4 = \displaystyle\sum_{k=1}^{4} k^2$

13. $S_3 = \displaystyle\sum_{k=1}^{3} (1/10^k)$

14. $S_5 = \displaystyle\sum_{k=1}^{5} (\tfrac{1}{3})^k$

15. $S_4 = \displaystyle\sum_{k=1}^{4} (-1)^k$

16. $S_6 = \displaystyle\sum_{k=1}^{6} (-1)^{k+1} k$

B *Write the first five terms of each sequence.*

17. $a_n = (-1)^{n+1} n^2$

18. $a_n = (-1)^{n+1}(1/2^n)$

19. $a_n = \tfrac{1}{3}[1 - (1/10^n)]$

20. $a_n = n[1 - (-1)^n]$

21. $a_n = n \cos(n\pi/2)$

22. $a_n = (1/n) + \sin(n\pi/2)$

23. $a_1 = 7; \ a_n = a_{n-1} - 4, \ n \geq 2$

24. $a_1 = a_2 = 1; \ a_n = a_{n-1} + a_{n-2}, \ n \geq 3$

25. $a_1 = 4; \ a_n = \tfrac{1}{4}a_{n-1}, \ n \geq 2$

26. $a_1 = 2; \ a_n = 2a_{n-1}, \ n \geq 2$

Find a_n in terms of n.

27. $4, 5, 6, 7, \ldots$

28. $-2, -1, 0, 1, \ldots$

29. $3, 6, 9, 12, \ldots$

30. $-2, -4, -6, -8, \ldots$

31. $\tfrac{1}{2}, \tfrac{2}{3}, \tfrac{3}{4}, \tfrac{4}{5}, \ldots$

32. $\tfrac{1}{2}, \tfrac{3}{4}, \tfrac{5}{6}, \tfrac{7}{8}, \ldots$

33. $1, -1, 1, -1, \ldots$

34. $1, -2, 3, -4, \ldots$

35. $-2, 4, -8, 16, \ldots$

36. $1, -3, 5, -7, \ldots$

37. $x, x^2/2, x^3/3, x^4/4, \ldots$

38. $x, -x^3, x^5, -x^7, \ldots$

Write each series in expanded form without sigma notation.

39. $\displaystyle\sum_{k=1}^{4} \dfrac{(-2)^{k+1}}{k}$

40. $\displaystyle\sum_{k=1}^{5} (-1)^{k+1}(2k - 1)^2$

41. $S_3 = \displaystyle\sum_{k=1}^{3} \dfrac{1}{k} x^{k+1}$

42. $S_5 = \displaystyle\sum_{k=1}^{5} x^{k-1}$

43. $\displaystyle\sum_{k=1}^{5} \dfrac{(-1)^{k+1}}{k} x^k$

44. $\displaystyle\sum_{k=0}^{4} \dfrac{(-1)^k x^{2k+1}}{2k + 1}$

Write each series using sigma notation.

45. $S_4 = 1^2 + 2^2 + 3^2 + 4^2$

46. $S_5 = 2 + 3 + 4 + 5 + 6$

47. $S_5 = 1/2 + 1/2^2 + 1/2^3 + 1/2^4 + 1/2^5$

48. $S_4 = 1 - \frac{1}{2} + \frac{1}{3} - \frac{1}{4}$

49. $S_n = 1 + 1/2^2 + 1/3^2 + \cdots + 1/n^2$

50. $S_n = 2 + \frac{3}{2} + \frac{4}{3} + \cdots + (n+1)/n$

51. $S_n = 1 - 4 + 9 - \cdots + (-1)^{n+1}n^2$

52. $S_n = \frac{1}{2} + \frac{1}{4} + \frac{1}{8} + \cdots + (-1)^{n+1}/2^n$

C   53. Show that $\displaystyle\sum_{k=1}^{n} ca_k = c \sum_{k=1}^{n} a_k$.

54. Show that $\displaystyle\sum_{k=1}^{n} (a_k + b_k) = \sum_{k=1}^{n} a_k + \sum_{k=1}^{n} b_k$.

The sequence

$$a_n = \frac{a_{n-1}^2 + N}{2a_{n-1}} \qquad n \geq 2 \qquad N \in R^+$$

can be used to find $\sqrt{N}$ to any decimal-place accuracy desired. To start the sequence, choose a_1 arbitrarily from the positive real numbers.

55. (A)   Find the first four terms of the sequence

$$a_1 = 3 \qquad a_n = \frac{a_{n-1}^2 + 2}{2a_{n-1}} \qquad n \geq 2$$

   (B)   Compare the terms with $\sqrt{2}$ from a table.

   (C)   Repeat (A) and (B) by letting a_1 be any other positive number, say, 1.

56. (A)   Find the first four terms of the sequence

$$a_1 = 2 \qquad a_n = \frac{a_{n-1}^2 + 5}{2a_{n-1}} \qquad n \geq 3$$

   (B)   Find $\sqrt{5}$ in a table and compare with (A).

   (C)   Repeat (A) and (B) by letting a_1 be any other positive number, say, 3.

In calculus, it can be shown that

$$e^x = \sum_{k=0}^{\infty} \frac{x^k}{k!} = 1 + \frac{x}{1!} + \frac{x^2}{2!} + \frac{x^3}{3!} + \cdots$$

$$\sin x = \sum_{k=0}^{\infty} \frac{(-1)^k x^{2k+1}}{(2k+1)!} = x - \frac{x^3}{3!} + \frac{x^5}{5!} - \frac{x^7}{7!} + \cdots$$

$$\cos x = \sum_{k=0}^{\infty} \frac{(-1)^k x^{2k}}{(2k)!} = 1 - \frac{x^2}{2!} + \frac{x^4}{4!} - \frac{x^6}{6!} + \cdots$$

where $0! = 1$ and $n! = 1 \cdot 2 \cdot 3 \cdots n$, $n \in N$.

57. Let $S_n = \sum_{k=0}^{n} (x^k/k!)$, and find S_2, S_4, and S_6 for $x = 2$; then compare with e^2 from a table.

58. Let

$$S_n = \sum_{k=0}^{n} \frac{(-1)^k x^{2k+1}}{(2k+1)!}$$

and find S_1, S_2, and S_3 for $x = \frac{1}{2}$; then compare with $\sin \frac{1}{2}$ from a table.

59. Let

$$S_n = \sum_{k=1}^{n} \frac{(-1)^k x^{2k}}{(2k)!}$$

and find S_1, S_2, and S_3 for $x = \frac{1}{2}$; then compare with $\cos \frac{1}{2}$ from a table.

60. The formula for the area of a regular inscribed polygon with n sides, inscribed in a circle with radius 1, is

$$A_n = \frac{n}{2} \sin \frac{2\pi}{n} \qquad n \geq 3$$

Find A_3, A_4, and A_6.

8.2 MATHEMATICAL INDUCTION

In common usage the word *induction* means the generalization from particular cases or facts. The ability to formulate general hypotheses from a limited number of facts is a distinguishing characteristic of a creative mathematician. The creative process does not stop here, however; these hypotheses must then be proved or disproved. In mathematics, we have a special method of proof called *mathematical induction* that ranks among the most important basic tools in a mathematician's tool box. This method of proof, using deductive reasoning, enters frequently into the second part of the process described above.

We illustrate the first part of the process by an example. Suppose we write down the sums of consecutive odd integers as follows:

$$1 = 1$$
$$1 + 3 = 4$$
$$1 + 3 + 5 = 9$$
$$1 + 3 + 5 + 7 = 16$$
$$1 + 3 + 5 + 7 + 9 = 25$$

Is there something very regular about 1, 4, 9, 16, and 25? You no doubt guessed that each is a perfect square, and, perhaps, even guessed that each is the square of the number of terms being added. Have we "discovered" a general property of integers? What does this property appear to be?

HYPOTHESIS P: The sum of the first n odd integers is n^2 for all positive integers n [that is, $1 + 3 + 5 + \cdots + (2n - 1) = n^2$ for $n \in N$].

Thus far we have used ordinary induction to arrive at Hypothesis P. But how do we prove that it is true for all positive integers? Continuing by one-by-one testing will never accomplish a general proof—not in your life time or all of your ancestors' life times. Mathematical induction is the answer to this dilemma. Before we discuss this method of proof, let us consider another hypothesis:

HYPOTHESIS Q: For each positive integer n, $n^2 - n + 41$ is a prime number.

It is important to recognize that a hypothesis can be proved false if it fails for only one case, called a *counterexample*. Let us check the hypothesis for a few particular cases.

n	$n^2 - n + 41$	Prime?
1	41	Yes
2	43	Yes
3	47	Yes
4	53	Yes
5	61	Yes

It certainly appears that Hypothesis Q has a "good chance" of being true. The reader may want to check a few more cases, and if he persists, he will find Q true for n up to 41. What happens at $n = 41$?

$$41^2 - 41 + 41 = 41^2$$

which is not prime. Thus, Q is false—$n = 41$ provides a counterexample. Here we see the danger of generalizing without proof from a few special cases. This example was discovered by Euler (1707–1783).

Now to discuss mathematical induction. To start, we state a rather "obvious" property of the integers as an axiom.

Axiom (Well-Ordering Principle)   Let S be any set that contains one or more positive integers; then there must be a positive integer in S that is smaller than all the others.

Sets in which we have a particular interest are sets of integers that are closed under the addition of 1. That is, if k is in the set, then $k + 1$ is in the set. We will refer to such sets as *inductive sets*. Now we state the important theorem of this section.

Theorem 1.
Principle of
Mathematical
Induction

If p is a positive integer and S is a set of integers such that (1) $p \in S$ and (2) S is inductive, then S contains all integers greater than or equal to p.

This theorem certainly seems reasonable, since if $p \in S$, then by hypothesis (2), $p + 1 \in S$; if $p + 1 \in S$, then by hypothesis (2), $p + 2 \in S$; and so on. Clearly, all integers greater than or equal to p are in S. The only catch to this "proof" is in the use of "and so on" and "clearly." We proceed now to a rigorous proof of this important theorem.

PROOF (BY CONTRADICTION)

Assume, under the hypothesis of the theorem, S does not contain all integers greater than or equal to p. Let G be the set of all integers greater than p not in S. From the well-ordering axiom, G has a least element, say r, which is not p, since, by hypothesis (1), $p \in S$. Thus $r - 1$, the integer preceding r, is in S. But by hypothesis (2), if $r - 1 \in S$, then $(r - 1) + 1 = r \in S$, which is a contradiction, since r is in G. Our assumption must be false, and we conclude that S contains all integers from p on.

Let us now use Theorem 1 to prove that Hypothesis P above is true, as well as several over conjectures.

Example 6. Prove $1 + 3 + 5 + \cdots + (2n - 1) = n^2$, $n \in N$.

PROOF

Write

$$P_n: 1 + 3 + 5 + \cdots + (2n - 1) = n^2$$
$$S = \{n \in N \mid P_n \text{ is true}\}$$

where S is the truth set for the open statement P_n. To show that $S = N$, we must establish both parts of Theorem 1.

PART 1: Show that $1 \in S$.

$$1 = 1^2$$
$$\therefore 1 \in S$$

PART 2: Show that S is inductive (that is, prove generally that $k \in S \Rightarrow k + 1 \in S$).

We want to show that if P_n is true for $n = k$, it follows logically that P_n

is true for $n = k + 1$. We write P_k and P_{k+1} first to obtain an idea of where we must start and where we must finish:

$$P_k: 1 + 3 + 5 + \cdots + (2k - 1) = k^2$$
$$P_{k+1}: 1 + 3 + 5 + \cdots + (2k - 1) + (2k + 1) = (k + 1)^2$$

Starting with P_k, we can add $2k + 1$ to both members, and after simplifying the right member we note that we have obtained P_{k+1} as a logical consequence of P_k:

$$1 + 3 + 5 + \cdots + (2k - 1) = k^2 \qquad (P_k)$$
$$1 + 3 + 5 + \cdots + (2k - 1) + (2k + 1) = k^2 + (2k + 1) \qquad \text{(equality}$$
$$= (k + 1)^2 \qquad \text{property)}$$

Thus, $k \in S \Rightarrow k + 1 \in S$, and S is inductive.

CONCLUSION: $S = N$.

Problem 6. Prove $1 + 2 + 3 + \cdots + n = n(n + 1)/2$, $n \in N$.

PROOF (SKETCH)

Write

$$P_n: 1 + 2 + 3 + \cdots + n = \frac{n(n + 1)}{2} \qquad \text{and} \qquad S = \{n \in N \mid P_n \text{ is true}\}$$

PART 1: Show that $1 \in S$.

$$1 = \frac{1(1 + 1)}{2}$$
$$= 1$$
$$\therefore 1 \in S$$

PART 2: Show that S is inductive. (Supply reasons.)

$$1 + 2 + 3 + \cdots + k = \frac{k(k + 1)}{2}$$

$$1 + 2 + 3 + \cdots + k + (k + 1) = \frac{k(k + 1)}{2} + (k + 1)$$

$$= \frac{(k + 1)(k + 2)}{2}$$

Thus, $k \in S \Rightarrow k + 1 \in S$, and S is inductive.

CONCLUSION: $S = N$.

We are now in a position to prove the laws of exponents for natural numbers n. First, we redefine a^n, $n \in N$, using a *recursive formula*:

$$a^1 = a$$
$$a^{n+1} = a^n a \qquad n \in N$$

Thus

$$a^4 = a^3 a = (a^2 a)a = [(a^1 a)a]a = [(aa)a]a$$

Example 7. Prove that $(xy)^n = x^n y^n$ for all positive integers n.

PROOF

Write

$$P_n: (xy)^n = x^n y^n \qquad \text{and} \qquad S = \{n \in N \,|\, P_n \text{ is true}\}$$

PART 1:   Show that $1 \in S$.

$$(xy)^1 = xy \qquad \text{(definition)}$$
$$= x^1 y^1 \qquad \text{(definition)}$$
$$\therefore 1 \in S$$

PART 2:   Show that S is inductive.

$$P_k: (xy)^k = x^k y^k$$
$$P_{k+1}: (xy)^{k+1} = x^{k+1} y^{k+1}$$

Here we start with the left member of P_{k+1} and use P_k to find the right member of P_{k+1}.

$$(xy)^{k+1} = (xy)^k (xy) \qquad \text{(definition)}$$
$$= x^k y^k xy \qquad \text{(use of } P_k)$$
$$= (x^k x)(y^k y) \qquad \text{(property of real numbers)}$$
$$= x^{k+1} y^{k+1} \qquad \text{(definition)}$$

Thus, $k \in S \Rightarrow k + 1 \in S$, and S is inductive.

CONCLUSION: $S = N$.

Problem 7. Prove that $(x/y)^n = x^n/y^n$ for all positive integers n.

Proof (SKETCH)

Write

$$P_n: \left(\frac{x}{y}\right)^n = \frac{x^n}{y^n} \quad \text{and} \quad S = \{n \in N \mid P_n \text{ is true}\}$$

PART 1:   Show that $1 \in S$. (Supply reasons.)

$$\left(\frac{x}{y}\right)^1 = \frac{x}{y}$$

$$= \frac{x^1}{y^1}$$

$\therefore 1 \in S$

PART 2:   Show that S is inductive. (Supply reasons.)

$$\left(\frac{x}{y}\right)^{k+1} = \left(\frac{x}{y}\right)^k \frac{x}{y}$$

$$= \frac{x^k}{y^k} \frac{x}{y}$$

$$= \frac{x^k x}{y^k y}$$

$$= \frac{x^{k+1}}{y^{k+1}}$$

Thus, $k \in S \Rightarrow k + 1 \in S$, and S is inductive.

CONCLUSION: $S = N$.

We consider one last example. (But first recall that integer p is *divisible* by integer q if $p = qr$ for some integer r.)

Example 8.   Prove that $4^{2n} - 1$ is divisible by 5 for all positive integers n.

Proof

Write

$$P_n: 4^{2n} - 1 \text{ is divisible by 5} \quad \text{and} \quad S = \{n \in N \mid P_n \text{ is true}\}$$

PART 1:   Show that $1 \in S$.

$4^{2 \cdot 1} - 1 = 15$ (which is divisible by 5)

$\therefore 1 \in S$

PART 2: Show that S is inductive.

$$P_k: 4^{2k} - 1 = 5r \qquad \text{for some integer } r$$
$$P_{k+1}: 4^{2(k+1)} - 1 = 5s \qquad \text{for some integer } s$$

$$
\begin{array}{ll}
4^{2k} - 1 = 5r & (P_k) \\
4^2(4^{2k} - 1) = 4^2(5r) & \text{(property of equality)} \\
4^{2k+2} - 4^2 = 4^2(5r) & \text{(property of a real number)} \\
4^{2(k+1)} - 1 = 15 + 4^2(5r) & \text{(property of equality)} \\
\qquad = 5(3 + 16r) & \text{(property of a real number)} \\
\qquad = 5s & \text{where } s = (3 + 16r), \text{ an integer}
\end{array}
$$

Thus, $k \in S \Rightarrow k + 1 \in S$, and S is inductive.

CONCLUSION: $S = N$.

Problem 8. Prove that $8^n - 1$ is divisible by 7 for all positive integers n.

PROOF (SKETCH)

Write

$$P_n: 8^n - 1 \text{ is divisible by 7} \qquad \text{and} \qquad S = \{n \in N \,|\, P_n \text{ is true}\}$$

PART 1: Show that $1 \in S$.

$$8^1 - 1 = 7$$
$$\therefore 1 \in S$$

PART 2: Show that S is inductive. (Supply reasons.)

$$
\begin{aligned}
8^k - 1 &= 7r \\
8(8^k - 1) &= 8(7r) \\
8^{k+1} - 1 &= 7 + 8(7r) \\
&= 7(1 + 8r)
\end{aligned}
$$

Thus, $k \in S \Rightarrow k + 1 \in S$, and S is inductive.

CONCLUSION: $S = N$.

We conclude this section by stating three famous problems. Instant worldwide fame awaits anyone who can prove or disprove either of the first two; neither has been proved or disproved to date.

Three Famous Problems

1. Goldbach's problem, 1742: Every positive even integer greater than 2 is the sum of two prime numbers.
2. Fermat's last theorem, 1637: For $n > 2$, $x^n + y^n = z^n$ does not have solutions in the integers.
3. Each positive integer can be expressed as the sum of four or fewer squares of positive integers. (Considered by the early Greeks and finally proved in 1772 by Lagrange.)

Exercise 65

A *Find the first positive integer n that causes the statement to fail.*

1. $(3 + 5)^n = 3^n + 5^n$
2. $n < 10$
3. $n^2 = 3n - 2$
4. $n^3 + 11n = 6n^2 + 6$

Verify each open statement P_n for $n = 1$, 2, and 3.

5. $P_n: 2 + 6 + 10 + \cdots + (4n - 2) = 2n^2$
6. $P_n: 4 + 8 + 12 + \cdots + 4n = 2n(n + 1)$
7. $P_n: a^5 a^n = a^{5+n}$
8. $P_n: (a^5)^n = a^{5n}$
9. $P_n: 9^n - 1$ is divisible by 4
10. $P_n: 4^n - 1$ is divisible by 3

Write P_k and P_{k+1} for each of the following.

11. P_n in Prob. 5
12. P_n in Prob. 6
13. P_n in Prob. 7
14. P_n in Prob. 8
15. P_n in Prob. 9
16. P_n in Prob. 10

Use mathematical induction to prove that each P_n holds for all positive integers n.

17. P_n in Prob. 5
18. P_n in Prob. 6
19. P_n in Prob. 7
20. P_n in Prob. 8
21. P_n in Prob. 9
22. P_n in Prob. 10

B *Use mathematical induction to prove each of the following propositions for all positive integers n, unless restricted otherwise.*

23. $2 + 2^2 + 2^3 + \cdots + 2^n = 2^{n+1} - 2$
24. $\frac{1}{2} + \frac{1}{4} + \frac{1}{8} + \cdots + 1/2^n = 1 - (\frac{1}{2})^n$
25. $1^2 + 3^2 + 5^2 + \cdots + (2n - 1)^2 = \frac{1}{3}(4n^3 - n)$
26. $1 + 8 + 16 + \cdots + 8(n - 1) = (2n - 1)^2$
27. $1^2 + 2^2 + 3^2 + \cdots + n^2 = n(n + 1)(2n + 1)/6$
28. $1 \cdot 2 + 2 \cdot 3 + 3 \cdot 4 + \cdots + n(n + 1) = n(n + 1)(n + 2)/3$
29. $a^n/a^3 = a^{n-3}$, $n > 3$
30. $a^5/a^n = 1/a^{n-5}$, $n > 5$

31. $a^m a^n = a^{m+n}$, m, $n \in N$. (*Hint:* Choose m as an arbitrary element of N, and then use induction on n.)
32. $(a^n)^m = a^{mn}$, m, $n \in N$
33. $x^n - 1$ is divisible by $x - 1$, $x \neq 1$ [divisible means that $x^n - 1 = (x - 1)Q(x)$ for some polynomial $Q(x)$].
34. $x^n - y^n$ is divisible by $x - y$, $x \neq y$.
35. $x^{2n} - 1$ is divisible by $x - 1$, $x \neq 1$.
36. $x^{2n} - 1$ is divisible by $x + 1$, $x \neq -1$.
37. $1^3 + 2^3 + 3^3 + \cdots + n^3 = (1 + 2 + 3 + \cdots + n)^2$. (*Hint:* See Prob. 6 following Example 6.)
38. $\dfrac{1}{1 \cdot 2 \cdot 3} + \dfrac{1}{2 \cdot 3 \cdot 4} + \dfrac{1}{3 \cdot 4 \cdot 5} + \cdots + \dfrac{1}{n(n + 1)(n + 2)} = \dfrac{n(n + 3)}{4(n + 1)(n + 2)}$

Discover a formula for each of the following, and prove your hypothesis using mathematical induction, $n \in N$.

39. $2 + 4 + 6 + \cdots + 2n$
40. $\dfrac{1}{1 \cdot 2} + \dfrac{1}{2 \cdot 3} + \dfrac{1}{3 \cdot 4} + \cdots + \dfrac{1}{n(n + 1)}$
41. The number of lines determined by n points in a plane, no three of which are collinear
42. The number of diagonals in a polygon with n sides

C *Prove the following true for all integers n as specified.*

43. $a > 1 \Rightarrow a^n > 1$, $n \in N$
44. $0 < a < 1 \Rightarrow 0 < a^n < 1$, $n \in N$
45. $n^2 > 2n$, $n \geq 3$
46. $2^n > n^2$, $n \geq 5$
47. $n! > 2^n$, $n \geq 4$, where $1! = 1$ and $(n + 1)! = (n + 1)n!$

48. Prove or disprove the generalization of the following two facts:
$$3^2 + 4^2 = 5^2$$
$$3^3 + 4^3 + 5^3 = 6^3$$

49. Prove or disprove: "$n^2 + 21n + 1$ is a prime number for all natural numbers n."
50. Prove DeMoivre's theorem: $z^n = (x + yi)^n = (r \text{ cis } \theta)^n = r^n \text{ cis } n\theta$, $n \in N$
51. Given that $\overline{z_1 z_2} = \bar{z}_1 \bar{z}_2$, prove that $\overline{z^n} = \bar{z}^n$, $n \in N$; z_1, $z_2 \in C$.
52. Prove that $\sin x + \sin 2x + \cdots + \sin nx = \sin \tfrac{1}{2}nx \sin \tfrac{1}{2}(n + 1)x / \sin \tfrac{1}{2}x$.

If $\{a_n\}$ and $\{b_n\}$ are two sequences, we write $\{a_n\} = \{b_n\}$ if and only if $a_n = b_n$, $n \in N$. Use mathematical induction to show that $\{a_n\} = \{b_n\}$ where

53. $a_1 = 1$, $a_n = a_{n-1} + 2$; $b_n = 2n - 1$
54. $a_1 = 2$, $a_n = a_{n-1} + 2$; $b_n = 2n$
55. $a_1 = 2$, $a_n = 2^2 a_{n-1}$; $b_n = 2^{2n-1}$
56. $a_1 = 2$, $a_n = 3a_{n-1}$; $b_n = 2 \cdot 3^{n-1}$

8.3 ARITHMETIC SEQUENCES AND SERIES

Consider the sequence

5, 9, 13, 17, ...

Can you guess what the fifth term is? If you guessed 21, you have observed that each term after the first can be obtained from the preceding one by adding 4 to it. This is an example of an arithmetic sequence. In general, a sequence

$$a_1, a_2, a_3, \ldots, a_n, \ldots$$

is called an *arithmetic sequence* (or an *arithmetic progression*) if there exists a constant d, called the *common difference*, such that

---

$$a_n = a_{n-1} + d \qquad \text{for every } n > 1$$

Example 9. Which sequence is an arithmetic sequence and what is its common difference?

(A)   1, 2, 3, 5, ...
(B)   3, 5, 7, 9, ...

SOLUTION

(B) is an arithmetic sequence with $d = 2$.

Problem 9. Repeat Example 9 with (A) $-4, -1, 2, 5, \ldots$, and (B) 2, 4, 8, 16, ...

ANSWER

(A) with $d = 3$.

Arithmetic sequences have several convenient properties. For example, it is easy to derive formulas for the nth term in terms of n and the sum of any number of consecutive terms. To obtain an nth-term formula, we note that if a is an arithmetic sequence, then

$$a_2 = a_1 + d$$
$$a_3 = a_2 + d = a_1 + 2d$$
$$a_4 = a_3 + d = a_1 + 3d$$

which suggests

$$a_n = a_1 + (n - 1)d \qquad \text{for every } n > 1$$

We have arrived at this formula by ordinary induction; its proof requires mathematical induction, which we leave as an exercise.

Example 10. If the first and tenth terms of an arithmetic sequence are 3 and 30, respectively, find the fiftieth term of the sequence.

SOLUTION

First find d:

$$a_n = a_1 + (n - 1)d$$
$$a_{10} = a_1 + (10 - 1)d$$
$$30 = 3 + 9d$$
$$d = 3$$

Now find a_{50}:

$$a_{50} = a_1 + (50 - 1)3$$
$$= 3 + 49 \cdot 3$$
$$= 150$$

Problem 10. If the first and fifteenth terms of an arithmetic sequence are -5 and 23, respectively, find the seventy-third term of the sequence.

ANSWER

139.

The sum of the terms of an arithmetic sequence is called an *arithmetic series*. We will derive two simple and very useful formulas for finding the sum of an arithmetic series. Let

$$S_n = a_1 + (a_1 + d) + \cdots + [a_1 + (n - 2)d] + [a_1 + (n - 1)d]$$

Reversing the order of the sum, we obtain

$$S_n = [a_1 + (n - 1)d] + [a_1 + (n - 2)d] + \cdots + (a_1 + d) + a_1$$

Adding left members and corresponding elements of the right members of the two equations, we see that

$$2S_n = [2a_1 + (n-1)d] + [2a_1 + (n-1)d] + \cdots + [2a_1 + (n-1)d]$$
$$= n[2a_1 + (n-1)d]$$

or

$$S_n = \frac{n}{2}[2a_1 + (n-1)d]$$

By replacing $a_1 + (n-1)d$ with a_n, we obtain a second useful formula for the sum:

$$S_n = \frac{n}{2}(a_1 + a_n)$$

The proof of the first sum formula by mathematical induction is left as an exercise.

Example 11. Find the sum of the first 26 terms of an arithmetic series if the first term is -7 and $d = 3$.

SOLUTION

$$S_n = \frac{n}{2}[2a_1 + (n-1)d]$$

$$S_{26} = \frac{26}{2}[2(-7) + (26-1)3]$$

$$= 793$$

Problem 11. Find the sum of the first 52 terms of an arithmetic series if the first term is 23 and $d = -2$.

ANSWER

$-1,456.$

Example 12. Find the sum of all the odd numbers between 51 and 99, inclusive.

SOLUTION

First find n:

$$a_n = a_1 + (n - 1)d$$
$$99 = 51 + (n - 1)2$$
$$n = 25$$

Now find S_{25}:

$$S_n = \frac{n}{2}(a_1 + a_n)$$

$$S_{25} = \frac{25}{2}(51 + 99)$$
$$= 1,875$$

Problem 12. Find the sum of all the even numbers between -22 and 52, inclusive.

ANSWER

570.

EXERCISE 66

A   1. Determine which of the following are arithmetic sequences. Find d and the next two terms for those that are.
   (A) $2, 4, 8, \ldots$ (B) $7, 6.5, 6, \ldots$
   (C) $-11, -16, -21, \ldots$ (D) $\frac{1}{2}, \frac{1}{6}, \frac{1}{18}, \ldots$
   2. Repeat Prob. 1 for
   (A) $5, -1, -7, \ldots$ (B) $12, 4, \frac{4}{3}, \ldots$
   (C) $\frac{1}{2}, \frac{2}{3}, \frac{3}{4}, \ldots$ (D) $16, 48, 80, \ldots$

Let $a_1, a_2, a_3, \ldots, a_n, \ldots$ be an arithmetic sequence. In Probs. 3 to 18 find the indicated quantities.

   3. $a_1 = -5, d = 4, a_2 = ?, a_3 = ?, a_4 = ?$
   4. $a_1 = -18, d = 3, a_2 = ?, a_3 = ?, a_4 = ?$
   5. $a_1 = -3, d = 5, a_{15} = ?, S_{11} = ?$
   6. $a_1 = 3, d = 4, a_{22} = ?, S_{21} = ?$
   7. $a_1 = 1, a_2 = 5, S_{21} = ?$
   8. $a_1 = 5, a_2 = 11, S_{11} = ?$
   9. $a_1 = 7, a_2 = 5, a_{15} = ?$
   10. $a_1 = -3, d = -4, a_{10} = ?$

B　11.　$a_1 = 3, a_{20} = 117, d = ?, a_{101} = ?$

12.　$a_1 = 7, a_8 = 28, d = ?, a_{25} = ?$

13.　$a_1 = -12, a_{40} = 22, S_{40} = ?$

14.　$a_1 = 24, a_{24} = -28; S_{24} = ?$

15.　$a_1 = \frac{1}{3}, a_2 = \frac{1}{2}, a_{11} = ?, S_{11} = ?$

16.　$a_1 = \frac{1}{6}, a_2 = \frac{1}{4}, a_{19} = ?, S_{19} = ?$

17.　$a_3 = 13, a_{10} = 55, a_1 = ?$

18.　$a_9 = -12, a_{13} = 3, a_1 = ?$

19.　$S_{51} = \sum_{k=1}^{51} (3k + 3) = ?$

20.　$S_{40} = \sum_{k=1}^{40} (2k - 3) = ?$

21.　Find $g(1) + g(2) + g(3) + \cdots + g(51)$ if $g(t) = 5 - t$.

22.　Find $f(1) + f(2) + f(3) + \cdots + f(20)$ if $f(x) = 2x - 5$.

23.　Find the sum of all the even integers between 21 and 135.

24.　Find the sum of all the odd integers between 100 and 500.

25.　Show that the sum of the first n odd natural numbers is n^2, using appropriate formulas from this section.

26.　Show that the sum of the first n even natural numbers is $n + n^2$, using appropriate formulas from this section.

27.　If in a given sequence $a_1 = -3$ and $a_n = a_{n-1} + 3$, $n > 1$, find a_n in terms of n.

28.　For the sequence in Prob. 27 find $S_n = \sum_{k=1}^{n} a_k$ in terms of n.

29.　An object falling from rest in a vacuum near the surface of the earth falls 16 ft during the first second, 48 ft during the second second, and 80 ft during the third second, and so on. (A) How far will the object fall during the eleventh second? (B) How far will the object fall in 11 sec? (C) How far will the object fall in t seconds?

30.　In investigating different job opportunities, you find that firm A will start you at $6,000 per year and guarantee you a raise of $300 each year, while firm B will start you at $7,000 per year, but will only guarantee you a raise of $200 each year. Over a 15-year period which firm will pay the greatest total amount?

C　31.　Prove, using mathematical induction, that if $\{a_n\}$ is an arithmetic sequence, then

$$a_n = a_1 + (n - 1)d$$

32.　Prove, using mathematical induction, that if $\{a_n\}$ is an arithmetic sequence, then

$$S_n = \frac{n}{2} [2a_1 + (n - 1)d]$$

33.　Show that $(x^2 + xy + y^2)$, $(y^2 + yz + z^2)$, and $(z^2 + xz + x^2)$ are consecutive terms of an arithmetic progression if x, y, and z are consecutive terms of an arithmetic progression. (U.S.S.R. Mathematical Olympiads, 1955–1956, Grade 9.)

34. Take 121 terms of each arithmetic progression 2, 7, 12, ... and 2, 5, 8, ... How many numbers will there be in common? (U.S.S.R. Mathematical Olympiads, 1955–1956, Grade 9.)

35. Given the system of equations

$$ax + by = c$$
$$dx + ey = f$$

where a, b, c, d, e, f is any arithmetic progression, show that the system has a unique solution.

8.4 GEOMETRIC SEQUENCES AND SERIES

Consider the sequence

$$2, -4, 8, -16, \ldots$$

Can you guess what the fifth and sixth terms are? If you guessed 32 and -64, respectively, you have observed that each term after the first can be obtained from the preceding one by multiplying it by -2. This is an example of a geometric sequence. In general, a sequence

$$a_1, a_2, a_3, \ldots, a_n, \ldots$$

is called a *geometric sequence* (or a *geometric progression*) if there exists a nonzero constant r, called the *common ratio*, such that

$$a_n = ra_{n-1} \qquad \text{for every } n > 1$$

Example 13. Which sequence is a geometric sequence and what is its common ratio?

(A) $2, 6, 8, 10, \ldots$
(B) $-1, 3, -9, 27, \ldots$

SOLUTION

(B) is a geometric sequence with $r = -3$.

Problem 13. Repeat Example 13 with (A) $\frac{1}{4}, \frac{1}{2}, 1, 2, \ldots$, and (B) $\frac{1}{2}, \frac{1}{4}, \frac{1}{16}, \frac{1}{256}, \ldots$.

ANSWER

(A) with $r = 2$.

Just as with arithmetic sequences, geometric sequences have several convenient properties. It is easy to derive formulas for the nth term in terms of n and the sum of any number of consecutive terms. To obtain an nth-term formula, we note that if a is a geometric sequence, then

$$a_2 = ra_1$$
$$a_3 = ra_2 = r^2a_1$$
$$a_4 = ra_3 = r^3a_1$$

which suggests that

$$a_n = a_1r^{n-1} \qquad \text{for every } n > 1$$

We have arrived at this formula using ordinary induction; its proof requires mathematical induction, which we leave as an exercise.

Example 14. Find the seventh term of the geometric sequence $1, \frac{1}{2}, \frac{1}{4}, \ldots$.

SOLUTION

$$r = \tfrac{1}{2}$$
$$a_n = a_1r^{n-1}$$
$$a_7 = 1(\tfrac{1}{2})^{7-1} = \tfrac{1}{64}$$

Problem 14. Find the eighth term of the geometric sequence $\frac{1}{64}, -\frac{1}{32}, \frac{1}{16}, \ldots$.

ANSWER

$-2.$

Example 15. If the first and tenth terms of a geometric sequence are 1 and 2, respectively, find the common ratio r.

SOLUTION

$$a_n = a_1r^{n-1}$$
$$2 = 1r^{10-1}$$
$$r = 2^{1/9} = 1.08 \qquad \text{(calculation by logarithms)}$$

Problem 15. If the first and eighth terms of a geometric sequence are 2 and 16, respectively, find the common ratio r.

ANSWER

$r = 1.346$.

The sum of the terms of a geometric sequence is called a *geometric series*. As was the case with an arithmetic series, we can derive two simple and very useful formulas for finding the *sum of a geometric series*. Let

$$S_n = a_1 + a_1 r + a_1 r^2 + a_1 r^3 + \cdots + a_1 r^{n-1}$$

and multiply both members by r to obtain

$$r S_n = a_1 r + a_1 r^2 + a_1 r^3 + \cdots + a_1 r^{n-1} + a_1 r^n$$

Now subtract the left member of the second equation from the left member of the first, and the right member of the second equation from the right member of the first to obtain

$$S_n - r S_n = a_1 - a_1 r^n$$
$$S_n(1 - r) = a_1 - a_1 r^n$$

Thus,

$$S_n = \frac{a_1 - a_1 r^n}{1 - r} \qquad r \neq 1$$

Since $a_n = a_1 r^{n-1}$, or $r a_n = a_1 r^n$, the sum formula can also be written in the form

$$S_n = \frac{a_1 - r a_n}{1 - r} \qquad r \neq 1$$

The proof of the first sum formula by mathematical induction is left as an exercise.

Example 16. Find the sum of the first 20 terms of a geometric series if the first term is 1 and $r = 2$.

SOLUTION

$$S_n = \frac{a_1 - a_1 r^n}{1 - r}$$

$$S_n = \frac{1 - 1 \cdot 2^{20}}{1 - 2} \approx 1,050,000 \qquad \text{(calculation by logarithms)}$$

Problem 16. Find the sum of the first 14 terms of a geometric series if the first term is $\frac{1}{64}$ and $r = -2$.

ANSWER

-85.33.

Infinite Geometric Series

Consider a geometric series with $a_1 = 5$ and $r = \frac{1}{2}$. What happens to the sum S_n as n increases? To answer this question, we first write the sum formula in the more convenient form

$$S_n = \frac{a_1 - a_1 r^n}{1 - r} = \frac{a_1}{1 - r} - \frac{a_1 r^n}{1 - r} \tag{1}$$

For $a_1 = 5$ and $r = \frac{1}{2}$,

$$S_n = 10 - 10\left(\frac{1}{2}\right)^n$$

$$S_2 = 10 - 10\left(\frac{1}{4}\right)$$

$$S_4 = 10 - 10\left(\frac{1}{16}\right)$$

$$S_{10} = 10 - 10\left(\frac{1}{1,024}\right)$$

$$S_{20} = 10 - 10\left(\frac{1}{1,048,576}\right)$$

It appears that $(\frac{1}{2})^n$ becomes smaller and smaller as n increases, and that the sum gets closer and closer to 10.

In general, it is possible to show that, if $|r| < 1$ (that is, $-1 < r < 1$), then r^n will tend to zero as n increases. Thus,

$$\frac{a_1 r^n}{1 - r}$$

in Eq. (1) will tend to zero as n increases, and S_n will tend to

$$\frac{a_1}{1 - r}$$

In other words, if $|r| < 1$, then S_n can be made as close to

$$\frac{a_1}{1 - r}$$

as we wish by taking n sufficiently large. Thus, we define

$$S_\infty = \frac{a_1}{1 - r} \qquad |r| < 1$$

and call this the *sum of an infinite geometric series*. If $|r| \geq 1$, an infinite geometric series has no sum.

Example 17. Represent the repeating decimal $0.45\overline{4545}$ as the quotient of two integers. (Recall that a repeating decimal names a rational number, and that any rational number can be represented as the quotient of two integers.)

SOLUTION

$$0.45\overline{4545} = 0.45 + 0.0045 + 0.000045 + \cdots$$

The right member of the equation is an infinite geometric series with $a_1 = 0.45$ and $r = 0.01$. Thus,

$$S_\infty = \frac{a_1}{1 - r} = \frac{0.45}{1 - 0.01} = \frac{0.45}{0.99} = \frac{5}{11}$$

Hence, $0.45\overline{4545}$ and $\frac{5}{11}$ name the same rational number. Check the result by dividing 5 by 11.

Problem 17. Repeat Example 17 for $0.81\overline{8181}$.

ANSWER

$\frac{9}{11}$.

EXERCISE 67

A 1. Determine which of the following are geometric sequences. Find r and the next two terms for those that are.

    (A) $2, -4, 8, \ldots$ (B) $7, 6.5, 6, \ldots$

    (C) $-11, -16, -21, \ldots$ (D) $\frac{1}{2}, \frac{1}{6}, \frac{1}{18}, \ldots$

2. Repeat Prob. 1 for:

    (A) $5, -1, -7, \ldots$ (B) $12, 4, \frac{4}{3}, \ldots$

    (C) $\frac{1}{2}, \frac{2}{3}, \frac{3}{4}, \ldots$ (D) $16, 48, 80, \ldots$

Let $a_1, a_2, a_3, \ldots, a_n, \ldots$ be a geometric sequence. Find each of the indicated quantities.

3. $a_1 = -6, r = -\frac{1}{2}, a_2 = ?, a_3 = ?, a_4 = ?$

4. $a_1 = 12, r = \frac{2}{3}, a_2 = ?, a_3 = ?, a_4 = ?$

5. $a_1 = 81, r = \frac{1}{3}, a_{10} = ?$

6. $a_1 = 64, r = \frac{1}{2}, a_{13} = ?$

7. $a_1 = 3, a_7 = 2{,}187, r = 3, S_7 = ?$

8. $a_1 = 1, a_7 = 729, r = -3, S_7 = ?$

B 9. $a_1 = 100, a_6 = 1, r = ?$

10. $a_1 = 10, a_{10} = 30, r = ?$

11. $a_1 = 5, r = -2, S_{10} = ?$

12. $a_1 = 3, r = 2, S_{10} = ?$

13. $a_1 = 9, a_4 = \frac{8}{3}, a_2 = ?, a_3 = ?$

14. $a_1 = 12, a_4 = -\frac{4}{9}, a_2 = ?, a_3 = ?$

15. $S_7 = \sum_{k=1}^{7} (-3)^{k-1} = ?$

16. $S_7 = \sum_{k=1}^{7} 3^k = ?$

17. Find $g(1) + g(2) + \cdots + g(10)$ if $g(x) = (\frac{1}{2})^x$.

18. Find $f(1) + f(2) + \cdots + f(10)$ if $f(x) = 2^x$.

19. Find a positive number x so that $-2 + x - 6$ is a geometric series.

20. Find a positive number x so that $6 + x + 8$ is a geometric series.

Find the sum of each infinite geometric series that has a sum.

21. $3 + 1 + \frac{1}{3} + \cdots$ 22. $16 + 4 + 1 + \cdots$

23. $2 + 4 + 8 + \cdots$ 24. $4 + 6 + 9 + \cdots$

25. $2 - \frac{1}{2} + \frac{1}{8} + \cdots$ 26. $21 - 3 + \frac{3}{7} + \cdots$

Represent each repeating decimal fraction as the quotient of two integers.

27. $0.7\overline{77}$ 28. $0.5\overline{55}$

29. $0.54\overline{54}$ 30. $0.272\overline{727}$

31. $3.216216\overline{216}$ 32. $5.636\overline{363}$

33. If P dollars is invested at r percent compounded annually, the amount A present after n years forms a geometric progression with a constant ratio $(1 + r)$. Write a formula for the amount present after n years. How long will it take for a sum of money P to double if invested at 6% interest compounded annually?

34. If a population of A_0 people grows at the constant rate of r percent per year, the population after t years forms a geometric progression with a constant ratio $(1 + r)$. Write a formula for the total population after t years. If the world's population is increasing at the rate of 2 percent per year, how long will it take to double?

35. A rotating flywheel coming to rest rotates 300 revolutions the first minute. If in each subsequent minute it rotates two-thirds as many times as in the preceding minute, how many revolutions will the wheel make before coming to rest?

36. The first swing of a bob on a pendulum is 10 in. If on each subsequent swing it travels 0.9 as far as on the preceding swing, how far will the bob travel before coming to rest?

c 37. If in a given sequence, $a_1 = -2$ and $a_n = -3a_{n-1}$, $n > 1$, find a_n in terms of n.

38. For the sequence in Prob. 37 find $S_n = \sum\limits_{k=1}^{n} a_k$ in terms of n.

39. Prove, using mathematical induction, that if $\{a_n\}$ is a geometric sequence, then

$$a_n = a_1 r^{n-1} \qquad n \in N$$

40. Prove, using mathematical induction, that if $\{a_n\}$ is a geometric sequence, then

$$S_n = \frac{a_1 - a_1 r^n}{1 - r} \qquad n \in N$$

41. The government, through a subsidy program, distributes $1,000,000. If we assume that each individual or agency spends 0.8 of what is received, and 0.8 of this is spent, and so on, how much total increase in spending results from this government action? (Let $a_1 = \$800,000$.)

42. Visualize a hypothetical 440-yd oval race track that has tapes stretched across the track at the halfway point and at each point that marks the halfway point of each remaining distance thereafter. A runner running around the track has to break the first tape before the second, the second before the third, and so on. From this point of view it appears that he will never finish the race. (This famous paradox is attributed to the Greek philosopher, Zeno, 495–435 B.C.) If we assume the runner runs at 440 yd per min, the times between tape breakings form an infinite geometric progression. What is the sum of this progression?

8.5 ADDITIONAL APPLICATIONS

This section includes additional applications involving progressions (mainly geometric) associated with many different fields. The problems are self-contained, and require no previous knowledge of the subjects concerned.

EXERCISE 68

Business and Economics

1. If you received $7,000 a year 11 years ago and now receive $14,000 per year, and if your salary has been increased the same amount each year, what is that yearly increase and how much money have you received from the company over the 11 years?

2. Let us suppose the government has reduced taxes so that you have $600 more in spendable income. What is the net effect of this extra $600 on the economy? According to the "multiplier" doctrine in economics, the effect of the $600 is multiplied. Let us assume that you spend 0.7 of the $600 on consumer goods, that the producers of these goods in turn spend 0.7 of what they receive on consumer goods, and that this chain continues indefinitely, forming a geometric progression. What is the total amount spent on consumer goods if the process continues indefinitely? (Let $a_1 = \$420$.)

Earth Sciences

3. If atmospheric pressure decreases (roughly) by a factor of 10 for each 10-mi increase in altitude up to 60 mi, and if the pressure is 15 lb per in.^{2} at sea level, what will the pressure be 40 mi up?

4. As dry air moves upward it expands, and in so doing cools at the rate of about 5°F for each 1,000-ft rise. This is known as the *adiabatic process*.
   (A) Temperatures at altitudes that are multiples of 1,000 form what kind of a sequence?
   (B) If the ground temperature is 80°F, write a formula for the temperature T_n in terms of n, if n is in thousands of feet.

Life Sciences—Ecology

5. A plant is eaten by an insect, an insect by a trout, a trout by a salmon, a salmon by a bear, and the bear is eaten by you. If only 20 percent of the energy is transformed from one stage to the next, how many calories must be supplied by plant food to provide you with 2,000 calories from the bear meat?

6. If there are 30 years in a generation, how many direct ancestors did each of us have 600 years ago? (By direct ancestors we mean parents, grandparents, great-grandparents, and so on.)

7. A single cholera bacterium divides every $\frac{1}{2}$ hour to produce two complete cholera bacteria. If we start with a colony of A_0 bacteria, in t hours (assuming adequate food supply) how many bacteria will we have?

8. One leukemic cell injected into a healthy mouse will divide into two cells in about $\frac{1}{2}$ day; at the end of the day these two cells will divide again, the doubling process continuing each half day until there are 1 billion cells, at which time the mouse dies. On which day after the experiment is started does this happen?

Astronomy

9. Ever since the time of the Greek astronomer Hipparchus (second century B.C.), the brightness of stars has been measured in terms of magnitude. The brightest stars (excluding the sun) are classed as magnitude 1, and the dimmest visible to the eye are classed as magnitude 6. In 1856, the English astronomer N. R. Pogson showed that first-magnitude stars are 100 times brighter than sixth-magnitude stars. If the ratio of brightness between consecutive magnitudes is constant, find this ratio. (*Hint:* If b_n is the brightness of an nth-magnitude star, find r for the geometric progression $b_1, b_2, b_3,$ ..., given $b_1 = 100b_6$.)

Music

10. The notes on a piano, as measured in cycles per second, form a geometric progression. (A) If A is 400 cycles per sec and A′, 12 notes higher, is 800 cycles per sec, find the constant ratio r. (B) Find the cycles per second for C, three notes higher than A.

Geometry

11. If the midpoints of the sides of an equilateral triangle are joined by straight lines, the new figure will be an equilateral triangle with a perimeter half the old. If we start with an equilateral triangle with perimeter 1, and form a sequence of "nested" equilateral triangles proceeding as above, what will be the total perimeter of all the triangles that can be formed in this way?

Photography

12. The shutter speeds and f-stops on a camera are given as follows:

Shutter speeds: $1, \frac{1}{2}, \frac{1}{4}, \frac{1}{8}, \frac{1}{15}, \frac{1}{30}, \frac{1}{60}, \frac{1}{125}, \frac{1}{250}, \frac{1}{500}$
f-stops: 1.4, 2, 2.8, 4, 5.6, 8, 10.3, 16

These are very close to being geometric progressions. Estimate their common ratios.

Puzzles

13. If you place 1 cent on the first square of a chess board, 2 cents on the second square, 4 cents on the third, and so on, continuing to double the amount until all 64 squares are covered, how much money will be on the sixty-fourth square? How much money will there be on the whole board?

14. If a sheet of very thin paper 0.001 in. thick is torn in half, and each half is again torn in half, and this process is repeated for a total of 32 times, how high will the stack of paper be if the pieces are placed one on top of the other? Give the answer to the nearest mile. (5,280 ft = 1 mi.)

15. Find the number of paths in the diamond array below that spell ALGEBRA. The paths must start with an A on the boundary and end at the A in the center. (*Hint:* Start at the center and work backward.)

```
            A
          A L A
        A L G L A
      A L G E G L A
    A L G E B E G L A
  A L G E B R B E G L A
A L G E B R A R B E G L A
  A L G E B R B E G L A
    A L G E B E G L A
      A L G E G L A
        A L G L A
          A L A
            A
```

8.6 BINOMIAL FORMULA

The binomial form

$$(a + b)^n \qquad n \in N$$

appears more frequently than one might expect. The coefficients of its expansion play an important role in probability studies. In this section we will derive the famous binomial formula which will enable us to accomplish an expansion directly for any natural number n. First, we introduce the useful concept of factorial.

The product of the first n natural numbers is symbolized by $n!$ and is referred to as *n factorial*. Symbolically,

$$1! = 1$$
$$n! = n(n-1)! \qquad \text{or} \qquad n! = n(n-1)(n-2) \cdots 3 \cdot 2 \cdot 1$$

In addition, we define

$$0! = 1$$

Example 18.   (A) $4! = 4 \cdot 3! = 4 \cdot 3 \cdot 2! = 4 \cdot 3 \cdot 2 \cdot 1! = 4 \cdot 3 \cdot 2 \cdot 1 = 24$

               (B) $5! = 5 \cdot 4 \cdot 3 \cdot 2 \cdot 1 = 120$

               (C) $\dfrac{7!}{6!} = \dfrac{7 \cdot \cancel{6!}}{\cancel{6!}} = 7$

               (D) $\dfrac{8!}{5!} = \dfrac{8 \cdot 7 \cdot 6 \cdot \cancel{5!}}{\cancel{5!}} = 336$

Problem 18.   Find

               (A) $6!$ (B) $6!/5!$ (C) $9!/6!$

ANSWER

(A) 720, (B) 6, (C) 504.

The symbol $\binom{n}{r}$ is frequently used in probability studies, and will be used by us shortly. It is called the *combinatorial symbol*, and is defined for nonnegative r and n, $r \leq n$, by the formula

$$\binom{n}{r} = \frac{n!}{r!(n-r)!} = \frac{n(n-1)(n-2) \cdots (n-r+1)}{r(r-1) \cdots 2 \cdot 1}$$

Example 19.   (A) $\dbinom{8}{3} = \dfrac{8!}{3!(8-3)!} = \dfrac{8!}{3!\,5!} = \dfrac{8 \cdot 7 \cdot 6 \cdot 5!}{3 \cdot 2 \cdot 1 \cdot 5!} = 56$

               (B) $\dbinom{7}{0} = \dfrac{7!}{0!(7-0)!} = \dfrac{7!}{7!} = 1$

Problem 19.   Find (A) $\dbinom{9}{2}$ and (B) $\dbinom{5}{5}$

ANSWER

(A) 36, (B) 1.

We will attempt to discover a formula for the expansion of $(a + b)^n$, using ordinary induction; that is, we will look at a few special cases and try to postulate a general formula from them. If successful, we will try to prove that the formula holds for all natural numbers, using mathematical induction. To start, let us calculate directly the first five powers of $(a + b)^n$:

$$(a + b)^1 = a + b$$
$$(a + b)^2 = a^2 + 2ab + b^2$$
$$(a + b)^3 = a^3 + 3a^2b + 3ab^2 + b^3$$
$$(a + b)^4 = a^4 + 4a^3b + 6a^2b^2 + 4ab^3 + b^4$$
$$(a + b)^5 = a^5 + 5a^4b + 10a^3b^2 + 10a^2b^3 + 5ab^4 + b^5$$

Observations

1. The expansion of $(a + b)^n$ has $n + 1$ terms.
2. The power of a starts at n and decreases 1 for each term until it is 0 in the last term.
3. The power of b starts at 0 in the first term and increases 1 for each term until it is n in the last term.
4. The sum of the powers of a and b in each term is the constant n.
5. The coefficient of any term after the first can be obtained from the preceding term as follows. In the preceding term multiply the coefficient by the exponent of a, and then divide this product by the number representing the position of the preceding term in the series.

We now postulate these same properties for the general case:

$$(a + b)^n = a^n + \frac{n}{1} a^{n-1}b + \frac{n(n - 1)}{1 \cdot 2} a^{n-2}b^2$$

$$+ \frac{n(n - 1)(n - 2)}{1 \cdot 2 \cdot 3} a^{n-3}b^3 + \cdots + b^n$$

$$= \frac{n!}{0!(n - 0)!} a^n + \frac{n!}{1!(n - 1)!} a^{n-1}b + \frac{n!}{2!(n - 2)!} a^{n-2}b^2$$

$$+ \frac{n!}{3!(n - 3)!} a^{n-3}b^3 + \cdots + \frac{n!}{n!(n - n)!} b^n$$

$$= \binom{n}{0}a^n + \binom{n}{1}a^{n-1}b + \binom{n}{2}a^{n-2}b^2 + \binom{n}{3}a^{n-3}b^3 + \cdots + \binom{n}{n}b^n$$

Thus, it appears that

$$(a + b)^n = \sum_{k=0}^{n} \binom{n}{k}a^{n-k}b^k \qquad n \geq 1$$

This result is known as the *binomial formula*, and we now proceed to prove that it holds for all natural numbers n.

Proof

Write

$$P_n: (a + b)^n = \sum_{j=1}^{n} \binom{n}{j} a^{n-j} b^j$$

$$S = \{n \in N \,|\, P_n \text{ is true}\}$$

PART 1:   Show that $1 \in S$.

$$\sum_{j=0}^{1} \binom{1}{j} a^{1-j} b^j = \binom{1}{0} a + \binom{1}{1} b = a + b = (a + b)^1$$

$$\therefore 1 \in S$$

PART 2:   Show that $k \in S \Rightarrow k + 1 \in S$.

$$P_k: (a + b)^k = \sum_{j=0}^{k} \binom{k}{j} a^{k-j} b^j$$

$$P_{k+1}: (a + b)^{k+1} = \sum_{j=0}^{k+1} \binom{k+1}{j} a^{k+1-j} b^j$$

Starting with P_k, we multiply both members by $a + b$ and try to obtain P_{k+1}:

$$(a + b)^k (a + b) = \left[\sum_{j=0}^{k} \binom{k}{j} a^{k-j} b^j \right] (a + b)$$

$$= \left[\binom{k}{0} a^k + \binom{k}{1} a^{k-1} b + \binom{k}{2} a^{k-2} b^2 + \cdots + \binom{k}{k} b^k \right] (a + b)$$

$$= \left[\binom{k}{0} a^{k+1} + \binom{k}{1} a^k b + \binom{k}{2} a^{k-1} b^2 + \cdots + \binom{k}{k} ab^k \right]$$

$$+ \left[\binom{k}{0} a^k b + \binom{k}{1} a^{k-1} b^2 + \cdots + \binom{k}{k-1} ab^k \right.$$

$$\left. + \binom{k}{k} b^{k+1} \right]$$

$$= \binom{k}{0} a^{k+1} + \left[\binom{k}{0} + \binom{k}{1} \right] a^k b$$

$$+ \left[\binom{k}{1} + \binom{k}{2} \right] a^{k-1} b^2 + \cdots$$

$$+ \left[\binom{k}{k-1} + \binom{k}{k} \right] ab^k + \binom{k}{k} b^{k+1}$$

We now use the facts (the proofs left as exercises) that

$$\binom{k}{r-1} + \binom{k}{r} = \binom{k+1}{r} \qquad \binom{k}{0} = \binom{k+1}{0} \qquad \binom{k}{k} = \binom{k+1}{k+1}$$

to rewrite the right side as

$$\binom{k+1}{0}a^{k+1} + \binom{k+1}{1}a^k b + \binom{k+1}{2}a^{k-1}b^2 + \cdots + \binom{k+1}{k}ab^k$$

$$+ \binom{k+1}{k+1}b^{k+1}$$

$$= \sum_{j=0}^{k+1} \binom{k+1}{j}a^{k+1-j}b^j$$

Thus, $k \in S \Rightarrow k + 1 \in S$, and S is inductive.

CONCLUSION: $S = N$

Example 20. Use the binomial formula to expand $(x + y)^6$.

SOLUTION

$$(x + y)^6 = \sum_{k=0}^{6} \binom{6}{k}x^{6-k}y^k$$

$$= \binom{6}{0}x^6 + \binom{6}{1}x^5 y + \binom{6}{2}x^4 y^2 + \binom{6}{3}x^3 y^3$$

$$+ \binom{6}{4}x^2 y^4 + \binom{6}{5}xy^5 + \binom{6}{6}y^6$$

$$= x^6 + 6x^5 y + 15x^4 y^2 + 20x^3 y^3 + 15x^2 y^4 + 6xy^5 + y^6$$

Problem 20. Use the binomial formula to expand $(x + 1)^5$.

ANSWER

$$x^5 + 5x^4 + 10x^3 + 10x^2 + 5x + 1.$$

Example 21. Use the binomial formula to find the fourth term in the expansion of $(x - 2)^{20}$.

SOLUTION

$$\text{Fourth term} = \binom{20}{3}x^{17}(-2)^3$$

$$= \frac{20 \cdot 19 \cdot 18}{3 \cdot 2 \cdot 1}x^{17}(-8)$$

$$= -9{,}120x^{17}$$

Problem 21. Use the binomial formula to find the fifth term in the expansion of $(u - 1)^{18}$.

ANSWER

$3,060u^{14}$.

Exercise 69

A *Evaluate*

1. $6!$
2. $4!$
3. $\dfrac{20!}{19!}$
4. $\dfrac{5!}{4!}$

5. $\dfrac{10!}{7!}$
6. $\dfrac{9!}{6!}$
7. $\dfrac{6!}{4!2!}$
8. $\dfrac{5!}{2!3!}$

9. $\dfrac{9!}{0!(9-0)!}$
10. $\dfrac{8!}{8!(8-8)!}$
11. $\dfrac{8!}{2!(8-2)!}$
12. $\dfrac{7!}{3!(7-3)!}$

Write as the quotient of two factorials.

13. 9
14. 12
15. $6 \cdot 7 \cdot 8$
16. $9 \cdot 10 \cdot 11 \cdot 12$

B *Evaluate*

17. $\binom{9}{5}$
18. $\binom{5}{2}$
19. $\binom{6}{5}$
20. $\binom{7}{1}$

21. $\binom{9}{9}$
22. $\binom{5}{0}$
23. $\binom{17}{13}$
24. $\binom{20}{16}$

Expand, using the binomial formula.

25. $(u + v)^5$
26. $(x + y)^4$
27. $(y - 1)^4$
28. $(x - 2)^5$
29. $(2x - y)^5$
30. $(m + 2n)^6$

Find the indicated term in each expansion.

31. $(u + v)^{15}$; seventh term
32. $(a + b)^{12}$; fifth term
33. $(2m + n)^{12}$; eleventh term
34. $(x + 2y)^{20}$; third term
35. $[(w/2) - 2]^{12}$; seventh term
36. $(x - 3)^{10}$; fourth term

C
37. Evaluate $(1.01)^{10}$ to four decimal places, using the binomial formula. (*Hint:* Let $1.01 = 1 + 0.01$.)
38. Evaluate $(0.99)^6$ to four decimal places, using the binomial formula.
39. Show that

$$\binom{n}{r} = \binom{n}{n-r}$$

40. Show that

$$\binom{n}{0} = \binom{n}{n}$$

41. Show that

$$\binom{k}{r-1} + \binom{k}{r} = \binom{k+1}{r}$$

42. Show that

$$\binom{k}{0} = \binom{k+1}{0}$$

43. Show that

$$\binom{k}{k} = \binom{k+1}{k+1}$$

44. Show that

$$\binom{n}{r}$$

is given by the recursive formula

$$\binom{n}{r} = \frac{n-r+1}{r}\binom{n}{r-1}$$

where

$$\binom{n}{0} = 1$$

45. Write $2^n = (1+1)^n$ and expand, using the binomial formula to obtain

$$2^n = \binom{n}{0} + \binom{n}{1} + \binom{n}{2} + \cdots + \binom{n}{n}$$

46. Can you guess what the next two rows in Pascal's triangle are? Compare the numbers in the triangle with the binomial coefficients obtained with the binomial formula.

```
    1
   1 1
  1 2 1
 1 3 3 1
1 4 6 4 1
```

Exercise 70   CHAPTER-REVIEW EXERCISES

A   1. Identify all arithmetic and all geometric sequences from the following list
of sequences.
(A) $16, -8, 4, \ldots$
(B) $5, 7, 9, \ldots$
(C) $-8, -5, -2, \ldots$
(D) $2, 3, 5, 8, \ldots$
(E) $-1, 2, -4, \ldots$

(A) Write the first four terms of each sequence, (B) find A_{10}, and (C) find S_{10}.

2. $a_n = 2n + 3$ 3. $a_n = 32(\frac{1}{2})^n$
4. $a_1 = -8; a_n = a_{n-1} + 3, n \geq 2$ 5. $a_1 = -1; a_n = (-2)a_{n-1}, n \geq 2$
6. Find S_∞ in Prob. 3.

Evaluate.

7. $6!$ 8. $\dfrac{22!}{19!}$ 9. $\dfrac{7!}{2!(7-2)!}$

Verify for $n = 1, 2,$ and 3.

10. $P_n: 5 + 7 + 9 + \cdots + (2n + 3) = n^2 + 4n$
11. $P_n: 2 + 4 + 8 + \cdots + 2^n = 2^{n+1} - 2$
12. $P_n: 49^n - 1$ is divisible by 6

Write P_k and P_{k+1}.

13. For P_n in Prob. 10
14. For P_n in Prob. 11
15. For P_n in Prob. 12

B   *Write without sigma notation and find the sum.*

16. $S_{10} = \sum\limits_{k=1}^{10} (2k - 8)$

17. $S_7 = \sum\limits_{k=1}^{7} \dfrac{16}{2^k}$

18. $S_\infty = 27 - 18 + 12 + \cdots = ?$
19. Write $S_n = \frac{1}{3} - \frac{1}{9} + \frac{1}{27} + \cdots + (-1)^{n+1}/3^n$ using sigma notation, and find
S_∞.
20. If in an arithmetic sequence $a_1 = 13$ and $a_7 = 31$, find the common difference d and the fifth term a_5.
21. Write $0.72\overline{72}$ as the quotient of two integers.

Evaluate.

22. $\dfrac{20!}{18!(20-18)!}$ 23. $\dbinom{16}{12}$ 24. $\dbinom{11}{11}$

25. Expand $(x - y)^5$ using the binomial formula.
26. Find the tenth term in the expansion of $(2x - y)^{12}$.

Establish each statement for all natural numbers, using mathematical induction.

27. P_n in Prob. 10
28. P_n in Prob. 11
29. P_n in Prob. 12

c 30. A free-falling body travels $g/2$ feet in the first second, $3g/2$ feet during the next second, $5g/2$ feet the next, and so on. Find the distance fallen during the twenty-fifth second, and the total distance fallen from the start to the end of the twenty-fifth second.

31. Expand $(x + i)^6$, i the complex unit, using the binomial formula.

Prove that each of the following statements holds for all positive integers, using mathematical induction.

32. $\displaystyle\sum_{k=1}^{n} k^3 = \left(\sum_{k=1}^{n} k\right)^2$

33. $x^{2n} - y^{2n}$ is divisible by $x - y$

34. $\dfrac{a^n}{a^m} = a^{n-m}; n > m; n, m \in N$

35. $\{a_n\} = \{b_n\}$ where $a_n = a_{n-1} + 2$, $a_1 = -3$, and $b_n = -5 + 2n$.
36. $(1!)1 + (2!)2 + (3!)3 + \cdots + (n!)n = (n+1)! - 1$ (U.S.S.R. Mathematical Olympiad, 1955–1956, Grade 10).

Answers

CHAPTER 1

Exercise 1

1. $\{1,2,3,4,5\}$ 3. $\{12,13,14,15,16\}$ 5. $\{3\}$ 7. $\{-7,7\}$ 9. $\{3\}$ 11. $\{-7,7\}$
13. $\{1,2,3,4,5\}$ 15. $\{3,4\}$ 17. $\varnothing$ 19. F   21. T   23. T   25. F   27. T
29. F   31. T   33. (A) T; (B) F; (C) F; (D) T; (E) F; (F) T
35. (A) $\{-4,4\}$; (B) $A = \{x \,|\, x^2 = 16\}$; (C) $-4 \in A$; $16 \notin A$ 37. $\{11,13\}$
39. (A) T; (B) T; (C) T; (D) T; (E) F; (F) T; (G) T; (H) T
41. (A) $\{3,5,7,9\}$; (B) $\{4,5,6,7,9\}$; (C) $\{3,4,5,6,7\}$; (D) $\{5,7\}$; (E) $\varnothing$; (F) $\varnothing$
43. (A) $A \cap B = \{2,4\} = B \cap A$; (B) $A \cap (B \cap C) = \{4\} = (A \cap B) \cap C$
45. (A) $\{2,4\}$; B $\{2,4\}$ 47. 10
49. $\varnothing$ is the empty set; $\{\varnothing\}$ and $\{0\}$ are each a set with one element.
51. $A \cup (B \cap C) = \{1,2,3,4,6\} = (A \cup B) \cap (A \cup C)$
53. (A) 2; (B) 4; (C) 8, 2^n
55. Associate each natural number n with the even number $2n$ and each even
number m with the natural number $m/2$. Infinite   57. (A) T; (B) F;
59. $\{a,b\}, \{a,c,d\}, \{a,c,e\}, \{a,d,e\}, \{b,c,d\}, \{b,c,e\}, \{b,d,e\}$

Exercise 2

1. (A) $\sqrt{2}$; (B) -3; (C) $-\frac{3}{4}$ 3. (A) R, Q, I; (B) R, Q; (C) R, Q; (D) R
5. (A) $=$; (B) $\neq$; (C) $\neq$ 7. Symmetric law
9. Transitive law or substitution principle   11. Substitution principle
13. (A) Commutative multiplication; (B) Associative multiplication;
(C) Closure and commutative addition; (D) Distributive; (E) Closure addition;
(F) Associative addition; (G) Distributive; (H) Closure multiplication
15. (A) $0.375\overline{00}$; (B) $2.5\overline{55}$; (C) $0.538461\overline{538461}$ 17. (A) $\frac{3}{11}$; (B) $\frac{106}{33}$
19. Incorrect use of the equality symbol
21. (A) Closure and commutative multiplication; (B) Closure and commutative
addition; (C) Closure and associative addition; (D) Closure addition and
distributive; (E) Closure addition and multiplication and associative
multiplication
23. $(8 - 4) - 2 \neq 8 - (4 - 2)$ and $(8 \div 4) \div 2 \neq 8 \div (4 \div 2)$; thus the set of
real numbers is not associative with respect to subtraction or division.

25. Exhibit a counterexample; e.g., $2 + (3 \cdot 4) \neq (2 + 3)(2 + 4)$.

27. $37(60 + 2) = 2{,}220 + 74 = 2{,}294$

29. (A) No additive identity, no additive inverse, no multiplicative inverse; (B) No multiplicative inverse   31. $3\frac{2}{3}$ and $-\frac{2}{3}$ 33. π and $-\pi$

35. (A) The set of natural numbers; (B) The set of integers

37. Repeated use of associative and commutative addition; additive inverse; additive identity; uniqueness of additive inverse

Exercise 3

1. Theorem 1B   3. Theorem 1C   5. Definition of subtraction   7. Theorem 2A

9. Theorem 2B   11. Theorem 2C   13. Theorem 3A   15. Theorem 3C

17. Theorem 4B   19. Theorem 5C   21. Theorem 6B   23. Theorem 6A

25. Theorem 7A   27. Theorem 7D   29. Theorem 8C   31. Theorem 8A

33. Theorem 9A   35. (A) Sometimes; (B) Never

37. By definition $a - b = a + (-b)$, and R is closed under addition.

39. 1. Definition of division and R is closed under multiplication; 2. Reflexive properties for $=$; 3. Given; 4. Substitution principle

41. 1. Definition of division; 2. Theorem 6C; 3. Definition of division

43. | *Statement* | *Reason* |
|---|---|
| 1. $(b + c)a = a(b + c)$ | 1. Closure for addition and commutative properties for multiplication |
| 2. $\quad = ab + ac$ | 2. Distributive properties |
| 3. $\quad = ba + ca$ | 3. Commutative properties for multiplication |

45. | *Statement* | *Reason* |
|---|---|
| 1. $(a + b) + (-a - b) = (a + b) + [(-a) + (-b)]$ | 1. Definition of subtraction |
| 2. $\quad = [(b + a) + (-a)] + (-b)$ | 2. Commutative and associative properties for addition |
| 3. $\quad = b + [a + (-a)] + (-b)$ | 3. Associative properties for addition |
| 4. $\quad = (b + 0) + (-b)$ | 4. Additive inverse properties |
| 5. $\quad = b + (-b)$ | 5. Additive identity properties |
| 6. $\quad = 0$ | 6. Additive inverse properties |
| 7. $\therefore (-a - b) = -(a + b)$ | 7. Theorem 2A |

47. | *Statement* | *Reason* |
|---|---|
| 1. $a/b + c/d = ad/bd + bc/bd$ | 1. Theorem 7D |
| 2. $\quad = (ad + bc)/bd$ | 2. Theorem 8A |

49. | *Statement* | *Reason* |
|---|---|
| 1. $aa^{-1} = 1$ | 1. Multiplicative inverse properties |
| 2. $a = (a^{-1})^{-1}$ | 2. Theorem 2B |
| 3. $(a^{-1})^{-1} = a$ | 3. Symmetric property of $=$ |

Exercise 4

1. $-9, -3$ 3. $0, -9, -9, 0$ 5. b, a 7. uv, wx 9. $\{1,2,3,4,5\}$
11. $\{-2,-1,0,1\}$ 13. $\{-3,-2,-1,0,1\}$ 15.

17.

19.

21.

23.

25. (A) $\{1,2,3,4,5,6,7\}$; (B) $\{100,101,102\}$; (C) $\{y\,|\,y>9,\ y\in N\}$
27. (A) $S=\{3,4,5,6\}$; (B) $S=\{t\,|\,2<t\leq6,\ t\in N\}$
29. (A) Empty; (B) Empty; (C) Infinite; (D) Infinite
31.

33.

35. 1. Definition $>$; 2. Add in zero in the form $z-z$; 4. Definition $>$
37. No. See Theorem 12.   39. (A) 4, 5; (B) No. See Theorem 12.
41. 1. $x>y\to x-y$ is positive   1. Definition $>$
    2. z is positive   2. Given
    3. $z(x-y)=zx-zy$ is positive   3. Sign properties and distributive properties
    4. $zx>zy$ 4. Definition $>$
43. Assume there is a rational number a/b, a and b integers, such that

$$\left(\frac{a}{b}\right)^2 = 3 \quad\text{or}\quad a^2 = 3b^2$$

If the right and left members are factored as the product of prime factors, then 3 would appear an odd number of times on the right and an even number of times on the left, if at all. This contradicts the fundamental theorem of arithmetic. Hence, there is no rational number whose square is 3.
45. $a=bq+r, 0<r<b$, or $a/b=q+r/b$, where $0<r/b<1$, but the latter implies that $0<a/b-q<1$ or $q<a/b<q+1$.

Exercise 5

1. $7-5i$ 3. $-3+2i$ 5. $17-2i$ 7. $\frac{7}{6}-\frac{9}{2}i$ 9. -8 or $-8+0i$
11. $12+6i$ 13. $15-3i$ 15. $8+i$ 17. 34 or $34+0i$
19. u^2+v^2 or $(u^2+v^2)+0i$ 21. $3+3i$ 23. $-2+7i$ 25. $3+2i$
27. $2+\sqrt{3}\,i$ 29. $2-2i$ 31. $-5+3i$ 33. $6+13i$ 35. $13+i$ 37. $3-4i$
39. $\frac{3}{25}+\frac{4}{25}i$ 41. $-\frac{1}{3}i$ or $0-\frac{1}{3}i$ 43. $-\frac{1}{3}-\frac{2}{3}i$ 45. $-6i$ or $0-6i$
47. 0 or $0+0i$ 49. $\pm5i$ 51. $3\pm2i$ 53. $-1, -i, 1, i, -1, -i, 1$
55. $x=3, y=-2$

57. 1. Definition of addition; 2. Property of real numbers; 3. Definition of addition   59. $x \geq 10$ 61. $i^{4k} = (i^4)^k = (i^2 \cdot i^2)^k = [(-1)(-1)]^k = 1^k = 1$
63. $i^{4k+2} = i^{4k}i^2 = 1(-1) = -1$
65. Let $a + bi$ be an arbitrary complex number; then, using the definition of addition, $(a + bi) + (0 + 0i) = (a + 0) + (b + 0)i = a + bi$.
67. Using the definition of addition, we have $(a + bi) + (-a - bi) = (a - a) + (b - b)i = 0 + 0i = 0$.
69. Let $a + bi$, $c + di$, and $e + fi$ be any three complex numbers; then, using the definition of addition followed by the definition of multiplication, $(a + bi)[(c + di) + (e + fi)] = (a + bi)[(c + e) + (d + f)i] = [a(c + e) - b(d + f)] + [a(d + f) + b(c + e)]i$. Now using the property of real numbers, we obtain $[(ac - bd) + (ae - bf)] + [(ad + bc) + (af + be)]i$. Finally, we use the definitions of addition and multiplication in complex numbers to obtain $(a + bi)(c + di) + (a + bi)(e + fi)$.

Exercise 6

1. $\{-6,6\}$ 2. (A) $\{1,3,4,5\}$; (B) $\{3,5\}$; (C) $\varnothing$; (D) $\{3,4,5\}$
3. (A) F; (B) T; (C) T; (D) T; (E) T   4. (A) T; (B) T; (C) T
5. Substitution principle
6. (A) Commutative properties for addition; (B) Associative properties for multiplication; (C) Distributive properties; (D) Closure property for multiplication   7. $-8, -10, -10, -8$
8. (A) x;   (B) x
$\qquad\quad -3\ -2\ -1\ 0\ 1\ 2\ 3 \qquad\qquad -3\ -2\ -1\ 0\ 1\ 2\ 3$
9. $3 - 6i$ 10. $15 + 3i$ 11. $2 + i$ 12. (A) $\{-5,5\}$; (B) $\{x \mid x^2 = 25\}$
13. (A) $\{-1,0,1,2,3\}$; (B) $\{1\}$; (C) No; (D) Yes; (E) No
14. (A) Commutative properties for addition; (B) Associative properties for addition; (C) Distributive properties   15. (A) $0.14285\overline{7142857}$; (B) $\frac{4}{33}$
16. No   17. Yes, since $a - b = a + (-b)$ and R is closed under addition.
18. ab, ac, ac, ab 19. $R, -4 \leq x < 3$ 20. $-1 - i$ 21. $\frac{4}{13} - \frac{7}{13}i$ 22. $5 + 4i$
23. $-i$ 24. $\varnothing$ 25. $A \cap B$ 26. (A) T; (B) F; (C) T
27. (A) All do; (B) Q, R 28. The set of integers
29.   *Statement*   *Reason*
   1. $a + c \in R$ 1. R is closed under addition
   2. $a + c = a + c$ 2. Reflexive properties for $=$
   3. $a + c = b + c$ 3. Substitution principle
30. $a > b \rightarrow a - b$ is positive, therefore, $a + c - b - c = (a + c) - (b + c)$ is positive; hence, $a + c > b + c$.   31. No
32. Assume there is a rational number a/b, a and b integers, such that $(a/b)^2 = 5$; that is, $a^2 = 5b^2$. If the right and left members are factored as the product of prime factors, then 5 would appear on the right an odd number of times and on the left an even number of times, if at all. This contradicts the fundamental theorem of arithmetic. Hence, there is no rational number whose square is 5.

33. 0 or $0 + 0i$. Let $a + bi$ be an arbitrary complex number, then by definition of addition $(a + bi) + (0 + 0i) = (a + 0) + (b + 0)i$, which by the real number property, is $a + bi$.   34. 1, multiplicative inverse property

CHAPTER 2

Exercise 7

1. $8x - 7$ 3. $6x^2 + 7x - 3$ 5. $2x - 3$ 7. $4x - 6$ 9. $6y^3 + 19y^2 + y - 6$
11. $2x + 3$ 13. $3x - 14$ 15. $a^3 + b^3$ 17. $y - 3$ 19. $x^2 + x + 1$
21. $4x - 1, R = 5$ 23. $x - 4, R = 3$ 25. 1   27. $2x^4 - 5x^3 + 5x^2 + 11x - 10$
29. $2y^2 + y - 3$ 31. $x^3 - 2x^2 + 4x - 8$ 33. $13x^2 - 26x + 10$
35. $x^3 + 6x^2y + 12xy^2 + 8y^3$ 37. $2y^2 - 5y + 13, R = -27$
39. $4x^3 - 14x^2 + 8x - 6$ 41. $2x^5 - 9x^4 + 11x^3 - x^2 - x - 2$
43. $3x^3 - 4x + 3, R = -8x$
45. (A) $x - y$; (B) $-x + y - z$; (C) $(y - 1)$; (D) $y^2 - 2y + 1$
47. A, C, D, E, G, H 49. (A) G; (B) H; (C) C; (D) A, E
51. $2x^2 - 2xy + 3y^2$ 53. $5x + 10(x - 5) + 25[(x - 5) + 2]$; $40x - 125$
55. $y(y - 8)$; $y^2 - 8y$ 57. $Q(x) = x - 3, R(x) = x + 2$
59. By the right-hand distributive property and substitution principle,
$7x + 5x = (7 + 5)x = 12x$
61. 1. Commutative addition; 2. Associative addition; 3. Associative addition;
4. Distributive; 5. Substitution; 6. Commutative addition; 7. Associative
addition; 8. Distributive; 9. Substitution   63. (A) m; (B) $m + n$
65. (A) 0; (B) 1

Exercise 8

1. $b^2 + 2b - 80$ 3. $x^2 - 49$ 5. $2x^2 + 9x + 9$ 7. $15x^2 - 11x - 14$
9. $16y^2 - 24y + 9$ 11. $25m^2 - 9n^2$ 13. $12m^2 + 17mn - 5n^2$
15. $4x^2 - 12xy + 9y^2$ 17. $(m - 3)(m - 4)$ 19. Prime   21. $(u + 4v)(u + 5v)$
23. $(t - 6)(t + 6)$ 25. Prime   27. Prime   29. $4(y - 3)(y - 4)$
31. $2t^2(t - 2)(t - 10)$ 33. $(2x + 3y)(3x + y)$ 35. $(5x - 4y)(5x + 4y)$
37. $(m - 6n)(m + 2n)$ 39. Prime   41. $(2x - 3y)(3x + 4y)$ 43. $2y(y^2 - y + 4)$
45. $xy(2x - y)(2x + y)$ 47. Prime
49. $[(a - b) - 2(c - d)][(a - b) + 2(c - d)] = (a - b - 2c + 2d)(a - b + 2c - 2d)$
51. $3mn(m - 2n)(m - 3n)$ 53. $(y - 1)(y^2 + y + 1)$
55. $(ab + 2)(a^2b^2 - 2ab + 4)$ 57. $(3 - xy)(9 + 3xy + x^2y^2)$
59. $(m - 2n)(x + y)$ 61. $(2m - 3n)(a + b)$ 63. $(x - 2)(x + 1)(x - 1)$
65. $(y - 3)(2y - 3)(2y + 3)$ 67. $(r^2 + s^2)(r - s)(r + s)$
69. $(x - 3)(x + 3)(x^2 + 2)$ 71. $[4(A + B) + 3][(A + B) - 2]$
73. $2a[3a - 2(x + 4)][3a + 2(x + 4)]$
75. $(x^3 - 1)(x^3 + 1) = (x - 1)(x^2 + x + 1)(x + 1)(x^2 - x + 1)$
77. $(y - x)(y - x - 1)$ 79. $[5 - (a + b)][5 + (a + b)]$
81. $(x^2 - x + 2)(x + 2)(x - 1)$ 83. The set of all real numbers
85. 6, 10, 12

Exercise 9

1. $2y/x^2$ 3. $3(x-y)/4xy$ 5. a 7. $x/(2x-3y)$ 9. $x-5$ 11. $20m^2n$
13. $3w^2 - wz$ 15. $2m^2 + 5mn + 2n^2$ 17. $(1-b)/a^2$ 19. $(x^2 - xy + y^2)/x^3$
21. $(2+x)/x$ 23. $(y^2+8)/8y^3$ 25. $(x-5)/(x-1)^2(x+1)$
27. $(3x-5)/(x-3)$ 29. $(x^2 - 6x + 7)/(x-2)$ 31. $2/(x+y)$
33. $(5a^2 - 2a - 5)/(a+1)(a-1)$ 35. $1/(x-1)$
37. $-17/[15(x-1)]$ or $17/[15(1-x)]$ 39. $(5m^2+1)/6(m+1)^2$
41. $x^2/(x^3+y^3)$ 43. $(x^2 - 2xy - y^2)/(ax^2 - ay^2 + bx^2 - by^2)$ 45. 1
47. $1, -2$ 49. 1 51. $x-y$

Exercise 10

1. $a+1$ 3. $1/m$ 5. $t(t-4)$ 7. $a^2/2$ 9. $1/(x-3)$ 11. $1/(y-x)$ 13. $-1/m$
15. $(t^2 - t + 1)/2(t-9)$ 17. $(x-y)^2/y^2(x+y)$ 19. $(x-y)/(x+y)$
21. $-m(m+n)/n$ 23. -1 25. $1/(1-x)$ 27. $-x$ 29. $(x-1)/x$
31. $r = 2r_R r_G/(r_R + r_G)$ 33. $(x+1)/(1/x+1) = (x+1)x/(1+x) = x$

Exercise 11

1. a^4 3. n^{14} 5. 1 7. 1 9. $6x^9$ 11. p^6q^{15} 13. a^{12}
15. $1/(8c^3d^6)$ 17. a^4b^{12}/c^8d^4 19. 10^{17} 21. $(2x)/y^2$ 23. n^2 25. 4×10^8
27. 3.5×10 29. 6×10^{-1} 31. 2.83×10^2 33. 1.7×10^{-2}
35. 4.93×10^3 37. 7.29×10^{-8} 39. 57.2 41. $40,000$ 43. 0.097
45. 0.005 47. $6,500,000,000$ 49. 0.0000000000063 51. $-1/x^8$
53. $4x^8/y^6$ 55. $5/(u-v+w)^3$ 57. $w^{12}/(u^{20}v^4)$ 59. $(27y^3)/(2x^3)$
61. $1/(x+y)^2$ 63. $(n^2+m^2)/mn$ 65. $1/xy$ 67. $xy/(y+x)$
69. 3×10 or 30 71. 3×10^{-4} or 0.0003 73. 6.6×10^{21} tons
75. $10^7; 6 \times 10^8$ 77. $(v-u)/(v+u)$ 79. y^{3n} 81. x^2 83. x^{n^2+n} 85. y^2/x
87. $(x/y)^{-n} = x^{-n}/(y^{-n}) = y^n/x^n = (y/x)^n$

Exercise 12

1. 4 3. 4 5. -8 7. Not defined 9. $\frac{4}{9}$ 11. $\frac{1}{125}$ 13. $\frac{1}{8}$
15. 49 17. $y^{3/5}$ 19. $a^{1/3}$ 21. $1/x^{1/2}$ 23. $n^{1/2}$ 25. $1/y^{1/2}$ 27. $2x/y^2$
29. $1/x^2y^3$ 31. Not defined 33. $m^{1/2}n^{1/3}$ 35. $\frac{5}{4}x^4y^2$ 37. $64y^{1/3}$
39. $a^{1/n}b^{1/m}$ 41. $6x - 2x^{19/3}$ 43. $x-y$ 45. $x - 2x^{1/2}y^{1/2} + y$
47. $1/x - 2/x^{1/2}y^{1/2} + 1/y$ 49. a 51. y^{m+1}
53. (A) Any negative number; (B) n even and x any negative number
55. The laws of exponents do not apply to $a^{m/n}$ when a is negative and n is even.
Note: $i = (-1)^{1/2}$.

Exercise 13

1. $\sqrt{7}$ 3. $\sqrt[4]{x^3}$ 5. $5\sqrt[3]{m^2}$ 7. $\sqrt[5]{(4ab^3)^2}$ 9. $\sqrt{a+b}$ 11. $\sqrt{a^2+b^2}$
13. $x^{1/7}$ 15. $a^{2/3}$ 17. $(2xy)^{3/4}$ 19. $3/y^{1/3}$ or $3y^{-1/3}$ 21. -3 23. $2a^2b^4$
25. $2mn^3$ 27. $3\sqrt{2}$ 29. $3mn^3\sqrt{3n}$ 31. $2ab^2\sqrt[4]{a}$ 33. $\sqrt[5]{x^3}$ 35. 3
37. $3xy$ 39. $\sqrt{7}/7$ 41. $\sqrt[4]{4}$ 43. $3m^2\sqrt{2mn}/2n$ 45. $\sqrt{42xy}/7y$
47. Is in the simplest radical form   49. $-3\sqrt{x}$ 51. $1/\sqrt[5]{(3m^2n^3)^3}$
53. $\sqrt[3]{\sqrt{x}+1/\sqrt{y}}$ 55. $-3x(a^3b)^{1/4}$ 57. $m^{2/3}-n^{1/2}$
59. $3/x^{1/2}+2/y^{1/2}$ or $3x^{-1/2}+2y^{-1/2}$ 61. $a^2b/2c^3$ 63. $-4x^3y^4\sqrt[3]{x^2y}$
65. $\sqrt[4]{2^3(x+y)^3}$ 67. $u^2v\sqrt[4]{24v}$ 69. $4u^2v^4\sqrt[3]{2uv}$ 71. $\sqrt{x-y}/(x-y)$
73. $\frac{2}{3}\sqrt[3]{6}$ 75. $2\sqrt[3]{6abc}$ 77. $\sqrt[5]{8m^2n^2}/2m$ 79. $m\sqrt[4]{1+4m^2}$ 81. $2x\sqrt[3]{4y^2}$
83. $2x^4y^3\sqrt[6]{2^5x^5y^5}$ 85. $\sqrt[6]{8x}$ 87. x^2y^{n+1}
89. (A) $\sqrt[n]{x^n}=(x^n)^{1/n}=x^{n/n}=x$; (B) $\sqrt[n]{xy}=(xy)^{1/n}=x^{1/n}y^{1/n}=\sqrt[n]{x}\sqrt[n]{y}$
91. (A) Any negative number; (B) n even and x any negative number
93. Laws of radicals do not apply when we take even roots of negative numbers.

Exercise 14

1. $-4\sqrt{x}$ 3. $-\sqrt[3]{u}$ 5. $2\sqrt{2}-2\sqrt{3}$ 7. $3\sqrt[3]{y}+3\sqrt[4]{y}$ 9. $3\sqrt{3}$
11. $2\sqrt{2}+6\sqrt{3}$ 13. $5-2\sqrt{5}$ 15. $5\sqrt{2}+5$ 17. $3m-\sqrt{mn}$ 19. $2\sqrt{2}-1$
21. $9+4\sqrt{5}$ 23. 25   25. $4x-9$ 27. $\sqrt{5}-2$ 29. $2\sqrt{6}+4$ 31. $\sqrt{3}-\sqrt{2}$
33. $(x+2\sqrt{x})/(x-4)$ 35. $3-2\sqrt{2}$ 37. $2\sqrt{6}+\sqrt{3}$ 39. $3\sqrt{2}$ 41. $\frac{3}{2}\sqrt[4]{2}$
43. $\frac{5}{2}\sqrt{2xy}$ 45. $10m-11\sqrt{m}-6$ 47. $u+\sqrt[3]{u^2v^2}-\sqrt[5]{u^3v^3}-v$
49. $6-6\sqrt{3}i$ 51. 1   53. No   55. 0 or $0+0i$ 57. $5+2\sqrt{6}$
59. $(x+5\sqrt{x}+6)/(x-9)$ 61. $(15\sqrt{a}+10a)/(9-4a)$
63. $(30+13\sqrt{6})/(-19)$ 65. $-\frac{4}{7}+(3\sqrt{3}/7)i$ 67. 1 or $1+0i$
69. $(\sqrt[3]{x^2}+\sqrt[3]{xy}+\sqrt[3]{y^2})/(x-y)$ 71. $(\sqrt[3]{x}-\sqrt[3]{y})/(x-y)$
73. $(\sqrt{x}-\sqrt{y}-\sqrt{z})[(x+y-z)+2\sqrt{xy}]/[(x+y-z)^2-4xy]$

Exercise 15

1. (A) x^3+3x^2+5x-2; (B) $x^3-3x^2-3x+22$;
(C) $3x^5+x^4-8x^3+24x^2+8x-64$;
(D) x^2-2x+4; (E) Prime   2. $11x^2-4x$
3. (A) $(3x-2)^2$; (B) Prime; (C) $3n(2n-5)(n+1)$ 4. $xy/(3x-2y)$
5. $(12a^3b-40b^2-5a)/30a^3b^2$ 6. $(7s-4)/6s(s-4)$
7. $(y+2)/y(y-2)$ 8. x 9. $6x^5y^{15}$ 10. c^6/d^{15} 11. $3u^4/v^2$ 12. $6\cdot10^2$
13. x^6/y^4 14. u 15. $(3a^2)/b$ 16. (A) $\sqrt[3]{(2mn)^2}$; (B) $3\sqrt[5]{x^2}$;

(C) $x^{5/7}$; (D) $-3(xy)^{2/3}$ 17. $2x^2y$ 18. $3x^2y\sqrt{x^2y}$ 19. $6x^2y^3\sqrt{xy}$
20. $2b\sqrt{3a}$ 21. $\sqrt{2xy}/2x$ 22. $\sqrt{7}-2\sqrt{3}$ 23. $(3\sqrt{5}+5)/4$ 24. $\sqrt[4]{y^3}$
25. (A) a, c, d; (B) a, d 26. $x^3 - 3x^2 + 2x + 4$, $R = -20$
27. $2x^3 - 4x^2 + 12x$ 28. (A) $y(y-2x)$; (B) $3(x-2y)(x^2+2xy+4y^2)$;
(C) $(y-b)(y-b-1)$ 29. $-1/(s+2)$ 30. y^2/x 31. $(x-y)/(x+y)$
32. $(pq)^4$ 33. c/a^2b^4 34. $\frac{1}{4}$ 35. $\frac{5}{9}$ 36. $(3x^2)/(2y^2)$
37. $x + 2x^{1/2}y^{1/2} + y$ 38. 2×10^{-3} or 0.002
39. (A) $-3\sqrt[3]{x^2}$; (B) $2/\sqrt[4]{(xy)^3}$; (C) $x/x^{3/5}$; (D) $x^{2/9}$ 40. $-6x^2y^2\sqrt[5]{3x^2y}$
41. $x\sqrt[3]{2x^2}$ 42. $\sqrt[5]{12x^3y^2}/2x$ 43. $y\sqrt[3]{2x^2y}$ 44. $3m\sqrt{m^2+n^2}$ 45. 0
46. $2x - 3\sqrt{xy} - 5y$ 47. $(6x + 3\sqrt{xy})/(4x - y)$ 48. $x = 3$
49. $Q(x) = 2x - 3$, $R(x) = x + 4$
50. 1. Definition of subtraction; 2. Sign property; 3. Right-hand distributive
property; 4. Substitution principle   51. The set of all real numbers   52. 6, 4
53. 1   54. $(x-2)(x+1)/2x$ 55. x^{m-1} 56. $a^2b^2/(a^3+b^3)$
57. (A) All nonnegative; (B) All; (C) All   58. $2xy\sqrt[6]{2xy}$ 59. $4\sqrt[12]{xy}$
60. $x^{(n+1)}$ 61. $(x\sqrt[3]{x} + \sqrt[3]{x^2y^2} + y\sqrt[3]{y})/(x^2 - y^2)$

CHAPTER 3

Exercise 16

1. 18   3. 9   5. 6   7. 9   9. 10   11. $\frac{31}{24}$ 13. $m = 3$ 15. No solution   17. $\frac{8}{5}$
19. $s = 2$ 21. No solution   23. $t = -4$ 25. $\frac{2}{3}$ 27. (A) F; (B) F
29. $d = (a_n - a_1)/(n - 1)$ 31. $f = d_1d_2/(d_1 + d_2)$ 33. $a = (A - 2bc)/(2b + 2c)$
35. $T_2 = T_1P_2V_2/P_1V_1$ 37. $x = (5y + 3)/(2 - 3y)$ 39. 1
41. $x = (by + cy - ac)/(a - y)$
43. Addition property of equality; subtraction property of equality;
both equations have the same solution set.
45. Replace "$+$" everywhere with "$-$" in Prob. 43.

Exercise 17

1. 4, 6, 8   3. 4 ft   5. 20 mi   7. $100   9. $1,600
11. Chemist: 40 hr; Assistant: 30 hr   13. 330 cps; 396 cps   15. 5,000
17. 315; 105; 105; 35   19. 150 cm   21. 14.52 years   23. 330 ft
25. 90 mi   27. 250 grams   29. 14,080 ft   31. 424 min or 7 hr and 4 min
33. 10 A.M.; 24 mi   35. 12 quarters, 6 dimes, 18 nickels   37. 4 ft
39. 15 min

Exercise 18

1. $x \geq -3$ ———●——→ x 3. $x < 2$ ←——○——— x
           -3 2
5. $M \geq 6$ ———●——→ M 7. $n \leq -3$ ←——●——— n
            6   -3

9. $u \leq \frac{2}{7}$ ——●———— u 11. $y < -7$ ——○———— y
$\quad\quad\quad \frac{2}{7} \quad\quad\quad\quad\quad\quad\quad\quad\quad -7$

13. $3 \leq m < 7$ ——●———○——▶ m 15. $p \geq 12$ ——●———▶ p
$\quad\quad\quad 3 \quad\quad 7 \quad\quad\quad\quad\quad\quad\quad\quad 12$

17. $x > -4\frac{2}{9}$ ——○——▶ x 19. $-9 \leq A \leq 9$ ——●———●——▶ A
$\quad\quad -4\frac{2}{9} \quad\quad\quad\quad\quad\quad\quad\quad -9 \quad\quad 9$

21. $41 \leq x < 59$ ——●———○——▶ x 23. $0 < w < 5$
$\quad\quad 41 \quad\quad 59$

25. $8,000 \leq h \leq 20,000$ 27. ≥ 98 29. $w \leq 3,300$ watts   31. Positive
33. (A) F; (B) T; (C) T
35. Multiplicative properties, Theorem 12, Chap. 1 for the first four "whys."
The last "why" is answered by the definition of equivalent inequalities.
37. Let r be a number such that $f(r) > g(r)$; then $f(r) + [-h(r)] >$
$g(r) + [-h(r)]$ by Theorem 12, Chap. 1. Also by the same theorem, if r is a
number such that $f(r) + [-h(r)] > g(r) + [-h(r)]$, then $f(r) > g(r)$. Thus,
$f(x) > g(x)$ and $f(x) - h(x) > g(x) - h(x)$ have the same solution sets; hence
they are equivalent.
39. Dividing by the negative quantity $(n - m)$ reverses the inequality sign.

Exercise 19

1. $x = \pm 7$ ——●——●——▶ x 3. $-7 \leq x \leq 7$ ——●———●——▶ x
$\quad\quad -7 \quad 7 \quad\quad\quad\quad\quad\quad\quad\quad -7 \quad 7$

5. $x \leq -7$ or $x \geq 7$ ◀——●——●——▶ x 7. $y = 2$ or 8 ——●——●——●——▶ y
$\quad\quad\quad -7 \quad 7 \quad\quad\quad\quad\quad\quad\quad 2 \quad 5 \quad 8$

9. $2 < y < 8$ ——○———○——▶ y 11. $y < 2$ or $y > 8$ ◀——○———○——▶ y
$\quad\quad 2 \quad\quad 8 \quad\quad\quad\quad\quad\quad\quad\quad 2 \quad\quad 8$

13. $u = -11$ or -5 ——●——●——●——▶ u
$\quad\quad\quad -11 \quad -8 \quad -5$

15. $-11 \leq u \leq -5$ ——●———●——▶ u
$\quad\quad\quad -11 \quad -5$

17. $u \leq -11$ or $u \geq -5$ ◀——●———●——▶ u
$\quad\quad\quad\quad -11 \quad -5$

19. $x = -4, \frac{4}{3}$ ——●——●——▶ x 21. $-\frac{9}{5} \leq x \leq 3$ ——●———●——▶ x
$\quad\quad -4 \quad \frac{4}{3} \quad\quad\quad\quad\quad\quad\quad -\frac{9}{5} \quad\quad 3$

23. $y < 3$ or $y > 5$ ◀——●———●——▶ y 25. $t = -\frac{4}{5}, \frac{18}{5}$ ——●———●——▶ t
$\quad\quad\quad 3 \quad\quad 5 \quad\quad\quad\quad\quad\quad\quad -\frac{4}{5} \quad \frac{18}{5}$

27. $-\frac{23}{7} < u < \frac{5}{7}$ ——○———○——▶ u 29. $x \leq -6$ or $x \geq 9$ ◀——●———●——▶ x
$\quad\quad -\frac{23}{7} \quad \frac{5}{7} \quad\quad\quad\quad\quad\quad\quad\quad -6 \quad 9$

31. $-35 < C < -\frac{5}{9}$ ——○———○——▶ C 33. $|x| \leq 17$ 35. $|x - 5| < 2$
$\quad\quad -35 \quad -\frac{5}{9}$

37. $|y + 2| \leq 5$ 39. $x \geq 5$ 41. $x < -8$ 43. $x \geq -\frac{3}{4}$ 45. $x < \frac{2}{5}$
47. All of the "whys" involve the definition of absolute value. First "why":
If $x > 0$, then $-x$ is negative and $|-x| = -(-x) = x$. Second "why":
If $x > 0$ then $|x| = x$. Third "why": If $x < 0$, then $-x$ is positive and
$|-x| = -x$. Fourth "why": If $x < 0$, then $|x| = -x$.

49. Case 1: If $x = 0$, then $|x|^2 = |0|^2 = 0^2 = 0 = 0^2 = x^2$. Case 2: If $x > 0$, then $|x| = x$; therefore $|x|^2 = x^2$. Case 3: If $x < 0$, then $|x| = -x$ and $(-x)^2 = x^2$; therefore $|x|^2 = x^2$. 51. $|x - 2| < e/2$

53. $|x + y| = \sqrt{(x+y)^2} = \sqrt{x^2 + 2xy + y^2} \leq \sqrt{|x|^2 + 2|x||y| + |y|^2}$
$= \sqrt{(|x| + |y|)^2} = |x| + |y|$

Exercise 20

1. 0, 3 3. 0, 2 5. 1, 5 7. $\frac{1}{3}, -8$ 9. $-2, 4$ 11. ± 5 13. $\pm 5i$
15. $\pm 2\sqrt{3}$ 17. $\pm \frac{4}{3}$ 19. $\pm \frac{5}{2}i$ 21. $-2, -8$ 23. $3 \pm 2i$ 25. $5 \pm 2\sqrt{7}$
27. $(-1 \pm \sqrt{5})/2$ 29. $2 \pm 2i$ 31. $(2 \pm \sqrt{2})/2$ 33. $(-3 \pm \sqrt{17})/4$
35. $3 \pm 2\sqrt{3}$ 37. $(3 \pm \sqrt{3})/2$ 39. $x = (1 \pm \sqrt{7})/3$
41. $(-m \pm \sqrt{m^2 - 4n})/2$ 43. $3, -5$ 45. $-4 \pm \sqrt{11}$ 47. $(3 \pm \sqrt{13})/2$
49. 0, 2 51. $-3 \pm 2i$ 53. $-\frac{1}{2}, 2$ 55. $2 \pm 2i$ 57. $-50, 2$
59. $t = \sqrt{2s/g}$ 61. $I = (E + \sqrt{E^2 - 4RP})/2R$
63. $[(-b + \sqrt{b^2 - 4ac})/2a][(-b - \sqrt{b^2 - 4ac})/2a] = [b^2 - (b^2 - 4ac)]/2a = c/a$
65. Substitute $r_1 = c/r_2 a$ into $r_1 + r_2 = -b/a$ to obtain $c/r_2 a + r_2 = -b/a$ or $ar_2^2 + br_2 + c = 0$. Similarly, substitute $r_2 = c/r_1 a$ into $r_1 + r_2 = -b/a$ to obtain after simplification $ar_1^2 + br_1 + c = 0$.
67. The $\pm$ in front still yields the same two numbers even if a is negative.

Exercise 21

1. 8, 13 3. 0, 2 5. 89 mi 7. 5.12 by 3.12 in. 9. $(-1 + \sqrt{5})/2$
11. 1 ft 13. $10\sqrt{2}$ ft, 14.14 ft 15. 60 mph
17. (A) $t = 0, 11$; y is zero at the beginning and end of flight;
(B) 10.91 sec, 0.09 sec 19. 13.08 hr; 8.08 hr 21. 5 mph; 12 mph 23. 20%

Exercise 22

1. 22 3. 8 5. No solution 7. 0, 4 9. $\pm 2, \pm \sqrt{2}i$ 11. $-\sqrt[3]{5}, \sqrt[3]{2}$
13. $\frac{1}{3}, -8$ 15. $-2, 3, 1/2 \pm \sqrt{7}/2\,i$ 17. No solution 19. 1 21. 2
23. $-\frac{3}{4}, \frac{1}{5}$ 25. $\pm 1, \pm 3$ 27. 1, 16 29. 2, 3, 7, 8 31. -2 33. 9, 16
35. 4, 81
37. Let r be a root of $f(x) = g(x)$; then $f(r) = g(r)$. And by closure for real number multiplication $[f(r)]^n = [g(r)]^n$.

Exercise 23

1. $\{x \mid -2 < x < 4\}$, ⟶○━━○⟶ x
   $-2 \quad 4$
3. $\{x \mid -5 < x < 2\}$, ⟶○━━○⟶ x
   $-5 \quad 2$

5. $\{x \mid x < -5 \text{ or } x > -2\}$, ⟵━━○⟶○━━⟶ x
   $-5 \quad -2$

7. $\{x \mid 0 \le x \le 8\}$, ⟶●━━●⟶ x
   $0 \quad 8$

9. $\{x \mid x \le -5 \text{ or } x \ge 0\}$, ⟵━━●⟶●━━⟶ x
   $-5 \quad 0$

11. $\{x \mid -3 \le x \le 3\}$, ⟶●━━●⟶ x
    $-3 \quad 3$

13. All real numbers. Graph: whole real line.   15. $\varnothing$

17. $\{x \mid -\sqrt{2} < x < \sqrt{2}\}$, ⟶○━━○⟶ x
    $-\sqrt{2} \quad \sqrt{2}$

19. $\{x \mid x \le 2 - \sqrt{3} \text{ or } x \ge 2 + \sqrt{3}\}$, ⟵━━●⟶●━━⟶ x
    $2 - \sqrt{3} \quad 2 + \sqrt{3}$

21. All real numbers. Graph: whole real line.

23. $\{x \mid x < 0 \text{ or } x > \frac{1}{4}\}$, ⟵━━○⟶○━━⟶ x
    $0 \quad \frac{1}{4}$

25. $\{x \mid 2 \le x < 3\}$, ⟶●━━○⟶ x
    $2 \quad 3$

27. $\{x \mid x \le -\frac{2}{3} \text{ or } x > 5\}$, ⟵━━●⟶○━━⟶ x
    $-\frac{2}{3} \quad 5$

29. $\{x \mid -5 \le x \le 0 \text{ or } x > 3\}$, ⟶●━━●⟶○━━⟶ x
    $-5 \quad 0 \quad 3$

31. $\{x \mid -1 < x < 2 \text{ or } x \ge 5\}$, ⟶○━━○⟶●━━⟶ x
    $-1 \quad 2 \quad 5$

33. $\{x \mid x \le -3 \text{ or } -2 \le x \le 2 \text{ or } x \ge 3\}$, ⟵━━●⟶●━━●⟶●━━⟶ x
    $-3 \quad -2 \quad 2 \quad 3$

35. $x < -5 \text{ or } x \ge 3$ 37. $2 \le t \le 8$

39. Replace r_1 and r_2 from the quadratic formula and multiply right member to obtain left member

41. $x^2 + y^2 \ge 2xy \Leftrightarrow x^2 - 2xy + y^2 \ge 0 \Leftrightarrow (x - y)^2 \ge 0$, which is true by the property of real numbers.   43. $\{x \mid -\frac{2}{3} < x < 0 \text{ or } 0 < x < 2\}$

45. $\{x \mid -2 \le x \le 2\}$ 47. $\frac{5}{3} < x \le 2$

Exercise 24

1. No solution   2. $\frac{30}{11}$ 3. $x \ge 1$ ⟶●━━⟶ x
   1

4. $-14 < y < -4$ ⟶○━━○⟶ y
   $-14 \quad -4$
5. $x < -1 \text{ or } x > 5$ ⟵━━○⟶○━━⟶ x
   $-1 \quad 5$

6. $\pm\sqrt{7}$ 7. $0, 2$ 8. $\frac{1}{2}, 3$ 9. $(-1 \pm \sqrt{5})/2$ 10. $(3 \pm \sqrt{33})/4$ 11. $2, 3$

12. $\pm 2, \pm 3i$ 13. $\frac{5}{3}$ or $-\frac{3}{5}$ 14. $0, 2$

15. $-5 < x < 4$ ──○──○──→ x 16. $x \le -3$ or $x \ge 7$ ←──●──●──→ x
$\qquad\qquad\quad -5 \quad 4$ $\qquad\qquad\qquad\qquad\qquad\qquad -3 \quad 7$

17. All real numbers. Graph: real line.   18. No solution   19. -15

20. 450 grams   21. $n = (a_n - a_1 + d)/d$ 22. $x \ge -19$ ──────●──→ x
$\qquad\qquad\qquad\qquad\qquad\qquad\qquad\qquad\qquad\qquad\qquad\qquad -19$

23. $\frac{1}{2} \le x \le 3$ ──●──●──→ x 24. $x < 2$ or $x > \frac{10}{3}$ ←──○──○──→ x
$\qquad\quad \frac{1}{2} \quad 3$ $\qquad\qquad\qquad\qquad\qquad\qquad 2 \quad \frac{10}{13}$

25. $(-5 \pm \sqrt{5})/2$ 26. $1 \pm \sqrt{2}\,i$ 27. $(1 \pm \sqrt{43})/3$ 28. $64, -\frac{27}{8}$

29. $\pm 1, \pm 2, \pm 2i, \pm i$ 30. $3, \frac{9}{4}$ 31. (A) $2,000$ and $8,000$; (B) $5,000$

32. $x = (13 \pm \sqrt{45})/2$ thousand, or approximately $3,146$ and $9,854$ 33. $\varnothing$

34. $(-1 - \sqrt{2}) < x < (-1 + \sqrt{2})$ ──────○────────○──→ x
$\qquad\qquad\qquad\qquad\qquad\qquad -1 - \sqrt{2} \quad -1 + \sqrt{2}$

35. $x < 0$ or $x > \frac{1}{2}$ 36. $x \le 1$ or $3 < x < 4$ ←──●──○──○──→ x
$\qquad\qquad\qquad\qquad\qquad\qquad\qquad\qquad\qquad\quad 1 \quad 3 \quad 4$

37. $\frac{3}{2}$ 38. The proof parallels the proof of Theorem 6 given in the text.

39. It follows from the given part that $|x + y| \le |x| + |y|$, and from the addition property of inequalities that $|x + y| + |z| \le |x| + |y| + |z|$, but $|x + y + z| \le |x + y| + |z|$; hence from the transitive property $|x + y + z| \le |x| + |y| + |z|$.   40. $|x - 3| < e/3$

41. $(3x \pm |x| \sqrt{33})/6$ 42. $9, 25$

43. $\{x \mid x < (-1 - \sqrt{2})$ or $(1 - \sqrt{2}) < x < 0$ or $0 < x < (-1 + \sqrt{2})$ or $x > (1 + \sqrt{2})\}$ 44. $x \ge 2$

CHAPTER 4

Exercise 25

1. $\{(-1,3), (-1,4), (-1,5), (-2,3), (-2,4), (-2,5)\}$

3. $\{(3,-1), (3,-2), (4,-1), (4,-2), (5,-1), (5,-2)\}$

5. $\{(3,7), (3,8), (4,7), (4,8), (5,7), (5,8)\}$

7.
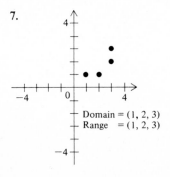
Domain = $(1, 2, 3)$
Range = $(1, 2, 3)$

9.
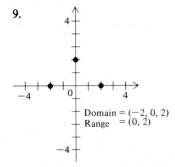
Domain = $(-2, 0, 2)$
Range = $(0, 2)$

11.

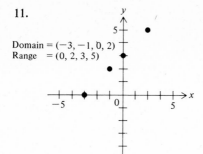

Domain = $(-3, -1, 0, 2)$
Range = $(0, 2, 3, 5)$

13.

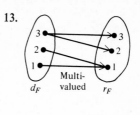

15.

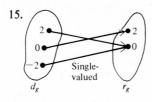

17.

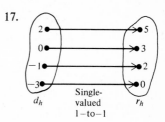

19. $NXN = \{(x,y) \mid x \in N \text{ and } y \in N\}$; (2,5), (3,7)
21. $NXI = \{(x,y) \mid x \in N \text{ and } y \in I\}$; (3,−7), (4,0)
23. $RXR = \{(x,y) \mid x \in R \text{ and } y \in R\}$; $(-\frac{2}{3}, \sqrt{2})$, $(\frac{2}{3}, 8)$

25.

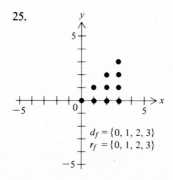

$d_f = \{0, 1, 2, 3\}$
$r_f = \{0, 1, 2, 3\}$

27.

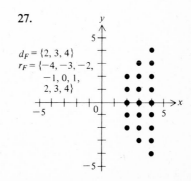

$d_F = \{2, 3, 4\}$
$r_F = \{-4, -3, -2, -1, 0, 1, 2, 3, 4\}$

29.

$F : x \to x^2 + 1$

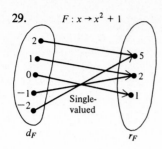

d_F Single-valued r_F

31.

$h : x \to x^3 + x$

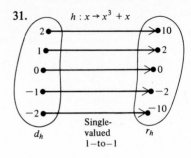

d_h Single-valued 1–to–1 r_h

33.

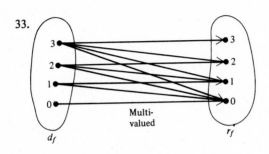

d_f Multi-valued r_f

35. (H,G) would be the best choice and (L, G) would be the worst [not (L, P) as might be expected (Why?).]

37. A, B, F **39.** A, B, C, F **41.** Both are. **43.** a divides b; $a \le b$

Exercise 26

1. 5 **3.** $5\sqrt{2}$

5.

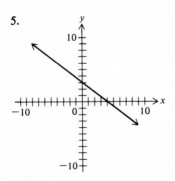

7.

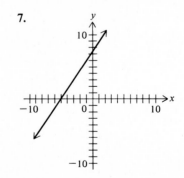

9.

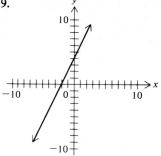

11.

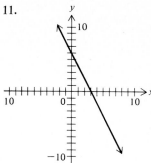

13.

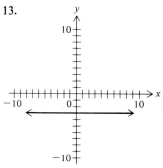

15.

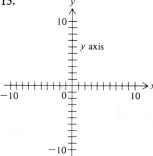

17.

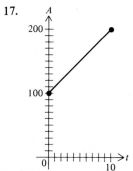

19.

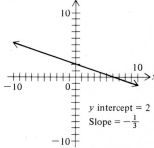

y intercept $= 2$

Slope $= -\frac{1}{3}$

21.

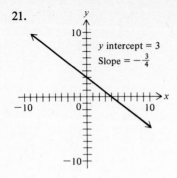

y intercept = 3

Slope = $-\frac{3}{4}$

23. $y = -x - 1$ **25.** $y = \frac{2}{3}x + \frac{3}{2}$

27. (A)

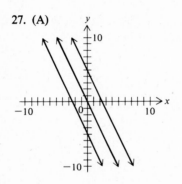

(B)

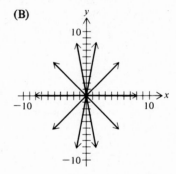

29. No.   **31.** They do.

33.

(C)

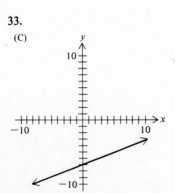

35.

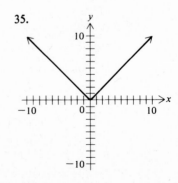

37. $y = x$ 39. $y = -\frac{1}{3}x - 2$ 41. $\frac{1}{2}$ 43. $\frac{1}{3}$ 45. $y = 4$
47. $x = 2$ 49. (A) $y = \frac{3}{2}x - \frac{1}{2}$; (B) $y = -\frac{2}{3}x - \frac{8}{3}$
51. $m_1 = \frac{3}{2} = m_2 \Rightarrow L_1 // L_2$ 53. No.   55. (A) $c = x/2 + 200$

(B)

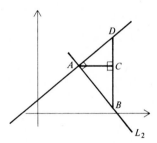

57. 7 or -3 59. $5x + 3y = -2$
61. First show that $\triangle ACD$ and $\triangle ABC$ are similar; then the result follows
immediately using proportional parts of similar triangles.

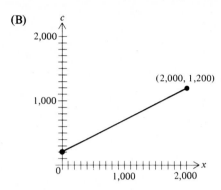

Exercise 27

1.

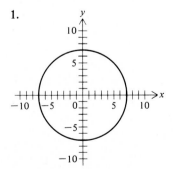

3.

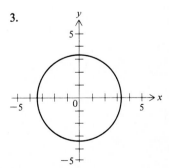

5.

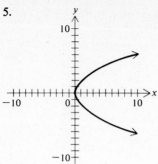

7.

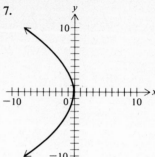

9.

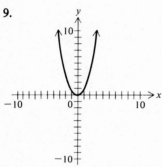

11.

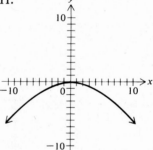

13.

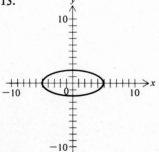

15.

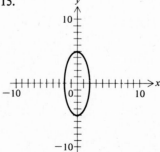

17.

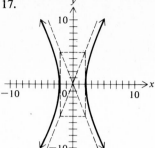

19.

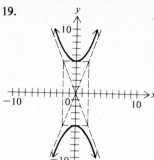

21.

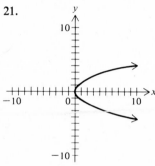

23.

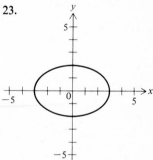

25.

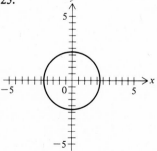

27.

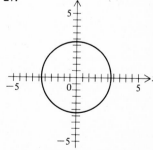

29. No graph   **31.** $x^2 + y^2 = 11$ **33.** $x^2 + y^2 = 25$ **35.** $(1,0), x = -1$
37. $(0, -\sqrt{21}), (0, \sqrt{21})$ **39.** $(-\sqrt{13}, 0), (\sqrt{13}, 0)$ **41.** $x^2 = -100y$
43. $(x + 4)^2 + (y - 5)^2 = 10$
45. Square both members of

$$\sqrt{(x - h)^2 + (y - k)^2} = r$$

47. $(x - 2)^2 = -4(y - 3)$ or $x^2 - 4x + 4y - 8 = 0$

Exercise 28

1.

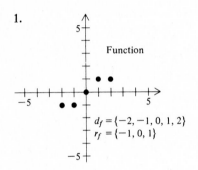

Function

$d_f = \{-2, -1, 0, 1, 2\}$
$r_f = \{-1, 0, 1\}$

3.

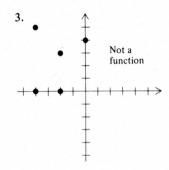

Not a function

5. 3   **7.** 2   **9.** 3   **11.** 0   **13.** -27 **15.** -6 **17.** 25   **19.** 22   **21.** -91
23. $3, 0$, not defined   **25.** $Y = \{-8, -5, -2, 1, 4\}$
27. $\{\frac{1}{6}, 0, -\frac{1}{4}, -\frac{2}{3}, -\frac{3}{2}\}$ **29.** $\{-8, -3, 0, 1\}$

31.

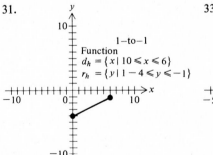

1-to-1
Function
$d_h = \{x \mid 10 \leqslant x \leqslant 6\}$
$r_h = \{y \mid 1 - 4 \leqslant y \leqslant -1\}$

33.

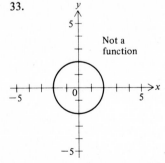

Not a function

35.

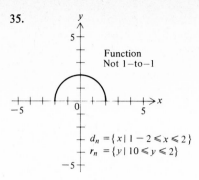

Function
Not 1−to−1

$d_n = \{x \mid 1 - 2 \leqslant x \leqslant 2\}$
$r_n = \{y \mid 10 \leqslant y \leqslant 2\}$

37. -1 39. $-6x - 7, -1$ 41. $4t^4 + 8t^2 + 4, 100$ 43. -2 45. h
47. (A) $g(t) = 16t^2, t \geq 0$; (B) 0, 16, 64, 144; (C) $64 + 16h$, the average
rate from $t = 2$ to $t = 2 + h$ (What happens when h approaches zero?)
49. $C = 300 + 50x, x \geq 0$ 51. $(f + g)(x) = x^2 + 2x - 1$; $(f + g)(-1) = -2$
53. $(fg)(x) = 2x^3 - x^2$, $(fg)(-2) = -20$
55. $d_{f \cdot g} = \{x \mid x \geq -2\}$, $r_{f \cdot g} = \{y \mid y \geq 0\}$ 57. (A) Yes; (B) Yes; (C) No.
59. $2ak + b$

61.

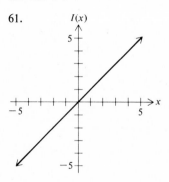

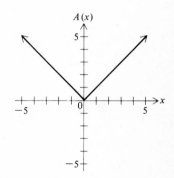

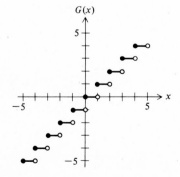

Exercise 29

1.

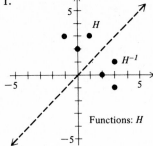

Functions: *H*

3.

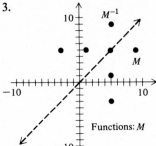

Functions: *M*

5.

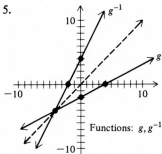

Functions: g, g^{-1}

7.

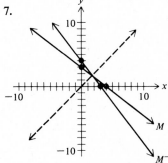

Functions: M, M^{-1}

9. Domain: $\{2, 3\}$, Range: $\{-1, 0, 1\}$ 11. Domain: $\{5\}$, Range: $\{-3, 1, 5, 9\}$
13. $g(x) = \frac{1}{2}x - 2, g^{-1}(x) = 2x + 4$ 15. $M(x) = -\frac{3}{4}x + 3, M^{-1}(x) = -\frac{4}{3}x + 4$

17.

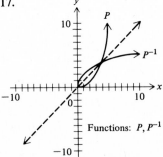

Functions: P, P^{-1}

19.

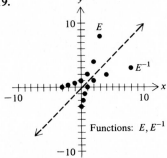

Functions: E, E^{-1}

21. Domain: $\{\frac{1}{8}, \frac{1}{4}, \frac{1}{2}, 0, 2, 4, 8\}$; Range: $\{-3, -2, -1, 0, 1, 2, 3\}$

23. $P(x) = x^2/4$, $P^{-1}(x) = \sqrt{4x}$ 25. $3, x$ 27. $2, x$

29. Since f is 1-to-1, f^{-1} is also 1-to-1. Thus f^{-1} is a single-valued relation and hence a function.

31. From Theorem 5, $(f \circ f^{-1})(x) = x$. Also, $I(x) = x$. Therefore, $f \circ f^{-1} = I$.

Exercise 30

1.

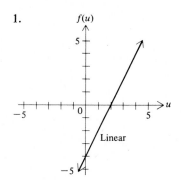

Linear

3.

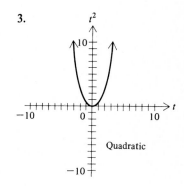

Quadratic

5.

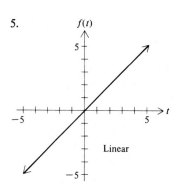

Linear

7.

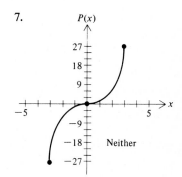

Neither

9. $-2, 2$ 11. No real solutions

13.

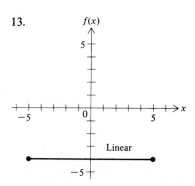

Linear

15.

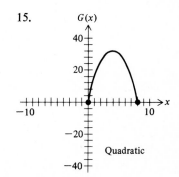

Quadratic

17.

Neither

19. $-1, 3$ **21.** $-2, 2$ **23.** 5   **25.** $-1, 4$ **27.** No real solution

29. (A)

(B) $t = 3$, time when ball reaches maximum height

31.

(A) $A(x) = 50x - x^2$
(B) Domain: $0 \leq x \leq 50$
(C)
(D) 25′ by 25′

33. 1.9   **35.** 1

Exercise 31

1. $F = kv^2$ 3. $f = k\sqrt{T}$ 5. $y = k/\sqrt{x}$ 7. $t = k/T$ 9. $R = kSTV$
11. $v = khr^2$ 13. 4   15. $9\sqrt{3}$ 17. $U = k(ab/c^3)$ 19. $L = k(wh^2/\ell)$
21. -12 23. 83 lb   25. 20 amperes
27. The new horsepower must be 8 times the old.   29. No effect

Exercise 32

1. $t^2 = kd^3$ 3. 1.47 hr (approximately)   5. 20 days   7. Quadrupled
9. 540 lb   11. (A) $\Delta S = kS$; (B) 10 oz; (C) 8 candlepower
13. 32 times per sec   15. $N = k(F/d)$ 17. 0.075 mi per sec   19. 20 days
21. The volume is increased by a factor of 8.

Exercise 33

1. $\{(-3,4), (-3,6), (-3,8), (-2,4), (-2,6), (-2,8)\}$
2. (A) Domain: $\{2, 3, 4, 5\}$, Range: $\{3, 4\}$; (B)
(C) Yes; (D)
(E) Single-valued

3.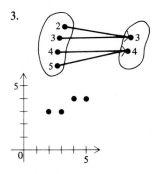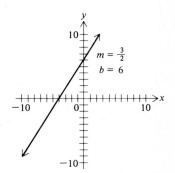

4. $\sqrt{73}$ 5. Not defined, 0

6.

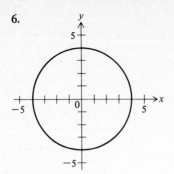

7.

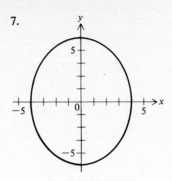

8.

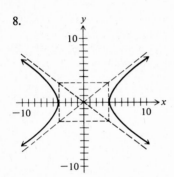

9.

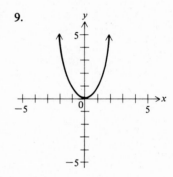

10. No. A function is a relation, but with the added property that each element in the domain is associated with exactly one element in the range.
11. $0, 6, 9, 6 - m$ 12. $-6, 0, -3, c - 2c^2$ 13. $Y = \{-17, -1, 15\}$

14.

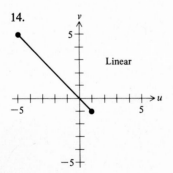

Linear

15.

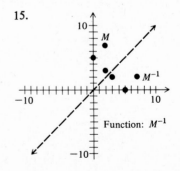

Function: M^{-1}

16. Domain: {3, 5, 7}, Range: {0, 2}   17. (A) $y = k(x/z)$, (B) $y = \frac{4}{3}$

18. $NXR = \{(x,y) \mid x \in N \text{ and } y \in R\}$ 19.

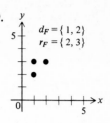

20. (A) $d_H = \{-2, 0, 2\}$; $r_H = \{-8, -2, 4\}$ (B)

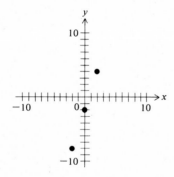

(C) Yes; (D)   (E) 1-to-1

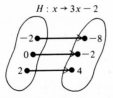

$H : x \to 3x - 2$

21. $y = -\frac{2}{3}x - 7$ 22. $y = -\frac{3}{2}x + 1$ 23. No.   24. $x^2 + y^2 = 169$

25.

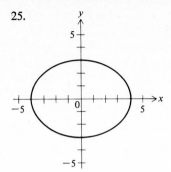

26.

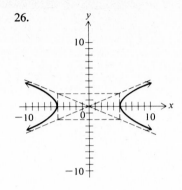

27.

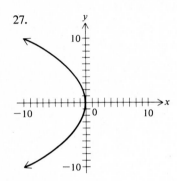

28. (A) 7; (B) 1; (C) $x^2 + x - 7$; (D) 3; (E) 3; (F) $-t^2 + 6t - 5$

29. $-2h - h^2$, $-2 - h$

30.

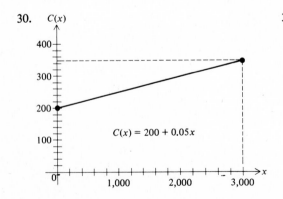

$C(x) = 200 + 0.05x$

31.

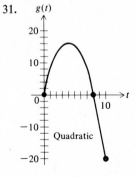

Quadratic

32. $-5, -1$

33.

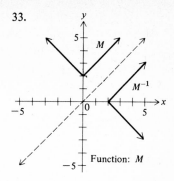

Function: M

34. (A) $M^{-1}(x) = 2x - 3$; (B) Yes; (C) 3; (D) a 35. $t = k (wa_i''/P)$
36. 8 footcandles, $\sqrt{2}$ ft
37. Yes, since it is reflexive, symmetric, and transitive.   38. $y = x - 3$
39. $(x - 3)^2 + (y + 2)^2 = 2$ 40. $(x - 2)^2 = 20(y + 3)$
41. (A) -1; (B) $(fg)(x) = f(x) \cdot g(x) = 5x - 5x^2$; (C) $(f \circ g)(x) = f[g(x)] = f(5)$
$= -20$ 42. (A) Yes; (B) Yes.

43.

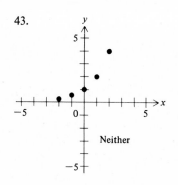

Neither

44. All but (B)   45. Doubled

CHAPTER 5

Exercise 34

1. $x + 6 + 15/(x - 3)$ 3. $2x - 1 - 1/(x + 4)$
5. $(2x^2 + 4x + 5) + 11/(x - 2)$ 7. $(3x^3 - 3x^2 + 3x - 4)$
9. $(2x^2 - 2x - 3) - 2/(x + 3)$ 11. $(2x^3 - 3x^2 - x - 5) - 10/(x - 5)$
13. $(3x^5 - 3x^4 + x^3 - 3)$ 15. $(x^4 - x^3 + x^2 - x + 1)$
17. $(4x^3 - 6x - 2) + 2/(x + \frac{1}{2})$ 19. $3x^2 - 3x + 3$
21. $2x^2 + 3.4x - 1.32 + 0.736/(x - 0.2)$ 23. $(x + 2)(4x^2 - 8x + 1)$

25. $(x + 2)(x^4 - 2x^3 + 4x^2 - 8x + 16)$

27. $(x + a)(x^4 - ax^3 + a^2x^2 - a^3x + a^4)$ 29. $[x^2 + (-3 + i)x - 3i](x - i)$

31. (A) In both cases: the coefficient of x is a_2; the constant term $a_2 r + a_1$, and the remainder $(a_2 r + a_1)r + a_0$; (B) The remainder expanded is $a_2 r^2 + a_1 r + a_0 = P(r)$.

Exercise 35

1. 4   3. 3   5. -6 7. 3, -5 9. $-\frac{1}{2}, 8, -2$ 11. Yes.   13. No.   15. Yes.

17. 0   19. -3 21. 0.427   23. $-4, -8, 1$ 25. $\frac{1}{8}, -\frac{3}{8}, -4$

27. $P(x) = [x - (3 + \sqrt{5})/2][x - (3 - \sqrt{5})/2]$

29. $P(x) = [x - (3 + i)][x - (3 - i)]$ 31. Yes.   33. No.   35. Yes.

37. $P(x) = (x - 3)(x + 2)$ 39. $P(x) = (x + 8)(x + 7)(x - 1)$

41. $P(x) = (x - \frac{3}{8})(x + \frac{1}{7})(x - 9)$

43. $P(2) = 10$. Both methods involve exactly the same operations on the same numbers.

45. (A) $P(r) = (a_2 r + a_1)r + a_0$; (B) $P(r) = R = (a_2 r + a_1)r + a_0$. Both are the same.

Exercise 36

1. $-3 - 5i$ 3. $-4i$ 5. -6 7. 34   9. $2 - 3i$ 11. $-5 - 31i$

13. $x^2 - 6x + 10$ 15. $x^2 - 8x + 41$ 17. $1 + i$ 19. $-2i$

21. $P(x) = [x - (1 - i)][x - (1 + i)]$ 23. $P(x) = (x - 2i)(x + 2i)$

25. $x^2 + y^2$ 27. $-i, 2 + 3i$ 29. $5i, 3$ 31. $3 + i, -1$

33. $P(x) = (x + 5i)(x - 5i)(x - 3)$ 35. $P(x) = [x - (3 - i)][x - (3 + i)](x + 1)$

37. No, since the coefficients of $P(x)$ are not all real.   39. $x^2 - 2ax + (a^2 + b^2)$

Exercise 37

1. 5, -7 (multiplicity 2); degree of $P(x)$ is 3

3. 2 (multiplicity 3), -3 (multiplicity 2), 1; degree of $P(x)$ is 6

5. $P(x) = (x + 2)^3(x - 1)^2$; degree 5

7. $P(x) = (x + 7)^3(x - \frac{2}{3})(x + 5)$; degree 5

9. $P(x) = (x - i\sqrt{3})^2(x + i\sqrt{3})^2(x - 4)^3$; degree 7

11. $P(x) = (x - 3)^2(x + 2)$ 13. $P(x) = (x - 1)(x + 1)(x - i)(x + i)$

15. $P(x) = (x - 2)^2(x + 2)(x - 3i)(x + 3i)$ 17. 3 (multiplicity 2) and -2

19. 1, $-1, i, -i$ 21. 2 (multiplicity 2), $-2, 3i, -3i$ 23. $n; 0$

25. A polynomial of degree n must have exactly n zeros. If the coefficients of the polynomial are real, then any complex zeros must occur in conjugate pairs and hence an even number of times. Thus if n is odd there must be at least one real zero.

Exercise 38

1. 1 positive, 1 negative   3. 0 positive, 2 or 0 negative
5. 1 or 3 positive, 0 negative   7. u.b. $= 2$, l.b. $= -1$ 9. u.b. $= 2$, l.b. $= -3$
11. u.b. $= 1$, l.b. $= -2$ 13. $P(3) = -2, P(4) = 2$
15. $P(-3) = -13, P(-2) = 3$ 17. $Q(1) = 4, Q(2) = -1$
19. (A) 0 or 2 positive, 1 negative; (B) u.b. $= 3$, l.b. $= -3$; (C) 1 is a zero and
one zero in each interval $(-3,-2)$ and $(1,2)$
21. (A) 1 positive, 0 or 2 negative; (B) u.b. $= 3$, l.b. $= -2$; (C) one real zero in
interval $(2,3)$ 23. (A) 1 positive, 1 or 3 negative; (B) u.b. $= 2$, l.b. $= -5$;
(C) Each interval contains exactly one real zero: $(-4,-3)$, $(-2,-1)$, $(-1,0)$,
and $(1,2)$.   25. (A) 1 or 3 positive, 0 or 2 negative; (B) u.b. $= 2$, l.b. $= -2$;
(C) At least one real zero in interval $(1,2)$ 27. By Descartes's rule of signs
$P(x)$ has one positive and one negative real zero. By the fundamental theorem of
algebra, $P(x)$ has four zeros. Therefore, the other two zeros must be complex.
29. By Descartes's rule of signs, $P(x)$ has no positive or negative zeros.
Since $P(0) = 0$, $P(-1) < 0$, and $P(1) > 0$, the graph crosses the x axis only
at the origin.

Exercise 39

1. $\pm1, \pm2, \pm4, \pm8$ 3. $\pm1, \pm2, \pm3, \pm6$ 5. $\pm1, \pm3, \pm\frac{1}{2}, \pm\frac{3}{2}$
7. $\pm1, \pm3, \pm5, \pm15, \pm\frac{1}{2}, \pm\frac{3}{2}, \pm\frac{5}{2}, \pm\frac{15}{2}$ 9. $-4, -1, 2$
11. No rational zeros   13. -1 (a double zero); $\frac{2}{3}$ 15. $-\frac{2}{3}$ 17. $-2, 2$
19. $-\frac{1}{2}, \frac{1}{3}, \frac{3}{2}$ 21. $1, (2 - \sqrt{2}), (2 + \sqrt{2})$ 23. -2 (a double root), $\sqrt{5}, -\sqrt{5}$
25. $1, -1, \frac{3}{2}, i, -i$ 27. $2(x - 1)[x - (2 - \sqrt{2})][x - (2 + \sqrt{2})]$
29. $2(x + 1)(x - 1)(x - \frac{3}{2})(x + i)(x - i)$
31. $P(x) = x^2 - 6$ has no rational zeros.
33. $P(x) = x^3 - 5$ has no rational zeros.   35. $P(x) = x^5 - 8$ has no
rational zeros.

37.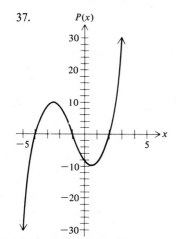

39.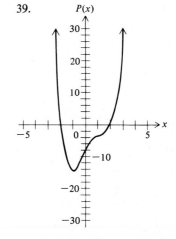

41.

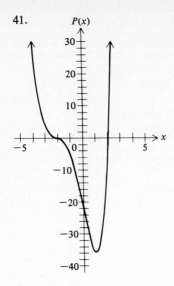

Exercise 40

1. 0.7   3. 1.8   5. 1, 1.5   7. $-\frac{3}{2}$, 1.2   9. 2.26   11. 2.18   13. 0.5 ft
15. 0.4 ft

Exercise 41

1. $A = 2, B = 5$ 3. $A = 7, B = -2$ 5. $A = 1, B = 2, C = 3$
7. $A = 2, B = 1, C = 3$ 9. $A = 0, B = 2, C = 2, D = -3$
11. $3/(x - 4) - 4/(x + 2)$ 13. $3/(3x + 4) - 1/(2x - 3)$
15. $2/x - 1/(x - 3) - 3/(x - 3)^2$ 17. $2/x + (3x - 1)/(x^2 + 2x + 3)$
19. $2x/(x^2 + 2) + (3x + 5)/(x^2 + 2)^2$ 21. $x - 2 + 3/(x - 2) - 2/(x - 3)$
23. $2/(x - 3) + (2x + 5)/(x^2 + 3x + 3)$ 25. $2/(x - 4) - 1/(x + 3) + 3/(x + 3)^2$
27. $2/(x - 2) - 3/(x - 2)^2 - 2x/(x^2 - x + 1)$
29. $x + 2 + 1/(2x - 1) - 2/(x + 2) + (x - 1)/(2x^2 - x + 1)$

Exercise 42

1. $2x^3 + 3x^2 - 1 = (x + 2)(2x^2 - x + 2) - 5$ 2. $P(3) = -8$
3. $2, -4, -1$ 4. $1 - i$
5. (A) 0 or 2 positive, 1 negative; (B) 0 positive, 1 negative
6. l.b.: -2 and -1, u.b.: 4   7. $P(1) = -5$ and $P(2) = 1$ are of opposite sign.
8. $\pm 1, \pm 2, \pm 3, \pm 6$ 9. $-1, 2, 3$ 10. $2/(x - 3) + 5/(x + 2)$
11. $P(x) = (x - \frac{2}{3})(3x^2 - 6x - 3) - 5$ 12. -4
13. $P(x) = [x - (1 + \sqrt{2})][x - (1 - \sqrt{2})]$
14. Yes, since $P(-1) = (-1)^{25} + 1 = 0$.
15. (A) 0 or 2 positive, 0 or 2

negative; (B) l.b.: -3, u.b.: 4; (C) -2 is a zero;
$(-1,0)$, $(0,1)$, and $(3,4)$ each contains a zero.   16. $-2, -\frac{1}{2}, 4$
17. $P(x) = 2(x + 2)(x + \frac{1}{2})(x - 4)$ 18. No rational zeros
19. $\frac{1}{2}, (1 + \sqrt{3}i)/2, (1 - \sqrt{3}i)/2$
20. $P(x) = 2(x - \frac{1}{2})[x - (1 + \sqrt{3}i)/2][x - (1 - \sqrt{3}i)/2]$
21. 1.4   22. $1/x - 2/(x - 2) + 3/(x - 2)^2$ 23. $3/x + (2x - 1)/(2x^2 - 3x + 3)$
24. $P(x) = [x - (1 + i)][x^2 + (1 + i)x + (3 + 2i)] + (3 + 5i)$
25. $P(x) = (x - \frac{1}{2})^2(x + 3)(x - 1)^3$; degree 6
26. $P(x) = (x + 5)[x - (2 - 3i)][x - (2 + 3i)]$; degree 3
27. $\frac{1}{2}, 3.0$ 28. $2/(x - 3) - 3/x + (x - 1)/(x^2 + 1)$

CHAPTER 6

Exercise 43

1.

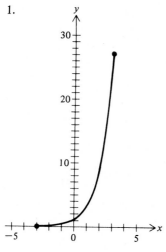

3.

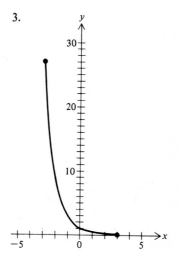

5.

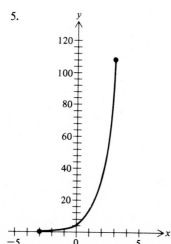

7.

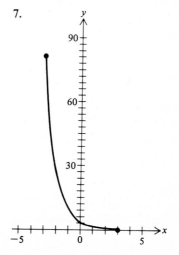

9.

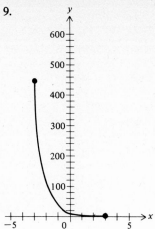

11.

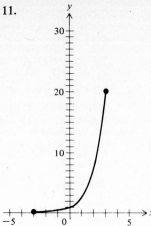

13.

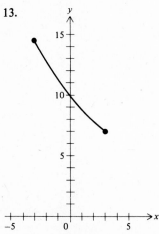

15.

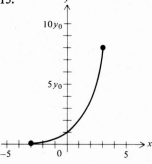

17.

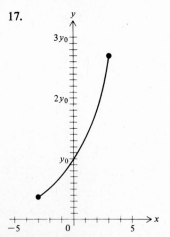

19.

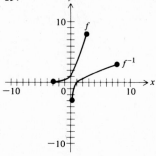

21.

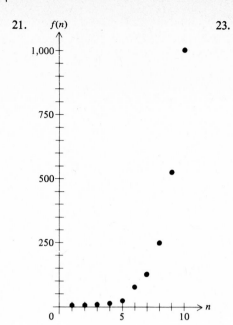

23.

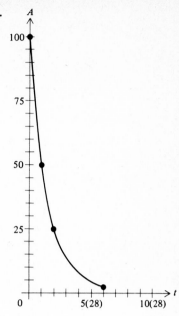

25.

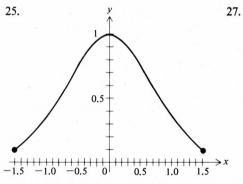

27.

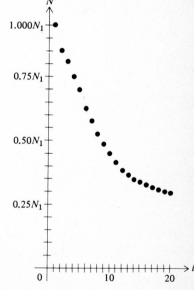

29.

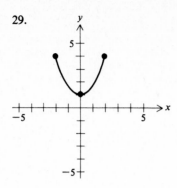

Exercise 44

1. $9 = 3^2$ 3. $81 = 3^4$ 5. $1,000 = 10^3$ 7. $1 = e^0$ 9. $\log_8 64 = 2$
11. $\log_{10} 10,000 = 4$ 13. $\log_v u = x$ 15. $\log_{27} 9 = \frac{2}{3}$ 17. 5   19. -4
21. 2   23. 3   25. $x = 4$ 27. $y = 2$ 29. $b = 4$ 31. $0.001 = 10^{-3}$
33. $3 = 81^{1/4}$ 35. $16 = (\frac{1}{2})^{-4}$ 37. $N = a^e$ 39. $\log_{10} 0.01 = -2$
41. $\log_e 1 = 0$ 43. $\log_2(\frac{1}{8}) = -3$ 45. $\log_{81} \frac{1}{3} = -\frac{1}{4}$ 47. $\log_{49} 7 = \frac{1}{2}$
49. u 51. $\frac{1}{2}$ 53. $\frac{3}{2}$ 55. 0   57. $\frac{3}{2}$ 59. 2   61. $y = -2$ 63. $b = 100$
65. Any positive real number except 1.
67. Domain of f is the set of all real numbers; the range of f is $\{1\}$. The domain of f^{-1} is $\{1\}$; the range of f^{-1} is the set of all real numbers. No, f^{-1} is not.

69. (A)

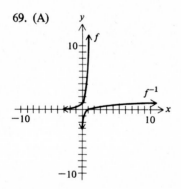

(B) Domain of f is the set of real numbers; range of f is the set of positive real numbers. The domain of f is the range of f^{-1} and the range of f is the domain of f^{-1}. (C) f^{-1} is called the logarithmic function with base 10.
71. -3

Exercise 45

1. $\log_b u + \log_b v$ 3. $\log_b A - \log_b B$ 5. $5 \log_b u$ 7. $\frac{3}{8} \log_b N$
9. $\frac{1}{2} \log_b Q$ 11. $\log_b u + \log_b v + \log_b w$ 13. $\log_b AB$ 15. $\log_b X/Y$
17. $\log_b wx/y$ 19. 3.40   21. -0.92 23. 3.30   25. $2 \log_b u + 7 \log_b v$
27. $-\log_b a$ 29. $\frac{1}{3} \log_b N - 2 \log_b p - 3 \log_b q$
31. $\frac{1}{4}(2 \log_b x + 3 \log_b y - \frac{1}{2} \log_b z)$ 33. $\log_b x^2/y$ 35. $\log_b x^3 y^2/z^4$
37. $\log_b \sqrt[5]{x^2 y^3}$ 39. 2.02   41. 0.23   43. -0.05 45. 8   47. $y = cb^{-kt}$
49. Let $u = \log_b M$ and $v = \log_b N$, then $M = b^u$ and $N = b^v$. Thus,
$\log_b M/N = \log_b b^u/b^v = \log_b b^{u-v} = u - v = \log_b M - \log_b N$.
51. $MN = b^{\log_b M} b^{\log_b N} = b^{\log_b M + \log_b N}$; hence, by definition of logarithm
$\log_b MN = \log_b M + \log_b N$.

Exercise 46

1. 0.3711   3. 0.7016   5. 1.8692   7. 6.4914   9. $0.8035 - 3$ 11. $0.6902 - 5$
13. 5.28   15. 9.36   17. $8.31 \times 10^4 = 83,100$ 19. $4.07 \times 10^{-1} = 0.407$
21. $2.78 \times 10 = 27.8$ 23. $9.14 \times 10^{-4} = 0.000914$ 25. $4.73 \times 10^{-3} = 0.00473$
27. $7.27 \times 10^{-1} = 0.727$ 29. $6.8 \times 10^{-4} = 0.00068$ 31. 0.3649
33. 5.8472   35. 1.8131   37. $0.6027 - 3$ 39. $0.9546 - 1$ 41. 5.8403
43. 5.204   45. $3.514 \times 10^5 = 351,400$ 47. $2.793 \times 10^3 = 2,793$
49. $4.017 \times 10^{-3} = 0.004017$ 51. $6.906 \times 10^{-1} = 0.6906$
53. $1.474 \times 10^{-1} = 0.1474$ 55. $0.2051 - 1$ 57. 4.8887   59. 6.0200
61. $0.5811 - 2$ 63. $0.1449 - 1$ 65. $y = 41.1$
67. $4.3062; 2.024 \times 10^4 = 20,240$ 69. $0.8552 - 8; 7.165 \times 10^{-8}$

Exercise 47

1. 77,340   3. 13.82   5. 168,600   7. 0.006745   9. 99.54   11. 3,581
13. 2.4×10^{-11} 15. 4.495   17. 0.6240   19. 0.0191   21. $-(7.98 \times 10^{-6})$
23. 151.2   25. 9.790   27. $-(4.462 \times 10^{-6})$ 29. 1.37×10^{12} 31. 0.02546
33. 7.6777   35. 2.475 sec   37. 1.642×10^{25} dollars   39. -1.415
41. (A) $t = kn^{3/2}$; (B) 39 or 40

Exercise 48

1. 2.9   3. 0.91   5. 6.0   7. 2.4   9. 80   11. 19   13. -2.4 15. 5.9
17. 0.063   19. 10   21. 4   23. 1.5117   25. 5.459   27. 390.2 mg   29. 28 years
31. \$21,430,000   33. $\log_a b = \log_b b/\log_b a = 1/\log_b a \Rightarrow (\log_a b)(\log_b a) = 1$

Exercise 49

1.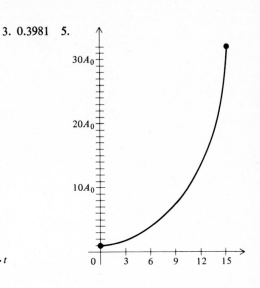

3. 0.3981 5.

7. 35 years, 55.5 years   9. 9.55×10^{-7} 11. \$1,338   13. 7.2%
15. 95 ft, 489 ft   17. 3.568 in.
19. $I = I_0 10^{N/10}$
    $\log I = \log I_0 + \log 10^{N/10}$
    $\log I = \log I_0 + N/10$
    $N/10 = \log I - \log I_0$
    $N/10 = \log I/I_0$
        $N = 10 \log I/I_0$

21.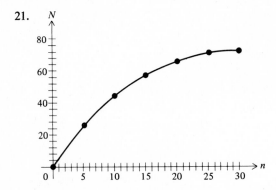

23. Factor of 8 (approximately)
25. 18,000,000 mi

Exercise 50

1. $x = 10^y$ 2. $\log_{10} m = n$ 3. 4   4. 5   5. 3   6. 114.1   7. 7.575
8. 884   9. 1.2   10. 25

11.

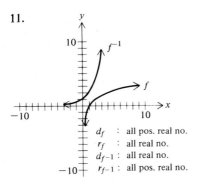

d_f : all pos. real no.
r_f : all real no.
$d_{f^{-1}}$: all real no.
$r_{f^{-1}}$: all pos. real no.

12. $y = e^x$ 13. $\log_e y = x$ 14. -2 15. $\frac{1}{3}$ 16. 64   17. e 18. 33
19. 0.02145   20. 0.2416   21. 0.839   22. 11.41   23. 42.36   24. 0.00247
25. 2.3   26. 92   27. $x = 1$ 28. 30   29. ± 2 30. 1.948   31. 24 years
32. If $\log_1 x = y$, then we would have to have $1^y = x$; that is, $1 = x$ for arbitrary positive x, which is impossible.
33. Let $u = \log_b M$ and $v = \log_b N$, then $M = b^u$ and $N = b^v$. Thus, $\log_b M/N = \log_b b^u/b^v = \log_b b^{u-v} = u - v = \log_b M - \log_b N$.   34. $y = ce^{-5t}$ 35. 4.605

36.

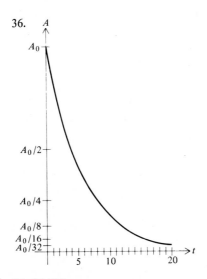

37. 37,200 years

CHAPTER 7

Exercise 51

1. $(2,-3)$ 3. No solution 5. $(-\frac{4}{3},1)$ 7. Infinite number of solutions
9. $(1,4)$ 11. $(-2,-3)$ 13. 14 nickels and 8 dimes 15. $52°; 38°$ 17. $(-2,3)$
19. $(1,-5)$ 21. $(\frac{4}{3},-2)$ 23. Infinite number of solutions 25. $(-2,2)$
27. $(1.1,0.3)$ 29. $(8,6)$ 31. $(-2,2)$
33. Eighty-four $\frac{1}{4}$-lb packages; sixty $\frac{1}{3}$-lb packages
35. 60 cc of 80% solution and 40 cc of 50% solution
37. (A) $1\frac{9}{13}$ sec, $7\frac{9}{13}$ sec; (B) Approximately 8,462 ft
39. Both companies pay \$136 on sales of \$1,700. The straight commission company pays better to the right of this point, and the other company pays better to the left. 41. It passes through the point of intersection.
43. $d = 141$ cm (approximately); move away from goal box; move toward goal box.

Exercise 52

1.

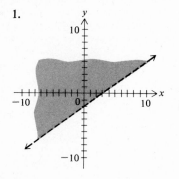

3.

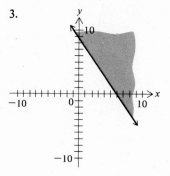

5.

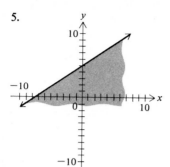

7.

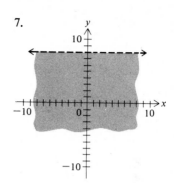

9.

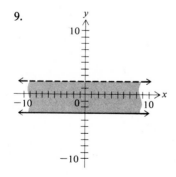

11.

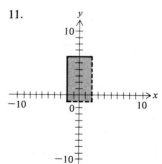

13.

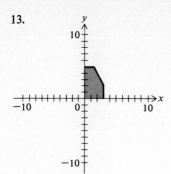

15.

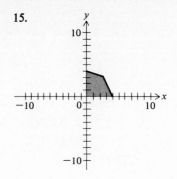

17.

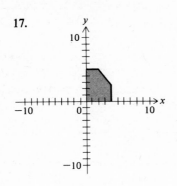

19.

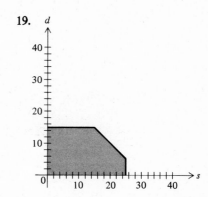

Exercise 53

1. 10 competition and no standard; maximum profit = $400.
3. 15 of each model; maximum profit = $11,250.

Exercise 54

1. $(-12,5), (-12,-5)$ 3. $(2,4), (-2,-4)$ 5. $(5i,-5i), (-5i,5i)$
7. $(3+4i,-1+2i), (3-4i,-1-2i)$ 9. $(2,4), (2,-4), (-2,4), (-2,-4)$
11. $(1,3), (1,-3), (-1,3), (-1,-3)$
13. $(-1+\sqrt{3}\,i,1+\sqrt{3}\,i), (-1-\sqrt{3}\,i,1-\sqrt{3}\,i)$ 15. $(0,-1), (-4,-3)$
17. $(2,2i), (2,-2i), (-2,2i), (-2,-2i)$ 19. $(2,\sqrt{2}), (2,-\sqrt{2}), (-1,i), (-1,-i)$
21. $(2,1), (-2,1), (2i,3), (-2i,3)$ 23. $(2,1), (-2,-1), (i,-2i), (-i,2i)$
25. $(2,2), (-2,-2), (\sqrt{2},-\sqrt{2}), (-\sqrt{2},\sqrt{2})$ 27. $(-3,1), (3,-1), (-i,i), (i,-i)$
29. $1/2+(\sqrt{3}/2)i$ and $1/2-(\sqrt{3}/2)i$ 31. $(2,4), (-2,-4)$
33. $(1,3), (1,-3), (-1,3), (-1,-3)$ 35. 12 in. by 5 in.

Exercise 55

1. $(1,4)$ 3. $(-1,-1,-2)$ 5. $(-1,-3)$ 7. $(0,-2,5)$ 9. $(3,-1,-2)$
11. No solution; the system is inconsistent.   13. $(\frac{1}{2},\frac{1}{3},-\frac{1}{2})$
15. $x^2 + y^2 - 4x - 4y - 17 = 0$ 17. A: 60 grams; B: 50 grams; C: 40 grams
19. $(2,0,0,-1)$ 21. For any real number k, $(k,-2k,-k)$ is a solution.
23. Interchanging two rows in an augmented matrix is the same as interchanging two equations in a system. By Theorem 3A, the two systems are equivalent; hence, the augmented matrices are row-equivalent.

Exercise 56

1. 2×2; 3×4; 1×4 3. 2   5. $[0\ 0\ 0\ 0]$ 7. C 9. None.

11.
$$-F = \begin{bmatrix} 3 & -4 \\ 0 & -5 \\ -2 & 1 \end{bmatrix}$$
13. $\begin{bmatrix} -1 & -3 \\ -5 & 4 \end{bmatrix}$ 15. $\begin{bmatrix} -5 & -1 \\ 5 & 4 \end{bmatrix}$ 17. Yes.

19. $[-4\ 5]$ 21. $\begin{bmatrix} 8 & -8 & 0 \\ 0 & 3 & 3 \end{bmatrix}$ 23. $\begin{bmatrix} -3 & 0 \\ 3 & -2 \end{bmatrix}$

25. $w = -1$, $x = 1$, $y = 7$, $z = -8$ 27. (A) No; (B) Yes; (C) Yes.

29. $\begin{bmatrix} -a & -b \\ -c & -d \end{bmatrix}$

Exercise 57

1. $\begin{bmatrix} -8 & 4 \\ 16 & -4 \end{bmatrix}$ 3. $\begin{bmatrix} 7 & 1 \\ -2 & 2 \end{bmatrix}$ 5. 10   7. -10 9. $[5\ \ -9]$ 11. $\begin{bmatrix} -6 \\ 14 \end{bmatrix}$

13. $\begin{bmatrix} 4 & -9 \\ -7 & 17 \end{bmatrix}$ 15. $\begin{bmatrix} 11 & 1 \\ -3 & 9 \end{bmatrix}$ 17. $\begin{bmatrix} -15 & 6 \\ -9 & -15 \\ 3 & 0 \end{bmatrix}$ 19. $\begin{bmatrix} 16 & -8 \\ 9 & 19 \\ -5 & 3 \end{bmatrix}$

21. -10 23. -15 25. $\begin{bmatrix} -6 & -8 \\ 4 & -7 \end{bmatrix}$ 27. $\begin{bmatrix} -8 & -8 & 3 \\ 3 & -4 & 5 \\ -2 & 0 & -1 \end{bmatrix}$ 29. $[6]$

31. $\begin{bmatrix} 2 & -4 & 4 \\ -1 & 2 & -2 \\ 1 & -2 & 2 \end{bmatrix}$ 33. $AB = \begin{bmatrix} 4 & 12 \\ 0 & 0 \end{bmatrix}$; $BA = \begin{bmatrix} 2 & 4 \\ -8 & -4 \end{bmatrix}$

35. Both members $= \begin{bmatrix} 4 & 2 \\ 8 & 4 \end{bmatrix}$

37.
$$(B+C)(B-C) = \begin{bmatrix} -15 & 5 \\ -30 & 10 \end{bmatrix}; \ B^2 - C^2 = \begin{bmatrix} -7 & 4 \\ -16 & 2 \end{bmatrix}$$

41.
$$\begin{bmatrix} 2 & -3 \\ 1 & 2 \end{bmatrix} \begin{bmatrix} x \\ y \end{bmatrix} = \begin{bmatrix} 5 \\ -1 \end{bmatrix} \Leftrightarrow \begin{bmatrix} 2-3x \\ x+2y \end{bmatrix} = \begin{bmatrix} 5 \\ -1 \end{bmatrix} \Leftrightarrow \begin{matrix} 2-3x = 5 \\ x+2y = -1 \end{matrix}$$

43.
(A) $u=0, v=7$; (B) $\begin{bmatrix} u \\ v \end{bmatrix} = \begin{bmatrix} (2x+y) \\ (3x-2y) \end{bmatrix} \Leftrightarrow \begin{matrix} u = 2x + y \\ v = 3x - 2y \end{matrix}, \ u=0, v=7;$

(C) $\begin{matrix} m = -x + 3y \\ n = 8x - 3y \end{matrix}, \ \begin{bmatrix} m \\ n \end{bmatrix} = \begin{bmatrix} -1 & 3 \\ 8 & -3 \end{bmatrix} \begin{bmatrix} x \\ y \end{bmatrix}, \begin{bmatrix} 1 & -1 \\ 1 & 2 \end{bmatrix} \begin{bmatrix} 2 & 1 \\ 3 & -2 \end{bmatrix} = \begin{bmatrix} -1 & 3 \\ 8 & -3 \end{bmatrix}$

Exercise 58

1.

(A) a, d, e; (B) $S = \begin{bmatrix} 0 & 0 & 0 & 1 & 0 \\ 0 & 0 & 0 & 1 & 1 \\ 0 & 0 & 0 & 0 & 0 \\ 1 & 1 & 0 & 0 & 1 \\ 0 & 1 & 0 & 1 & 0 \end{bmatrix}$;

(C) $S^2 = \begin{bmatrix} 1 & 1 & 0 & 0 & 1 \\ 1 & 2 & 0 & 1 & 1 \\ 0 & 0 & 0 & 0 & 0 \\ 0 & 1 & 0 & 3 & 1 \\ 1 & 1 & 0 & 1 & 2 \end{bmatrix}, \begin{matrix} a-1 \\ b-2 \\ c-0; \\ d-3 \\ e-2 \end{matrix}$ (D) $S^3 = \begin{bmatrix} 0 & 1 & 0 & 3 & 1 \\ 1 & 2 & 0 & 4 & 3 \\ 0 & 0 & 0 & 0 & 0 \\ 3 & 4 & 0 & 2 & 4 \\ 1 & 3 & 0 & 4 & 2 \end{bmatrix}$, clique $\{b,d,e\}$

Exercise 59

1. 8   3. -20 5. -0.88 7. $\begin{vmatrix} a_{22} & a_{23} \\ a_{32} & a_{33} \end{vmatrix}$ 9. $\begin{vmatrix} a_{11} & a_{12} \\ a_{31} & a_{32} \end{vmatrix}$

11. $(-1)^{1+1} \begin{vmatrix} a_{22} & a_{23} \\ a_{32} & a_{33} \end{vmatrix}$ 13. $(-1)^{2+3} \begin{vmatrix} a_{11} & a_{12} \\ a_{31} & a_{32} \end{vmatrix}$ 15. $\begin{vmatrix} 1 & -2 \\ -4 & 8 \end{vmatrix}$

17. $\begin{vmatrix} -2 & 0 \\ 5 & -2 \end{vmatrix}$ 19. $(-1)^{1+1} \begin{vmatrix} 1 & -2 \\ -4 & 8 \end{vmatrix} = 0$ 21. $(-1)^{3+2} \begin{vmatrix} -2 & 0 \\ 5 & -2 \end{vmatrix} = -4$

23. 10   25. -21 27. -40

29. $(-1)^{1+1} \begin{vmatrix} a_{22} & a_{23} & a_{24} \\ a_{32} & a_{33} & a_{34} \\ a_{42} & a_{43} & a_{44} \end{vmatrix}$ 31. $(-1)^{4+3} \begin{vmatrix} a_{11} & a_{12} & a_{14} \\ a_{21} & a_{22} & a_{24} \\ a_{31} & a_{32} & a_{34} \end{vmatrix}$ 33. 22

35. -12 37. 0   39. 6   41. 60   43. $\begin{vmatrix} a & b \\ ka & kb \end{vmatrix} = akb - kab = 0$

45. $\begin{vmatrix} a & b \\ c & d \end{vmatrix} = ad - cb = ad - bc = \begin{vmatrix} a & c \\ b & d \end{vmatrix}$ 49. $49 = (-7)(-7)$

Exercise 60

1. Theorem 9   3. Theorem 9   5. Theorem 10   7. Theorem 11
9. Theorem 13   11. $x = 0$ 13. $x = 5$ 15. 25   17. -12 19. Theorem 9
21. Theorem 10   23. Theorem 13   25. $x = 5, y = 0$ 27. $x = -3, y = 10$
29. -28 31. 106   33. 0   35. 6   37. 14
39. Expand the left member of the equation using minors or definition (3).
41. Expand both members of the equation and compare.
43. This follows from Theorem 12.
45. Expand the determinant about the first row to obtain $(y_1 - y_2)x$
$- (x_1 - x_2)y + (x_1 y_2 - x_2 y_1) = 0$; then show that the two points satisfy this
linear equation.
47. If the determinant is zero, then the area of the triangle formed by the
three points is zero. The only way that this can happen is if the three points
are on the same line; that is, the points are collinear.

Exercise 61

1. $\begin{bmatrix} -1 & 4 \\ 2 & 7 \end{bmatrix}$ 3. $\begin{bmatrix} 2 & -1 & 3 \\ 5 & 6 & 1 \\ 4 & 0 & 2 \end{bmatrix}$ 5. $\begin{bmatrix} -2 & 1 \\ 5 & 0 \end{bmatrix}$ 7. $\begin{bmatrix} 6 & 3 & 1 \\ -5 & -1 & 4 \\ 2 & 4 & 7 \end{bmatrix}$

9. $\begin{bmatrix} 3 & -1 \\ -5 & 2 \end{bmatrix}$ 11. $\frac{1}{2}\begin{bmatrix} 8 & -3 \\ -2 & 1 \end{bmatrix}$

13. $-\frac{1}{2}\begin{bmatrix} -2 & 1 & 4 \\ 0 & 0 & -2 \\ 0 & -1 & 2 \end{bmatrix}$ 15. Does not exist   17. $-\frac{1}{4}\begin{bmatrix} -1 & -1 & -1 \\ -2 & 2 & -2 \\ 3 & -1 & -1 \end{bmatrix}$

19. $a = 3, b = -1, c = -5, d = 2$

23. $\left(\begin{bmatrix} 2 & 1 \\ 5 & 3 \end{bmatrix}\begin{bmatrix} 1 & 3 \\ 2 & 8 \end{bmatrix}\right)^{-1} = \begin{bmatrix} 4 & 14 \\ 11 & 39 \end{bmatrix}^{-1} = \frac{1}{2}\begin{bmatrix} 39 & -14 \\ -11 & 4 \end{bmatrix};$

$\begin{bmatrix} 1 & 3 \\ 2 & 8 \end{bmatrix}^{-1}\begin{bmatrix} 2 & 1 \\ 5 & 3 \end{bmatrix}^{-1} = \frac{1}{2}\begin{bmatrix} 8 & -3 \\ -2 & 1 \end{bmatrix}\begin{bmatrix} 3 & -1 \\ -5 & 2 \end{bmatrix} = \frac{1}{2}\begin{bmatrix} 39 & -14 \\ -11 & 4 \end{bmatrix}$

25. Evaluate both sides to obtain $\begin{bmatrix} 3 & -5 \\ -1 & 2 \end{bmatrix}$

Exercise 62

1. $\begin{bmatrix} 1 & 2 \\ 1 & 3 \end{bmatrix}\begin{bmatrix} x \\ y \end{bmatrix} = \begin{bmatrix} 1 \\ -1 \end{bmatrix}$ 3. $2x - 3y = -1$ 5. $x = 5, y = -2$
$\qquad\qquad\qquad\qquad -x + 4y = 0$

7. $x = 1, y = -1$ 9. $x = -1, y = 1$ 11. $x = 1, y = -1$ 13. $x = -1, y = 1$

15. $x = 2, y = -2, z = -1$ 17. $x = 2, y = -1, z = 2$
19. $x = 2, y = -3, z = -1$ 21. $x = 1, y = -1, z = 2$
23. $x = 2, y = -3, z = -1$ 25. $x = 1, y = -1, z = 2$

Exercise 63

1. $x = 2, y = 3$ 2.

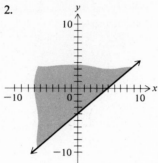

3. $(1 + i, 2i), (1 - i, -2i)$ 4. $(1, -1), (\frac{7}{5}, -\frac{1}{5})$ 5. $\begin{bmatrix} 4 & -1 \\ -1 & 6 \end{bmatrix}$ 6. $\begin{bmatrix} 0 & -5 \\ 7 & 3 \end{bmatrix}$

7. $\begin{bmatrix} -1 & 4 \\ 2 & 7 \end{bmatrix}$ 8. $\begin{bmatrix} 1 & 0 & 2 \\ -1 & 5 & 2 \end{bmatrix}$ 9. $\begin{bmatrix} u & x \\ v & y \end{bmatrix}$ 10. $-\frac{1}{9}\begin{bmatrix} 2 & -1 \\ -5 & -2 \end{bmatrix}$

11. -17 12. 0   13. 5×3 14. $x = 2, y = -1$
15. For any real number k, $[k, (8 + 4k)/3]$ is a solution. The system is dependent.
16. Forty-eight $\frac{1}{2}$-lb packages; seventy-two $\frac{1}{3}$-lb packages

17.

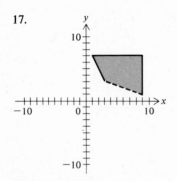

18. $(2, \sqrt{2}), (2, -\sqrt{2}), (-1, i), (-1, -i)$ 19. $(1, 3), (1, -3), (-1, 3), (-1, -3)$
20. $(\sqrt{5} + 1)/2$ and $(\sqrt{5} - 1)/2$

21. $\begin{bmatrix} 6 & 3 & -2 \\ 5 & -4 & 1 \\ 0 & 2 & -1 \end{bmatrix}$ 22. $\begin{bmatrix} 1 & 0 & 0 \\ 0 & 1 & 0 \\ 0 & 0 & 1 \end{bmatrix}$ 23. $\begin{bmatrix} 2 & -1 & 3 \\ 5 & 0 & 2 \\ 7 & 1 & 4 \end{bmatrix}$ 24. $-\frac{11}{12}$

25. 35   26. -35 27. Does not exist

28. $\frac{1}{3}\begin{bmatrix} -1 & 1 & 1 \\ 3 & 0 & 0 \\ -1 & 1 & -2 \end{bmatrix}$ 29. $\begin{bmatrix} 0 & 0 & 0 \\ 0 & 0 & 0 \\ 0 & 0 & 0 \end{bmatrix}$ 30. $\begin{bmatrix} 1 & 0 \\ 0 & 1 \end{bmatrix}$

31. $\dfrac{\begin{vmatrix} a_1 & k_1 \\ a_2 & k_2 \end{vmatrix}}{\begin{vmatrix} a_1 & b_1 \\ a_2 & b_2 \end{vmatrix}}$ 32. $x = -1,\ y = 2,\ z = 1$ 33. $(4,3),\ (-4,3),\ (4,-3),\ (-4,-3)$

34. $(2,2),\ (-2,-2),\ (\sqrt{2},-\sqrt{2}),\ (-\sqrt{2},\sqrt{2})$ 35. 9 and 12

36. A: 12 hr; B: 12 hr; C: 6 hr   37. -14 38. 42

39. $\begin{vmatrix} u & v \\ w & x \end{vmatrix} = ux - wv = -(wv - ux) = -\begin{vmatrix} w & x \\ u & v \end{vmatrix}$

40. $\begin{vmatrix} u + kv & v \\ w + kx & x \end{vmatrix} = (u + kv)x - (w + kx)v = (ux - wv) + (kvx - kvx) = \begin{vmatrix} u & v \\ w & x \end{vmatrix}$

43. $x = 2,\ y = -1,\ z = 2$

CHAPTER 8

Exercise 64

1. $-1, 0, 1, 2$ 3. $0, \frac{1}{3}, \frac{1}{2}, \frac{3}{5}$ 5. $4, -8, 16, -32$ 7. 6   9. $\frac{99}{101}$
11. $S_5 = 1 + 2 + 3 + 4 + 5$ 13. $S_3 = \frac{1}{10} + \frac{1}{100} + \frac{1}{1000}$
15. $S_4 = -1 + 1 - 1 + 1$ 17. $1, -4, 9, -16, 25$
19. $0.3, 0.33, 0.333, 0.3333, 0.33333$ 21. $0, -2, 0, 4, 0$ 23. $7, 3, -1, -5$
25. $4, 1, \frac{1}{4}, \frac{1}{16}, \frac{1}{64}$ 27. $a_n = n + 3$ 29. $a_n = 3n$ 31. $a_n = n/(n+1)$
33. $a_n = (-1)^{n+1}$ 35. $a_n = (-2)^n$ 37. $a_n = x^n/n$ 39. $\frac{4}{1} - \frac{8}{2} + \frac{16}{3} - \frac{32}{4}$
41. $S_3 = x^2 + x^3/2 + x^4/3$ 43. $x - x^2/2 + x^3/3 - x^4/4 + x^5/5$

45. $S_4 = \sum_{k=1}^{4} k^2$ 47. $S_5 = \sum_{k=1}^{5} 1/2^k$ 49. $S_n = \sum_{k=1}^{n} 1/k^2$ 51. $S_n = \sum_{k=1}^{n} (-1)^{k+1} k^2$

55. (A) $3, 1.83, 1.46, 1.415$; (B) Table $\sqrt{2} = 1.414$; (C) $1, 1.5, 1.417, 1.414$
57. $S_2 = 3,\ S_4 = 7,\ S_6 = 7.356$; Table $e^2 = 7.391$
59. $S_1 = 1,\ S_2 = 0.8750,\ S_3 = 0.8776$; Table $\cos \frac{1}{2} = 0.8776$

Exercise 65

1. Fails at $n = 2$ 3. Fails at $n = 3$
5. $P_1: 2 = 2 \cdot 1^2$; $P_2: 2 + 6 = 2 \cdot 2^2$; $P_3: 2 + 6 + 10 = 2 \cdot 3^2$
7. $P_1: a^5 a = a^{5+1}$; $P_2: a^5 a^2 = a^5(a^1 a) = (a^5 a)a = a^6 a = a^7 = a^{5+2}$;

P_3: $a^5a^3 = a^5(a^2a) = a^5(a^1a)a = [(a^5a)a]a = a^8 = a^{5+3}$

9. P_1: $9^1 - 1 = 8$ is divided by 4; P_2: $9^2 - 1 = 80$ is divided by 4; P_3: $9^3 - 1 = 728$ is divided by 4.

11. P_k: $2 + 6 + 10 + \cdots + (4k - 2) = 2k^2$; P_{k+1}: $2 + 6 + 10 + \cdots + (4k - 2) + (4k + 2) = 2(k + 1)^2$ 13. P_k: $a^5a^k = a^{5+k}$; P_{k+1}: $a^5a^{k+1} = a^{5+k+1}$

15. P_k: $9^k - 1 = 4r$; P_{k+1}: $9^{k+1} - 1 = 4s$ $s \in N$

39. Formula: $2 + 4 + 6 + \cdots + 2n = n(n + 1)$

41. $1 + 2 + 3 + \cdots + (n - 1) = n(n - 1)/2$, $n \geq 2$

49. Prime up to $n = 17$, fails at $n = 18$

Exercise 66

1. (B) $d = -0.5$; 5.5, 5; (C) $d = -5$; -26, -31 3. $a_2 = -1$, $a_3 = 3$, $a_4 = 7$

5. $a_{15} = 67$, $S_{11} = 242$ 7. $S_{21} = 861$ 9. $a_{15} = -21$ 11. $d \doteq 6$, $a_{101} = 603$

13. $S_{40} = 200$ 15. $a_{11} = 2$, $S_{11} = \frac{77}{6}$ 17. $a_1 = 1$ 19. $S_{51} = 4{,}131$

21. $-1{,}071$ 23. 4,446   27. $a_n = -3 + (n - 1)3$

29. (A) 336 ft; (B) 1,936 ft; (C) $16t^2$ 33. Hint: $y = x + d$, $z = x + 2d$

35. $x = -1$, $y = 2$

Exercise 67

1. (A) $r = -2$; -16, 32; (D) $r = \frac{1}{3}$; $\frac{1}{54}$, $\frac{1}{162}$ 3. $a_2 = 3$, $a_3 = -\frac{3}{2}$, $a_4 = \frac{3}{4}$

5. $a_{10} = \frac{1}{243}$ 7. $S_7 = 3{,}279$ 9. $r = 0.398$ 11. $S_{10} = -1{,}705$

13. $a_2 = 6$, $a_3 = 4$ 15. $S_7 = 547$ 17. $\frac{1{,}023}{1{,}024}$ 19. $x = 2\sqrt{3}$ 21. $S_\infty = \frac{9}{2}$

23. No sum   25. $S_\infty = \frac{8}{5}$ 27. $\frac{7}{9}$ 29. $\frac{6}{11}$ 31. $3\frac{24}{111}$ or $\frac{357}{111}$

33. $A = P(1 + r)^n$; Approximately 12 years   35. 900   37. $a_n = -3(-2)^{n-1}$

41. $4{,}000{,}000

Exercise 68

1. $700 per year; $115,500   3. 0.0015 lb per in.^{2} 5. 1,250,000   7. $A = A_0 2^{2t}$

9. $r = 10^{-0.4} = 0.398$ 11. 2   13. 9.185×10^{16} dollars; 1.827×10^{17} dollars

15. 252

Exercise 69

1. 720   3. 20   5. 720   7. 15   9. 1   11. 28   13. $9!/8!$ 15. $8!/5!$ 17. 126

19. 6   21. 1   23. 2,380   25. $u^5 + 5u^4v + 10u^3v^2 + 10u^2v^3 + 5uv^4 + v^5$

27. $y^4 - 4y^3 + 6y^2 - 4y + 1$

29. $32x^5 - 80x^4y + 80x^3y^2 - 40x^2y^3 + 10xy^4 - y^5$ 31. $5{,}005u^9v^6$

33. $264m^2n^{10}$ 35. $924w^6$ 37. 1.1045

39. $\dbinom{n}{r} = n!/r!(n - r)! = n!/(n - r)![n - (n - r)]! = \dbinom{n}{n - r}$

41. $\binom{k}{r-1} + \binom{k}{r} = k!/(r-1)!(k-r+1)! + k!/r!(k-r)! =$

$[rk! + (k+1-r)k!]/r!(k+1-r)! = (k+1)!/r!(k+1-r)! = \binom{k+1}{r}$

43. $\binom{k}{k} = k!/k!(k-k)! = 1 = (k+1)!/(k+1)![(k+1)-(k+1)]! = \binom{k+1}{k+1}$

Exercise 70

1. Arithmetic: (B) and (C); Geometric: (A) and (E)   2. (A) 5, 7, 9, 11; (B) $a_{10} = 23$; (C) $S_{10} = 140$ 3. (A) 16, 8, 4, 2; (B) $a_{10} = \frac{1}{32}$; (C) $S_{10} = 31\frac{31}{32}$
4. (A) $-8, -5, -2, 1$; (B) $a_{10} = 19$; (C) $S_{10} = 55$
5. (A) $-1, 2, -4, 8$; (B) $a_{10} = 512$; (C) $S_{10} = 341$ 6. $S_\infty = 32$ 7. 720
8. $20 \cdot 21 \cdot 22 = 9,240$ 9. 21
10. $P_1: 5 = 1^2 + 4 \cdot 1$; $P_2: 5 + 7 = 2^2 + 4 \cdot 2$; $P_3: 5 + 7 + 9 = 3^2 + 4 \cdot 3$
11. $P_1: 2 = 2^{1+1} - 2$; $P_2: 2 + 4 = 2^{2+1} - 2$; $P_3: 2 + 4 + 8 = 2^{3+1} - 2$
12. $P_1: 49^1 - 1 = 48$ is divided by 6; $P_2: 49^2 - 1 = 2,400$ is divided by 6; $P_3: 49^3 - 1 = 117,648$ is divided by 6
13. $P_k: 5 + 7 + 9 + \cdots + (2k + 3) = k^2 + 4k$; $P_{k+1}: 5 + 7 + 9 + \cdots + (2k + 3) + (2k + 5) = (k + 1)^2 + 4(k + 1)$
14. $P_k: 2 + 4 + 8 + \cdots + 2^k = 2^{k+1} - 2$; $P_{k+1}: 2 + 4 + 8 + \cdots + 2^k + 2^{k+1} = 2^{k+2} - 2$ 15. $P_k: 49^k - 1 = 6r$ for some integer r; $P_{k+1}: 49^{k+1} - 1 = 6s$ for some integer s.   16. $S_{10} = -6 - 4 - 2 + 0 + 2 + 4 + 6 + 8 + 10 + 12 = 30$
17. $S_7 = 8 + 4 + 2 + 1 + \frac{1}{2} + \frac{1}{4} + \frac{1}{8} = 15\frac{7}{8}$ 18. $S = \frac{81}{5}$

19. $S_n = \sum_{k=1}^{n} (-1)^{k+1}/3^k$, $S_\infty = \frac{1}{4}$ 20. $d = 3$; $a_5 = 25$ 21. $\frac{8}{11}$

22. 190   23. 1,820   24. 1   25. $x^5 - 5x^4y + 10x^3y^2 - 10x^2y^3 + 5xy^4 - y^5$
26. $-5,280x^3y^9$ 30. $49g/2$ ft; $625g/2$ ft
31. $x^6 + 6ix^5 - 15x^4 - 20ix^3 + 15x^2 + 6ix - 1$

TABLE 1   Squares and Square Roots (0 to 199)

n	n^2	$\sqrt{n}$	n	n^2	$\sqrt{n}$	n	n^2	$\sqrt{n}$	n	n^2	$\sqrt{n}$
0	0	0.000	50	2,500	7.071	100	10,000	10.000	150	22,500	12.247
1	1	1.000	51	2,601	7.141	101	10,201	10.050	151	22,801	12.288
2	4	1.414	52	2,704	7.211	102	10,404	10.100	152	23,104	12.329
3	9	1.732	53	2,809	7.280	103	10,609	10.149	153	23,409	12.369
4	16	2.000	54	2,916	7.348	104	10,816	10.198	154	23,716	12.410
5	25	2.236	55	3,025	7.416	105	11,025	10.247	155	24,025	12.450
6	36	2.449	56	3,136	7.483	106	11,236	10.296	156	24,336	12.490
7	49	2.646	57	3,249	7.550	107	11,449	10.344	157	24,649	12.530
8	64	2.828	58	3,364	7.616	108	11,664	10.392	158	24,964	12.570
9	81	3.000	59	3,481	7.681	109	11,881	10.440	159	25,281	12.610
10	100	3.162	60	3,600	7.746	110	12,100	10.488	160	25,600	12.649
11	121	3.317	61	3,721	7.810	111	12,321	10.536	161	25,921	12.689
12	144	3.464	62	3,844	7.874	112	12,544	10.583	162	26,244	12.728
13	169	3.606	63	3,969	7.937	113	12,769	10.630	163	26,569	12.767
14	196	3.742	64	4,096	8.000	114	12,996	10.677	164	26,896	12.806
15	225	3.873	65	4,225	8.062	115	13,225	10.724	165	27,225	12.845
16	256	4.000	66	4,356	8.124	116	13,456	10.770	166	27,556	12.884
17	289	4.123	67	4,489	8.185	117	13,689	10.817	167	27,889	12.923
18	324	4.243	68	4,624	8.246	118	13,924	10.863	168	28,224	12.961
19	361	4.359	69	4,761	8.307	119	14,161	10.909	169	28,561	13.000
20	400	4.472	70	4,900	8.367	120	14,400	10.954	170	28,900	13.038
21	441	4.583	71	5,041	8.426	121	14,641	11.000	171	29,241	13.077
22	484	4.690	72	5,184	8.485	122	14,884	11.045	172	29,584	13.115
23	529	4.796	73	5,329	8.544	123	15,129	11.091	173	29,929	13.153
24	576	4.899	74	5,476	8.602	124	15,376	11.136	174	30,276	13.191
25	625	5.000	75	5,625	8.660	125	15,625	11.180	175	30,625	13.229
26	676	5.099	76	5,776	8.718	126	15,876	11.225	176	30,976	13.266
27	729	5.196	77	5,929	8.775	127	16,129	11.269	177	31,329	13.304
28	784	5.292	78	6,084	8.832	128	16,384	11.314	178	31,684	13.342
29	841	5.385	79	6,241	8.888	129	16,641	11.358	179	32,041	13.379
30	900	5.477	80	6,400	8.944	130	16,900	11.402	180	32,400	13.416
31	961	5.568	81	6,561	9.000	131	17,161	11.446	181	32,761	13.454
32	1,024	5.657	82	6,724	9.055	132	17,424	11.489	182	33,124	13.491
33	1,089	5.745	83	6,889	9.110	133	17,689	11.533	183	33,489	13.528
34	1,156	5.831	84	7,056	9.165	134	17,956	11.576	184	33,856	13.565
35	1,225	5.916	85	7,225	9.220	135	18,225	11.619	185	34,225	13.601
36	1,296	6.000	86	7,396	9.274	136	18,496	11.662	186	34,596	13.638
37	1,369	6.083	87	7,569	9.327	137	18,769	11.705	187	34,969	13.675
38	1,444	6.164	88	7,744	9.381	138	19,044	11.747	188	35,344	13.711
39	1,521	6.245	89	7,921	9.434	139	19,321	11.790	189	35,721	13.748
40	1,600	6.325	90	8,100	9.487	140	19,600	11.832	190	36,100	13.784
41	1,681	6.403	91	8,281	9.539	141	19,881	11.874	191	36,481	13.820
42	1,764	6.481	92	8,464	9.592	142	20,164	11.916	192	36,864	13.856
43	1,849	6.557	93	8,649	9.644	143	20,449	11.958	193	37,249	13.892
44	1,936	6.633	94	8,836	9.659	144	20,736	12.000	194	37,636	13.928
45	2,025	6.708	95	9,025	9.747	145	21,025	12.042	195	38,025	13.964
46	2,116	6.782	96	9,216	9.798	146	21,316	12.083	196	38,416	14.000
47	2,209	6.856	97	9,409	9.849	147	21,609	12.124	197	38,809	14.036
48	2,304	6.928	98	9,604	9.899	148	21,904	12.166	198	39,204	14.071
49	2,401	7.000	99	9,801	9.950	149	22,201	12.207	199	39,601	14.107
n	n^2	$\sqrt{n}$	n	n^2	$\sqrt{n}$	n	n^2	$\sqrt{n}$	n	n^2	$\sqrt{n}$

TABLE 2   Values of e^x and e^{-x} (0.00 to 3.00)

x	e^x	e^{-x}	x	e^x	e^{-x}	x	e^x	e^{-x}
0.00	1.000	1.000	0.50	1.649	0.607	1.00	2.718	0.368
0.01	1.010	0.990	0.51	1.665	0.600	1.01	2.746	0.364
0.02	1.020	0.980	0.52	1.682	0.595	1.02	2.773	0.361
0.03	1.031	0.970	0.53	1.699	0.589	1.03	2.801	0.357
0.04	1.041	0.961	0.54	1.716	0.583	1.04	2.829	0.353
0.05	1.051	0.951	0.55	1.733	0.577	1.05	2.858	0.350
0.06	1.062	0.942	0.56	1.751	0.571	1.06	2.886	0.346
0.07	1.073	0.932	0.57	1.768	0.566	1.07	2.915	0.343
0.08	1.083	0.923	0.58	1.786	0.560	1.08	2.945	0.340
0.09	1.094	0.914	0.59	1.804	0.554	1.09	2.974	0.336
0.10	1.105	0.905	0.60	1.822	0.549	1.10	3.004	0.333
0.11	1.116	0.896	0.61	1.840	0.543	1.11	3.034	0.330
0.12	1.127	0.887	0.62	1.859	0.538	1.12	3.065	0.326
0.13	1.139	0.878	0.63	1.878	0.533	1.13	3.096	0.323
0.14	1.150	0.869	0.64	1.896	0.527	1.14	3.127	0.320
0.15	1.162	0.861	0.65	1.916	0.522	1.15	3.158	0.317
0.16	1.174	0.852	0.66	1.935	0.517	1.16	3.190	0.313
0.17	1.185	0.844	0.67	1.954	0.512	1.17	3.222	0.310
0.18	1.197	0.835	0.68	1.974	0.507	1.18	3.254	0.307
0.19	1.209	0.827	0.69	1.994	0.502	1.19	3.287	0.304
0.20	1.221	0.819	0.70	2.014	0.497	1.20	3.320	0.301
0.21	1.234	0.811	0.71	2.034	0.492	1.21	3.353	0.298
0.22	1.246	0.803	0.72	2.054	0.487	1.22	3.387	0.295
0.23	1.259	0.795	0.73	2.075	0.482	1.23	3.421	0.292
0.24	1.271	0.787	0.74	2.096	0.477	1.24	3.456	0.289
0.25	1.284	0.779	0.75	2.117	0.472	1.25	3.490	0.287
0.26	1.297	0.771	0.76	2.138	0.468	1.26	3.525	0.284
0.27	1.310	0.763	0.77	2.160	0.463	1.27	3.561	0.281
0.28	1.323	0.756	0.78	2.182	0.458	1.28	3.597	0.278
0.29	1.336	0.748	0.79	2.203	0.454	1.29	3.633	0.275
0.30	1.350	0.741	0.80	2.226	0.449	1.30	3.669	0.273
0.31	1.363	0.733	0.81	2.248	0.445	1.31	3.706	0.270
0.32	1.377	0.726	0.82	2.270	0.440	1.32	3.743	0.267
0.33	1.391	0.719	0.83	2.293	0.436	1.33	3.781	0.264
0.34	1.405	0.712	0.84	2.316	0.432	1.34	3.819	0.262
0.35	1.419	0.705	0.85	2.340	0.427	1.35	3.857	0.259
0.36	1.433	0.698	0.86	2.363	0.423	1.36	3.896	0.257
0.37	1.448	0.691	0.87	2.387	0.419	1.37	3.935	0.254
0.38	1.462	0.684	0.88	2.411	0.415	1.38	3.975	0.252
0.39	1.477	0.677	0.89	2.435	0.411	1.39	4.015	0.249
0.40	1.492	0.670	0.90	2.460	0.407	1.40	4.055	0.247
0.41	1.507	0.664	0.91	2.484	0.403	1.41	4.096	0.244
0.42	1.522	0.657	0.92	2.509	0.399	1.42	4.137	0.242
0.43	1.537	0.651	0.93	2.535	0.395	1.43	4.179	0.239
0.44	1.553	0.644	0.94	2.560	0.391	1.44	4.221	0.237
0.45	1.568	0.638	0.95	2.586	0.387	1.45	4.263	0.235
0.46	1.584	0.631	0.96	2.612	0.383	1.46	4.306	0.232
0.47	1.600	0.625	0.97	2.638	0.379	1.47	4.349	0.230
0.48	1.616	0.619	0.98	2.664	0.375	1.48	4.393	0.228
0.49	1.632	0.613	0.99	2.691	0.372	1.49	4.437	0.225

TABLE 2 (*continued*)

x	e^x	e^{-x}	x	e^x	e^{-x}	x	e^x	e^{-x}
1.50	4.482	0.223	2.00	7.389	0.135	2.50	12.182	0.082
1.51	4.527	0.221	2.01	7.463	0.134	2.51	12.305	0.081
1.52	4.572	0.219	2.02	7.538	0.133	2.52	12.429	0.080
1.53	4.618	0.217	2.03	7.614	0.131	2.53	12.554	0.080
1.54	4.665	0.214	2.04	7.691	0.130	2.54	12.680	0.079
1.55	4.712	0.212	2.05	7.768	0.129	2.55	12.807	0.078
1.56	4.759	0.210	2.06	7.846	0.127	2.56	12.936	0.077
1.57	4.807	0.208	2.07	7.925	0.126	2.57	13.066	0.077
1.58	4.855	0.206	2.08	8.004	0.125	2.58	13.197	0.076
1.59	4.904	0.204	2.09	8.085	0.124	2.59	13.330	0.075
1.60	4.953	0.202	2.10	8.166	0.122	2.60	13.464	0.074
1.61	5.003	0.200	2.11	8.248	0.121	2.61	13.599	0.074
1.62	5.053	0.198	2.12	8.331	0.120	2.62	13.736	0.073
1.63	5.104	0.196	2.13	8.415	0.119	2.63	13.874	0.072
1.64	5.155	0.194	2.14	8.499	0.118	2.64	14.013	0.071
1.65	5.207	0.192	2.15	8.585	0.116	2.65	14.154	0.071
1.66	5.259	0.190	2.16	8.671	0.115	2.66	14.296	0.070
1.67	5.312	0.188	2.17	8.758	0.114	2.67	14.440	0.069
1.68	5.366	0.186	2.18	8.846	0.113	2.68	14.585	0.069
1.69	5.420	0.185	2.19	8.935	0.112	2.69	14.732	0.068
1.70	5.474	0.183	2.20	9.025	0.111	2.70	14.880	0.067
1.71	5.529	0.181	2.21	9.116	0.110	2.71	15.029	0.067
1.72	5.585	0.179	2.22	9.207	0.109	2.72	15.180	0.066
1.73	5.641	0.177	2.23	9.300	0.108	2.73	15.333	0.065
1.74	5.697	0.176	2.24	9.393	0.106	2.74	15.487	0.065
1.75	5.755	0.174	2.25	9.488	0.105	2.75	15.643	0.064
1.76	5.812	0.172	2.26	9.583	0.104	2.76	15.800	0.063
1.77	5.871	0.170	2.27	9.679	0.103	2.77	15.959	0.063
1.78	5.930	0.169	2.28	9.777	0.102	2.78	16.119	0.062
1.79	5.989	0.167	2.29	9.875	0.101	2.79	16.281	0.061
1.80	6.050	0.165	2.30	9.974	0.100	2.80	16.445	0.061
1.81	6.110	0.164	2.31	10.074	0.099	2.81	16.610	0.060
1.82	6.172	0.162	2.32	10.176	0.098	2.82	16.777	0.060
1.83	6.234	0.160	2.33	10.278	0.097	2.83	16.945	0.059
1.84	6.297	0.159	2.34	10.381	0.096	2.84	17.116	0.058
1.85	6.360	0.157	2.35	10.486	0.095	2.85	17.288	0.058
1.86	6.424	0.156	2.36	10.591	0.094	2.86	17.462	0.057
1.87	6.488	0.154	2.37	10.697	0.093	2.87	17.637	0.057
1.88	6.553	0.153	2.38	10.805	0.093	2.88	17.814	0.056
1.89	6.619	0.151	2.39	10.913	0.092	2.89	17.993	0.056
1.90	6.686	0.150	2.40	11.023	0.091	2.90	18.174	0.055
1.91	6.753	0.148	2.41	11.134	0.090	2.91	18.357	0.054
1.92	6.821	0.147	2.42	11.246	0.089	2.92	18.541	0.054
1.93	6.890	0.145	2.43	11.359	0.088	2.93	18.728	0.053
1.94	6.959	0.144	2.44	11.473	0.087	2.94	18.916	0.053
1.95	7.029	0.142	2.45	11.588	0.086	2.95	19.106	0.052
1.96	7.099	0.141	2.46	11.705	0.085	2.96	19.298	0.052
1.97	7.171	0.139	2.47	11.822	0.085	2.97	19.492	0.051
1.98	7.243	0.138	2.48	11.941	0.084	2.98	19.688	0.051
1.99	7.316	0.137	2.49	12.061	0.083	2.99	19.886	0.050
						3.00	20.086	0.050

TABLE 3   Common Logarithms

N	0	1	2	3	4	5	6	7	8	9
1.0	0.0000	0.004321	0.008600	0.01284	0.01703	0.02119	0.02531	0.02938	0.03342	0.03743
1.1	0.04139	0.04532	0.04922	0.05308	0.05690	0.06070	0.06446	0.06819	0.07188	0.07555
1.2	0.07918	0.08279	0.08636	0.08991	0.09342	0.09691	0.1004	0.1038	0.1072	0.1106
1.3	0.1139	0.1173	0.1206	0.1239	0.1271	0.1303	0.1335	0.1367	0.1399	0.1430
1.4	0.1461	0.1492	0.1523	0.1553	0.1584	0.1614	0.1644	0.1673	0.1703	0.1732
1.5	0.1761	0.1790	0.1818	0.1847	0.1875	0.1903	0.1931	0.1959	0.1987	0.2014
1.6	0.2041	0.2068	0.2095	0.2122	0.2148	0.2175	0.2201	0.2227	0.2253	0.2279
1.7	0.2304	0.2330	0.2355	0.2380	0.2405	0.2430	0.2455	0.2480	0.2504	0.2529
1.8	0.2553	0.2577	0.2601	0.2625	0.2648	0.2673	0.2695	0.2718	0.2742	0.2765
1.9	0.2788	0.2810	0.2833	0.2856	0.2878	0.2900	0.2923	0.2945	0.2967	0.2989
2.0	0.3010	0.3032	0.3054	0.3075	0.3096	0.3118	0.3139	0.3160	0.3181	0.3201
2.1	0.3222	0.3243	0.3263	0.3284	0.3304	0.3324	0.3345	0.3365	0.3385	0.3404
2.2	0.3424	0.3444	0.3464	0.3483	0.3502	0.3522	0.3541	0.3560	0.3579	0.3598
2.3	0.3617	0.3636	0.3655	0.3674	0.3692	0.3711	0.3729	0.3747	0.3766	0.3784
2.4	0.3802	0.3820	0.3838	0.3856	0.3874	0.3892	0.3909	0.3927	0.3945	0.3962
2.5	0.3979	0.3997	0.4014	0.4031	0.4048	0.4065	0.4082	0.4099	0.4116	0.4133
2.6	0.4150	0.4166	0.4183	0.4200	0.4216	0.4232	0.4249	0.4265	0.4281	0.4298
2.7	0.4314	0.4330	0.4346	0.4362	0.4378	0.4393	0.4409	0.4425	0.4440	0.4456
2.8	0.4472	0.4487	0.4502	0.4518	0.4533	0.4548	0.4564	0.4579	0.4594	0.4609
2.9	0.4624	0.4639	0.4654	0.4669	0.4683	0.4698	0.4713	0.4728	0.4742	0.4757
3.0	0.4771	0.4786	0.4800	0.4814	0.4829	0.4843	0.4857	0.4871	0.4886	0.4900
3.1	0.4914	0.4928	0.4942	0.4955	0.4969	0.4983	0.4997	0.5011	0.5024	0.5038
3.2	0.5051	0.5065	0.5079	0.5092	0.5105	0.5119	0.5132	0.5145	0.5159	0.5172
3.3	0.5185	0.5198	0.5211	0.5224	0.5237	0.5250	0.5263	0.5276	0.5289	0.5302
3.4	0.5315	0.5328	0.5340	0.5353	0.5366	0.5378	0.5391	0.5403	0.5416	0.5428
3.5	0.5441	0.5453	0.5465	0.5478	0.5490	0.5502	0.5514	0.5527	0.5539	0.5551
3.6	0.5563	0.5575	0.5587	0.5599	0.5611	0.5623	0.5635	0.5647	0.5658	0.5670
3.7	0.5682	0.5694	0.5705	0.5717	0.5729	0.5740	0.5752	0.5763	0.5775	0.5786
3.8	0.5798	0.5809	0.5821	0.5832	0.5843	0.5855	0.5866	0.5877	0.5888	0.5899
3.9	0.5911	0.5922	0.5933	0.5944	0.5955	0.5966	0.5977	0.5988	0.5999	0.6010
4.0	0.6021	0.6031	0.6042	0.6053	0.6064	0.6075	0.6085	0.6096	0.6107	0.6117
4.1	0.6128	0.6138	0.6149	0.6160	0.6170	0.6180	0.6191	0.6201	0.6212	0.6222
4.2	0.6232	0.6243	0.6253	0.6263	0.6274	0.6284	0.6294	0.6304	0.6314	0.6325
4.3	0.6335	0.6345	0.6355	0.6365	0.6375	0.6385	0.6395	0.6405	0.6415	0.6425
4.4	0.6435	0.6444	0.6454	0.6464	0.6474	0.6484	0.6493	0.6503	0.6513	0.6522
4.5	0.6532	0.6542	0.6551	0.6561	0.6571	0.6580	0.6590	0.6599	0.6609	0.6618
4.6	0.6628	0.6637	0.6646	0.6656	0.6665	0.6675	0.6684	0.6693	0.6702	0.6712
4.7	0.6721	0.6730	0.6739	0.6749	0.6758	0.6767	0.6776	0.6785	0.6794	0.6803
4.8	0.6812	0.6821	0.6830	0.6839	0.6848	0.6857	0.6866	0.6875	0.6884	0.6893
4.9	0.6902	0.6911	0.6920	0.6928	0.6937	0.6946	0.6955	0.6964	0.6972	0.6981
5.0	0.6990	0.6998	0.7007	0.7016	0.7024	0.7033	0.7042	0.7050	0.7059	0.7067
5.1	0.7076	0.7084	0.7093	0.7101	0.7110	0.7118	0.7126	0.7135	0.7143	0.7152
5.2	0.7160	0.7168	0.7177	0.7185	0.7193	0.7202	0.7210	0.7218	0.7226	0.7235
5.3	0.7243	0.7251	0.7259	0.7267	0.7275	0.7284	0.7292	0.7300	0.7308	0.7316
5.4	0.7324	0.7332	0.7340	0.7348	0.7356	0.7364	0.7372	0.7380	0.7388	0.7396

By permission from Thomas L. Wade and Howard E. Taylor, *Fundamental Mathematics*, McGraw-Hill Book Company, New York, 1960.

TABLE 3 (*continued*)

N	0	1	2	3	4	5	6	7	8	9
5.5	0.7404	0.7412	0.7419	0.7427	0.7435	0.7443	0.7451	0.7459	0.7466	0.7474
5.6	0.7482	0.7490	0.7497	0.7505	0.7513	0.7520	0.7528	0.7536	0.7543	0.7551
5.7	0.7559	0.7566	0.7574	0.7582	0.7589	0.7597	0.7604	0.7612	0.7619	0.7627
5.8	0.7634	0.7642	0.7649	0.7657	0.7664	0.7672	0.7679	0.7686	0.7694	0.7701
5.9	0.7709	0.7716	0.7723	0.7731	0.7738	0.7745	0.7752	0.7760	0.7767	0.7774
6.0	0.7782	0.7789	0.7796	0.7803	0.7810	0.7818	0.7825	0.7832	0.7839	0.7846
6.1	0.7853	0.7860	0.7868	0.7875	0.7882	0.7889	0.7896	0.7903	0.7910	0.7917
6.2	0.7924	0.7931	0.7938	0.7945	0.7952	0.7959	0.7966	0.7973	0.7980	0.7987
6.3	0.7993	0.8000	0.8007	0.8014	0.8021	0.8028	0.8035	0.8041	0.8048	0.8055
6.4	0.8062	0.8069	0.8075	0.8082	0.8089	0.8096	0.8102	0.8109	0.8116	0.8122
6.5	0.8129	0.8136	0.8142	0.8149	0.8156	0.8162	0.8169	0.8176	0.8182	0.8189
6.6	0.8195	0.8202	0.8209	0.8215	0.8222	0.8228	0.8235	0.8241	0.8248	0.8254
6.7	0.8261	0.8267	0.8274	0.8280	0.8287	0.8293	0.8299	0.8306	0.8312	0.8319
6.8	0.8325	0.8331	0.8338	0.8344	0.8351	0.8357	0.8363	0.8370	0.8376	0.8382
6.9	0.8388	0.8395	0.8401	0.8407	0.8414	0.8420	0.8426	0.8432	0.8439	0.8445
7.0	0.8451	0.8457	0.8463	0.8470	0.8476	0.8482	0.8488	0.8494	0.8500	0.8506
7.1	0.8513	0.8519	0.8525	0.8531	0.8537	0.8543	0.8549	0.8555	0.8561	0.8567
7.2	0.8573	0.8579	0.8585	0.8591	0.8597	0.8603	0.8609	0.8615	0.8621	0.8627
7.3	0.8633	0.8639	0.8645	0.8651	0.8657	0.8663	0.8669	0.8675	0.8681	0.8686
7.4	0.8692	0.8698	0.8704	0.8710	0.8716	0.8722	0.8727	0.8733	0.8739	0.8745
7.5	0.8751	0.8756	0.8762	0.8768	0.8774	0.8779	0.8785	0.8791	0.8797	0.8802
7.6	0.8808	0.8814	0.8820	0.8825	0.8831	0.8837	0.8842	0.8848	0.8854	0.8859
7.7	0.8865	0.8871	0.8876	0.8882	0.8887	0.8893	0.8899	0.8904	0.8910	0.8915
7.8	0.8921	0.8927	0.8932	0.8938	0.8943	0.8949	0.8954	0.8960	0.8965	0.8971
7.9	0.8976	0.8982	0.8987	0.8993	0.8998	0.9004	0.9009	0.9015	0.9020	0.9025
8.0	0.9031	0.9036	0.9042	0.9047	0.9053	0.9058	0.9063	0.9069	0.9074	0.9079
8.1	0.9085	0.9090	0.9096	0.9101	0.9106	0.9112	0.9117	0.9122	0.9128	0.9133
8.2	0.9138	0.9143	0.9149	0.9154	0.9159	0.9165	0.9170	0.9175	0.9180	0.9186
8.3	0.9191	0.9196	0.9201	0.9206	0.9212	0.9217	0.9222	0.9227	0.9232	0.9238
8.4	0.9243	0.9248	0.9253	0.9258	0.9263	0.9269	0.9274	0.9279	0.9284	0.9289
8.5	0.9294	0.9299	0.9304	0.9309	0.9315	0.9320	0.9325	0.9330	0.9335	0.9340
8.6	0.9345	0.9350	0.9355	0.9360	0.9365	0.9370	0.9375	0.9380	0.9385	0.9390
8.7	0.9395	0.9400	0.9405	0.9410	0.9415	0.9420	0.9425	0.9430	0.9435	0.9440
8.8	0.9445	0.9450	0.9455	0.9460	0.9465	0.9469	0.9474	0.9479	0.9484	0.9489
8.9	0.9494	0.9499	0.9504	0.9509	0.9513	0.9518	0.9523	0.9528	0.9533	0.9538
9.0	0.9542	0.9547	0.9552	0.9557	0.9562	0.9566	0.9571	0.9576	0.9581	0.9586
9.1	0.9590	0.9595	0.9600	0.9605	0.9609	0.9614	0.9619	0.9624	0.9628	0.9633
9.2	0.9638	0.9643	0.9647	0.9652	0.9657	0.9661	0.9666	0.9671	0.9675	0.9680
9.3	0.9685	0.9689	0.9694	0.9699	0.9703	0.9708	0.9713	0.9717	0.9722	0.9727
9.4	0.9731	0.9736	0.9741	0.9745	0.9750	0.9754	0.9759	0.9763	0.9768	0.9773
9.5	0.9777	0.9782	0.9786	0.9791	0.9795	0.9800	0.9805	0.9809	0.9814	0.9818
9.6	0.9823	0.9827	0.9832	0.9836	0.9841	0.9845	0.9850	0.9854	0.9859	0.9863
9.7	0.9868	0.9872	0.9877	0.9881	0.9886	0.9890	0.9894	0.9899	0.9903	0.9908
9.8	0.9912	0.9917	0.9921	0.9926	0.9930	0.9934	0.9939	0.9943	0.9948	0.9952
9.9	0.9956	0.9961	0.9965	0.9969	0.9974	0.9978	0.9983	0.9987	0.9991	0.9996

Index